WILLIAM SMITH'S
FOSSILS REUNITED

WILLIAM SMITH'S FOSSILS REUNITED

STRATA IDENTIFIED BY ORGANIZED FOSSILS
AND
A STRATIGRAPHICAL SYSTEM OF ORGANIZED FOSSILS
BY
WILLIAM SMITH

WITH FOSSIL PHOTOGRAPHS FROM HIS COLLECTION AT THE
NATURAL HISTORY MUSEUM

Peter Wigley (Editor & Compiler)
with Jill Darrell, Diana Clements and Hugh Torrens

———•|•———

THE DOLAN CHARITABLE TRUST
in association with HALSGROVE PUBLISHING

First published in Great Britain in 2018

British Library Cataloguing-in-Publication Data
A CIP record for this title is available from the British Library

ISBN 978 0 85704 337 5

Halsgrove
Halsgrove House,
Ryelands Business Park,
Bagley Road, Wellington, Somerset TA21 9PZ
Tel: 01823 653777   Fax: 01823 216796
email: sales@halsgrove.com

Part of the Halsgrove group of companies
Information on all Halsgrove titles is available at: www.halsgrove.com

Printed and bound by Parksons Graphics, India

Portrait of William Smith and 1815 Geological Map of England and Wales (A Map)
© The Geological Society

1815 Geological Map of England and Wales (P Map)
© Manuscripts and Special Collections, The University of Nottingham

Portrait of William Smith (1769-1839) in oils, by Hugues Fourau, 1837.
(GSL/POR/15, courtesy of The Geological Society of London)

TABLE OF CONTENTS

TABLE OF CONTENTS (cont.)

LIST OF PLATES

FOREWORD

William Smith is perhaps best known for his geological map, *A delineation of the strata of England and Wales, with part of Scotland* which he published in 1815. His "Great Map", the first of its kind, may well have been the pinnacle of his achievements but importantly the map was based on his novel concept of an "Order of Strata". His first attempt at defining that order was in the Bath district, in part, resulting from his pioneering work on the Somerset Coal Canal. After several iterations he finally produced a table showing 34 different strata in "their order of superposition" which was applicable to much of the country. It was Smith's intimate knowledge of the fossils within each stratum that helped him to define this sequence. Through insight and experience, he knew that particular fossils identified particular strata. It was this knowledge that enabled him to differentiate the strata even though in some cases they had similar lithology. He also demonstrated that some fossils had longer geological age ranges than others and were thus less useful in defining strata.

Fossils were William Smith's tools of his trade and he collected them avidly from the late 18th century onwards. However, as good a geologist as he was, he was a poor business man and was constantly encumbered by debt. In an attempt to pay off some of his debts he was forced to sell his wonderful collection of fossils to a less than enthusiastic British Museum in 1816. It was at this time that he started on an important, albeit unfinished, publication, *Strata Identified by Organized Fossils*. Smith collaborated with the talented naturalist and illustrator James Sowerby to make engravings of key fossils which he then arranged stratigraphically together with descriptions of the strata. Unfortunately only four of the seven parts were ever completed. Similarly, he only completed the first part of his other publication *A Stratigraphical System of Organized Fossils* which he intended to be a descriptive catalogue of his collection at the British Museum.

In this reprint of these two classic publications, the text and fossil illustrations have been digitized and the latter reunited with new photographs of the actual specimens now housed in the Natural History Museum. From surviving Smith manuscripts, his fossil sketches and corresponding photographs have been added and the final part of *A Stratigraphical System of Organized Fossils* has been transcribed.

William Smith was both a brilliant and practical geologist; early on in his career he recognized the significance of his "Science of the Strata". Stratigraphy has made huge advances during the past 200 years, yet for all these advances, there is a direct link back to William Smith's original work. All those who use stratigraphy professionally, either in the world of resource exploration, or in academia, owe Smith an enormous debt of gratitude. It is important that his contribution to science continues to be remembered and it is hoped that this new publication of his original work will, to some degree, keep that memory nurtured and alive.

Sir David Attenborough OM FRS
Patron, The Dinosaur Society UK

ACKNOWLEDGEMENTS

The original suggestion to digitize and reprint *Strata Identified by Organized Fossils* and *A Stratigraphical System of Organized Fossils* came from Dave Williams of Lostwithiel in 2015. Dave also provided his personal copies of Smith's publications to the editor for digitization. We are extremely grateful to Dave for allowing the Editor to subject this precious collection to the rigours of the digital process. Upon completion of the digital versions of these two publications, Dave and Hugh Torrens suggested inclusion of photographs of some of Smith's fossils in the reprinted publications.

At the same time the Natural History Museum (NHM) put on a special exhibition to mark the bicentenary of the publication of William Smith's Map of England and Wales. Jill Darrell and Diana Clements were invited by the organizers to display four of the plate fossils in the way shown in this volume. This provided them with the impetus to find and display the specimens for the rest of the plates. We thank the NHM and the organizers of the special exhibition in this regard and also to the NHM for giving permission to reproduce photographs of Smith's fossils in this volume.

Kevin Webb has photographed all of the specimens and we are extremely grateful to him for the care he has taken in orientating them as closely as possible to the original plates.

Many colleagues in the Earth Science Department of the Natural History Museum have helped with the identifications of the specimens and we thank them for their assistance for that and other aspects. In particular Joe Collins, John Cooper, Tim Ewin, Andy Gale, Mike Howarth, Paul Kenrick, Alison Longbottom, Noel Morris, Simon Parfitt, Brian Rosen, Andrew Smith, Lil Stevens, Paul Taylor, John Todd and Steve Tracey.

The authors also thank and acknowledge the Oxford University Museum of Natural History (OUMNH) for giving permission to publish a transcription of Part II of *A Stratigraphical System of Organized Fossils* from a manuscript held in the William Smith Archive. OUMNH also provided scans of four sketches of unpublished fossil plates and permission for them to be included in this publication. The Editor would like to extend special thanks to Kate Diston, Head of Print and Digital Collections at the Museum for all her help and also to Paul Smith the Director of the Museum. The authors are also grateful to The Geological Society for permission to publish the Smith portrait and the 1815 "A" map, and to the Manuscript and Special Collections, The University of Nottingham for permission to publish the Smith 1815 "P" map.

The Editor is extremely indebted to Peter Dolan and Dave Williams for their financial support for this project and to Malcolm Butler and the Trustees of the UK Onshore Seismic Library. The Editor would also like to extend his personal thanks to Jill and Diana for their persistence and attention to detail in locating and identifying the fossils, to Dee Edwards for proof reading this work and to Hugh Torrens for his encyclopaedic knowledge of all things "Smithian". Dick Moody, Paul Henderson, Caroline Wigley and Kate Wigley provided valuable advice and guidance during the course of this project

This book reproduces William Smith's text as printed in the original editions of *Strata Identified by Organized Fossils* and *A Stratigraphical System of Organized Fossils*. The contents and language reflect the beliefs, practices and terminology of their times, and have not been updated. All additional text was authored by the editor for which he accepts full responsibility.

Finally, we would like to thank Sir David Attenborough OM FRS for finding time in his extraordinarily busy schedule to prepare the Preface to this volume.

WILLIAM SMITH'S FOSSILS REUNITED

Introduction

William Smith is universally remembered for his pioneering map of the Geology of England and Wales and later more detailed county geology maps. However, it is also important to consider that he authored two stratigraphically significant publications, *Strata Identified by Organized Fossils* and later, *A Stratigraphical System of Organized Fossils with reference to the specimens of the original geological collection in the British Museum*. In these two important publications Smith attempted to identify strata based on the fossil assemblages they contained and also to define a comprehensive stratigraphic system for the organization of "near seven hundred species" (page 1 of *A Stratigraphical System of Organized Fossils*). These formed part of his fossil collection sold to the British Museum in 1816. These two publications are exceedingly rare, two hundred and fifty copies of the first were printed and two hundred and fifteen of the second (Hugh Torrens, pers. comm. 2018). In the present publication photographs of Smith's own fossils have been reunited with republished versions of his ground-breaking books.

Strata Identified by Organized Fossils

This publication was planned by William Smith to be issued monthly in seven parts, of quarto size each tied in a blue wrapper. The order of publication started with the youngest strata and continued with progressively older strata; in the event only four parts were ever published. As is implied by the title, Smith intended to show that he could identify many of his mapped strata by assemblages of characteristic fossils contained within them. Smith used the innovative idea of having the engraved plates printed on a variety of coloured papers, the colour of which matched the colours of the strata on his *Geological Map of England and Wales* and his *Geological Table of Organized Fossils*. By this means the fossils could be directly related to their stratigraphic position and location on his map. The fossil plates were engraved by the renowned illustrator, naturalist and mineralogist, James Sowerby (1757-1822) from fossils provided by Smith (Cox, L.R. 1942, p. 53). It is also thought that Smith's young nephew, John Phillips (1800-1874), may have helped his uncle prepare both publications and also assisted in the preparation of the fossil collection for sale to the British Museum.

Interestingly, in the introductory text Smith emphasized the benefits to agriculture of his stratigraphical method, reminding the reader that the nature of the soil resulted from the strata which it rests upon. He also referred to his recently published map of the strata and distinguished between those fossils found in situ, which he used to identify his strata, and other "Gravel" or "Alluvial Fossils" which he thought had been torn from the strata by a great body of water, rounded by attrition and moved considerable distances. The term "diluvial" was also used by Smith, a possible reference to the great biblical flood. After the Introduction he described in general terms the distribution of fossiliferous strata across the country and compared them to less fossiliferous and un-fossiliferous tracts, mostly west of a curved line from Exeter to Teesmouth. For each of his principal stratigraphic groups Smith provided a standardized summary of the soil, subsoil, nature of any excavations or "hollow-ways", the stratum and water. This is followed by listings of the fossil assemblages and their locations.

The first part (No 1) was published in June 1816 and details Stratum No.1, his London Clay (which he considered his youngest stratum but which is now part of the Eocene), Crag which Smith defined as a localized stratum of shells and sands overlying the chalk in Norfolk and Suffolk (now considered to be Plio-Pleistocene and therefore younger than the London Clay) and finally the Upper Chalk. Also included as a frontispiece is an engraving of a large tooth from Norfolk which Smith describes to be from "some extinct monstrous unknown animal", now know to be a molar from a mastodon.

The following part (No 2) published in October 1816 consisted of five plates and text describing the Lower or Hard (Grey) Chalk and three strata beneath the chalk, the Green or Chlorite Sand (2 plates), the Micaceous Brick Earth and the Portland Stone. The Chalk strata are now considered to be part of the Upper Cretaceous Series, the Greensand and Brick Earth (Gault) are Lower-Upper Cretaceous and the Portland Stone Upper Jurassic.

The third part (No 3) was published almost a year later in September 1817 and, as in the previous part, consists of five plates and text covering the Oak Tree Clay, Coral Rag and Pisolite (2 plates), Clunch Clay and Shale and Kelloways Stone. Today we recognize all these strata as being within the Jurassic with Smith's names being replaced by the Kimmeridge Clay, Coralline Oolite, Oxford Clay and Kellaways Rock.

The fourth and final published part (No 4) did not appear until 1819, and consisted of a further five plates, Cornbrash, Forest Marble, Clay over the Oolite (now considered to be Bradford Clay), Upper Oolite (Great Oolite) and Fuller's Earth Rock.

The year 1819 was Smith's *annus horribilis* as he was unable to pay his debts and ultimately imprisoned for non-payment. Upon his release he retreated into self-imposed exile in the north of England with his nephew John Phillips. It is therefore unsurprising that publication ceased. However, we know Smith planned for a further three parts to his publication. Indeed he was at pains to point this out on the blue paper wrappers that accompanied parts three and four, which referred subscribers to those sections of his geological table already covered by the publication and assured them that there will be no more than seven parts (see page 13). The oldest published strata discussed by Smith was the Fuller's Earth Rock (Stratum No 21 on his table), a fossiliferous limestone within the Fuller's Earth which is a locally calcareous mudstone. In Part I of *Stratigraphical System of Organized Fossils*, Smith had described fossils from three formations below the Fuller's Earth Rock, namely: Under Oolite (22), Sand and Sandstone (23) and Marlstone (24). In a manuscript version of Part II of *Stratigraphical System of Organized Fossils* (WS/F/1/3, William Smith Archive, Oxford University Museum of Natural History) Smith had written further sections on the Blue Marl (25), Lias (26), Redland Limestone (29) and Mountain Limestone (31). The OUMNH archive also contains draft sketches of plates for the Blue Marl, Lias (two sketches) and Redland Limestone.

Leslie Cox has shown (Cox, L.R. 1942, p. 55) that the three missing parts were to have consisted of:
Part 5, Under Oolite, Sand & Sandstone, Marlstone and Blue Marl
Part 6, Blue Lias, Lias (two plates) Redland Limestone, Coal Measures (2 plates)
Part 7, Mountain Limestone, Clay Stone (of Golden Grove), Llandeilo Stone, Alluvial Fossils (2 plates).

In *Stratigraphical System of Organized Fossils* (p. 110) Smith listed fossils for two Under Oolite plates which he intended to add to Part 5 with nine specimens on the first plate and eight in the second. Similarly, in the description of fossils in the Sand and Sandstone (Stratum No. 23) section he designated three specimens for that plate and a further seven for the Marlstone (Stratum No. 24).

It should also be noted that in the introduction to the publication Smith recorded that he intended to discuss alluvial fossils in the final part of the book.

The publication was a collaboration between Smith and James Sowerby. Smith first introduced himself to

Sowerby by letter on 15th March, 1808 (Cox, L.R. 1942, p. 53) and was evidently seeking to reassure him that there would be no conflict between his work and Sowerby's *The Mineral Conchology of Great Britain*, which he was then preparing. He wrote:

"If I understand the nature of your intended publication on the organized fossils aright I think it will not in any way interfere with mine, yours being, as I apprehend, arranged according to the most approved Systems of Conchology for the purposes of comparison with recent shells, mine as they are found in the strata for the purpose of elucidating the formation of the earth."

Then later in the letter: " I have long wished to be upon terms of intimacy with men of such scientific eminence as yourself, but I have met so many pilferers of information ever since the perfection of my Geological System that I had begun to think such men considered all unpublished observations as lawful plunder."

Two months later on the 20th May, 1808 (Cox, L.R., 1942 p. 54) Smith met Sowerby and the same day wrote proposing a collaboration: "I have long had an inclination of making proposals to you respecting the completion of my work on the strata, which your conversation of this day has rather encouraged me to hope might not prove unacceptable. You seem to be as well convinced of the utility of the geological information I have collected as I am of your very superior method of conducting the publication of such works, and, as I feel myself in some degree incompetent to such a scientific explanation as the subject deserves, I should be glad to know whether, by your taking a certain share of the profits of the publication, you would engage to manage the engraving and the supervising of the manuscripts, sale of the work, etc. I am confident that your abilities and the public announcement of your name to the work would make a great addition to my list of subscribers, and I therefore should expect to give a good proportion of the profits".

The purpose of the venture, aside from the public dissemination of scientific knowledge, was to make money for both Smith and Sowerby. In the event neither benefitted financially, John Phillips recounted in his *Memoirs of William Smith, LLD* (1844) that a Mr. William Lowndes, a friend of Smith, advanced him £50 for the cost of the first number. Sowerby had estimated his cost for each part at £50 and the gross profit on a run of 250 copies would be £93 15s. (individual numbers were priced at 7s 6d, or highly finished at 10s 6d). When the cost of printing and booksellers' percentages were deducted there would have been little chance of any profit either for Smith, Sowerby or indeed repayment of Lowndes's loan. James Sowerby died in 1822, without completing any further parts. However, it is known that in 1828 Roderick Murchison wrote to Smith passing on a request from James De Carl Sowerby (son of James Sowerby) for him to send Part 5 to him which he eventually did in 1837 (Cox, L.R. 1942, p. 56). There is no record as to whether or not Sowerby ever made any progress with the elusive Part 5. Paul Henderson has written a fascinating biography of James Sowerby in his book *James Sowerby: the Enlightenment's natural historian* (Henderson. P. 2015).

As with his map, it seems that there was a degree of hostility from the geological establishment regarding both Smith's publications. In December 1817 Etheldred Benett (1776-1845), the indefatigable lady fossil collector and geologist, well connected to the Geological Society, wrote to Gideon Mantell:

"Smith's Stratigraphical System I have only just caught sight of. It was sent to Mr [Aylmer Bourke] Lambert [1761-1842], to myself and several other People in this neighbourhood, as Subscribers – not one of whom had subscribed to it – and, of course we all returned it! If any Geological friends form a good opinion of it, I shall buy it, but not else, as I do not like his other work!" (pers. comm. Hugh Torrens, 2018).

William Smith's fossil collection and its sale to the British Museum

William Smith had collected fossils for many years. His fossils were the tools of his trade and were essential to his "Science of the Strata". In 1815, when his financial circumstances were at an all time low, he started negotiations to sell this valuable resource to the British Museum. The story of the sale of his geological collection (for it contained rocks as well as fossils) was well documented by the late Joan Eyles (Eyles, J.M., 1967). Most of the following account is sourced from her eloquently written article, supplemented by information from Hugh Torrens (Torrens, H. S. 2016). In 1815, the British Museum was wholly funded by the government through the Treasury and luckily most of the correspondence concerning the sale was preserved in the Public Records Office (now part of the National Archive). During this time the Treasury maintained a register of letters received, together with the original letters, books recording letters sent and Treasury Minute Books. Joan Eyles researched all these documents together with correspondence in the William Smith Archive, previously at the Department of Geology and Mineralogy, Oxford University and now at the Oxford University Museum of Natural History (OUMNH).

The early nineteenth century was a turbulent time; the Napoleonic wars raged from 1803 until 1815 and after the wars there was a severe economic recession which had profound financial implications for Smith. In 1798 Smith had purchased a small estate at Tucking Mill beside the Somerset Coal Canal. He had tried to dispose of the property in 1807 (Torrens, H.S., 2003) but was only partially successful and in 1811 made the ruinous decision to build a small railroad from the newly-opened Kingham Fields Quarry on the edge of Combe Down to a stone-sawing mill he built on a wharf beside the canal. This venture was funded by borrowed capital which Smith anticipated he could easily repay from sales of his geological map. The venture failed due to the poor quality of the quarried stone and Smith was left with a considerable burden of debt. Although his great map was finally published in 1815, sales were not as good as he had hoped and consequently he started negotiations to sell his fossil collection on 1st July of that year. His diary entry for the day notes a meeting with three MPs, one of whom, Nicholas Vansittart (1766-1851) was the Chancellor of the Exchequer, who incidentally had previously been involved in a lunatic attempt to find coal in Sussex (Torrens, H.S., 2002, 2003). They advised Smith to make a submission (a memorial in their terminology) to the Treasury which he did later in the month. His memorial outlined his expertise as a surveyor and map maker, the time and expense he had incurred in collecting the fossils from each stratum and the usefulness of his discoveries to agriculture and mining. The last paragraph requested that the Treasury consider purchase of his collection for the British Museum.

Although Smith was not a member of the Geological Society of London and could not rely on the help of the gentlemanly members, he was surprisingly well connected to the upper echelons of society. It would be unthinkable today to expect the Chancellor of the Exchequer to be concerned with the sale of a collection to the British Museum. Hugh Torrens (Torrens, H.S., 2003) believes Sir Joseph Banks, then President of the Royal Society and one of the Trustees of the Museum, helped instigate the sale. Banks was certainly consulted on the sale of additional fossils and also provided Smith with some hard to find scientific works which Smith used in the preparation of the fossil catalogue. Smith's friend, William Lowndes (1752-1828), Chief Commissioner of the Tax Office, also proved to be a valued supporter during the course of the sale. This is the same William Lowndes who was to lend Smith money to finance publication of *Strata Identified by Organized Fossils*. Also of great assistance was one Thomas Hoblyn (1778-1860), Senior Clerk to the Treasury and later Chief Clerk. It was to Hoblyn that Smith wrote at the end of September 1815 pleading for an advance of "five or seven hundred pounds" on the sale. He had evidently expected the final price to be significantly higher but in the event the total price (including a payment for a catalogue and additional specimens) was only £700.

It was at this time that officials from the British Museum became involved in the negotiations to establish the value of the collection. The Principal Librarian, Joseph Planta (1744-1827), Under Librarian, Charles Konig (1774-1851) and also the chemist Charles Hatchett (1765-1847) visited Smith's home in Buckingham Street on October 10th, 1815. Their first response, even though Smith and his brother had spent time cleaning, arranging and labelling fossils, was to complain at the lack of a proper catalogue. However, despite any formal valuation being made, Smith was granted an advance of £100 and started in earnest, with the help of his young nephew John Phillips, on the creation of a written catalogue. By the end of 1815, Hatchett, Planta and Konig had visited Smith for a second time and recommended that Smith be paid a total of £500, this sum was to be paid in stages and conditional on receipt of the collection and its subsequent "arrangement" by Smith at the Museum. It is likely that Smith would have been very unhappy with this valuation, particularly as he would have been aware that in 1810 a mineral collection of over 14,000 items had been purchased for £13,727 by the museum. However, Charles Hatchett had sold them 7,000 mineral specimens for £700 in 1799, which was comparable to the price Smith received. Nevertheless he had no recourse other than to accept and immediately informed the Treasury that the collection was ready for removal; he was, of course, anxious to receive the second payment and did so shortly after. However, the removal of the collection was delayed; Smith was informed by Konig that the space the Museum had allocated for it was not yet ready so in the meantime Smith continued cataloguing the collection.

Time passed and still no word came from Konig on the readiness of the Museum to accept and house the collection. In desperation Smith again wrote to the Treasury complaining that, as the space in the Museum was still not ready, he had been forced to arrange the specimens in the required order in his own house. Furthermore he informed them that he and Phillips had spent four months completing this task and asked that he receive additional remuneration for the time spent. It is not until June 1816 that the Museum finally took possession of the collection and Smith received the final settlement of £200.

Smith was evidently still unhappy with the settlement and wrote firstly to the Trustees of the Museum and afterwards to the Treasury emphasizing just how much additional work he had undertaken. This request met with an annoyed response from Planta to the Treasury stating that Smith had failed to arrange the specimens at the Museum's apartments thus negating their usefulness and secondly he was unconvinced that Smith had in any way enhanced the value of the collection through additional work. Again Smith prevailed on Lowndes to visit the Museum and report on the collection. During the visit Planta and Konig revealed that the sloping display cases requested by Smith had not been made. Lowndes then wrote to the Treasury recommending further recompense for additional work carried out. In another memorial Smith enlarged on the nature of the additional work, namely that he had arranged the specimens according to Class, Order, Genera and Species as well as the strata from which they came. He also outlined his coding system which he used to label the fossils, the specimens being marked with a capital letter for the genus (in the order in which they were listed for each stratum), then a number for the species and finally a lower case letter for the location. This system uniquely identifies the specimen within each stratum. Not all the specimens are marked with a code, particularly the smaller ones and the bones and teeth. It is unclear when exactly they were labelled in this way and whether or not they are labelled in Smith's own hand or those of his nephew, John Phillips. This is the first time a numbering system was used on a collection of fossils that signified scientific attributes of the specimens. (Hugh Torrens pers. comm.). Smith also referred to the "scientific catalogue" which he had prepared. It is this catalogue which formed the basis of his publication *A Stratigraphical System of Organized Fossils with reference to the specimens of the original geological collection in the British Museum,* which he published in August 1817. Finally he mentioned new material which he had recently collected from a 300 foot well sunk near the Wilts and Berks Canal at Swindon from which he obtained some fine specimens. He offered these and others he had recently collected for sale to the Museum. In due course Smith does indeed receive an further £100 for the extra work on the catalogue but no mention was made of the sale of new fossils.

Presumably because of his mounting debt, Smith showed dogged determination in trying to extract as much money as possible from the Treasury. In August 1817 he wrote again to the Treasury offering three hundred new specimens which he has collected from various parts of the country, ranging stratigraphically from the Crag to the Under Oolite. On behalf of the Trustees, Planta and Konig respond favourably but in a subsequent report to the Treasury, however, Konig declined to place a value on the collection, "it being a matter which he feels himself wholly inadequate to appreciate". Hugh Torrens (Torrens, H.S., 2016, p. 36) has noted that even as late as 1827 Konig was to write "Glass cases were fitted up with sloping shelves for the reception of the greater part of Mr William Smith's collection of Secondary Fossils. [It] is a method not likely to meet with the approbation of the Trustees. It does not appear to possess any advantage over the common way of arranging rocks and fossils, neither are Geologists agreed with regard to several supposed facts intended to be illustrated, and explained, by that arrangement; not to mention that the nomenclature used by W. Smith has not been generally adopted by writers on this subject.", (BM Archives, Original Letters and Papers VI, between ff. 2265–2266). It is clear from this that Konig had no real understanding of Smith's concept, he just did not comprehend stratigraphy, he merely wanted to curate and catalogue.

To his credit, Konig did consult with Sir Joseph Banks about the value of the additional specimens and it was probably Banks's recommendation that secured a further £100. In total Smith received £700, spread over a two year period, for a total of 2,657 specimens (John Phillips, 1844, p. 79). Smith did make further appeals to the Board of Trustees for publication costs of the catalogue but his requests were unanswered.

The indifference shown by officials at the Museum was confirmed in a letter to the *Philosophical Magazine* in 1819 which reported that a request to the Museum to view the Smith collection was answered by "it was not in order, and could not be seen" (Eyles, J.M., 1967). Twenty years later Thomas Hoblyn (now retired) reported that "The specimens remain in the Boxes at the Museum unopened !!!". Furthermore, writing in 1844 Phillips said: "The present state of this "the first stratigraphical collection" ever made, is unknown". However things changed significantly for the better after the opening of the Natural History Museum in 1881, (then known as British Museum (Natural History)). The specimens were transferred to the building in South Kensington and when the new paleontological galleries were opened in 1885-1886 Smith's fossils were at last put on display (Eyles, J.M., 1967). In 1930 it was thought that some 2,000 of the original specimens remained (Cox, L.R., 1930) and currently the number located (including 240 rock specimens) is about the same. At the present time, although not on permanent display, they are carefully preserved and temporary loans of selected specimens have been made to institutions and organizations with a special interest in William Smith. Of note are the Enlightenment Gallery at the British Museum and the Rotunda Museum in Scarborough.

The whole process concerning the sale of Smith's fossil collection to the British Museum must have been both stressful and demeaning for Smith. Time and time again he was forced into the embarrassing position of having to plead for cash advances on the sale in order to fend off his debtors. Smith undoubtedly felt that his collection had been significantly undervalued, as indeed it had been. He was certainly a victim of the economic climate at the time but, this being true, it was officials from the British Museum who were asked by the Treasury to value the collection. It can be argued that if these officials had really understood Smith's pioneering concept of stratigraphy, of which the fossils were a physical expression, then they might have placed a far greater value on the collection. Generally, both civil servants and MPs at the Treasury responded favourably to the Museum's recommendations, many were sympathetic to Smith's situation and were usually prompt to make payments when asked to do so.

A Stratigraphical System of Organized Fossils with reference to the specimens of the original geological collection in the British Museum

At first glance the title of this 1817 publication appears very similar to Smith's *Strata Identified by Organized Fossils* and it is certainly true that there is a degree of overlap. However, in this publication Smith attempted to lay out, for the first time, a systematic arrangement of fossil species ordered according to the position of the strata in which they were embedded. It also served as a catalogue for most of the specimens in his fossil collection. Indeed, in the introduction to the publication he makes it clear that the book is intended to be used in conjunction with his fossil collection, which he expected to be publicly available at the British Museum and because of this believed the inclusion of any engraved figures was unnecessary. Smith does, however, refer readers back to *Strata Identified by Organized Fossils*, his joint venture with Sowerby, and as a further reference suggests consultation of Sowerby's own publication, *Mineral Conchology*. This catalogue goes beyond *Strata Identified* in that it lists the fossils that came to the British Museum and in the Introduction Smith outlines his system in great detail. The fossil names have also been revised by Smith in some instances and locations are not always identical. Smith said he preferred to use Lamarck's system for his taxonomy, which he believed extended and improved on that of Linnaeus. However, he accepted that because of the abundance and variety of English fossil species, many did not fit into the Lamarckian system and because of that he has mostly followed Linnaeus using many new genera defined by Sowerby, Parkinson and others. Smith admitted that his own knowledge of fossil species and genera may be limited but gave a list of numerous scientific works which he had consulted for the purpose of "giving to the specimens the most appropriate and descriptive names". Of interest is another comment which Smith made in the Introduction (vi) which demonstrated his practical and pragmatic approach to science. He said: "My observations on this and on other branches of the subject are entirely original, and unincumbered [sic] with theories for I have none to support: nor do I refer my reader to foreign countries to prove what I advance".

For each of his stratigraphic units Smith describes his fossils in the same order, namely: Zoophites, Testacea, Echini, Crustacea and Bones of large Animals and Fish remains (teeth, palates, vertebrae, etc.). Each species is listed, usually by number e.g. Species 1, Species 2 etc. and these are used for the numeral in the codes inscribed on the specimens. Many species are also identified, often with reference to a plate figure in *Strata Identified,* or in Sowerby's *Mineral Conchology* and occasionally other sources. Usually there is a short description of each species, with a list of the locations where the specimens were found. Smith also included a copy of his *Geological Table of British Organized Fossils*. This remarkable figure, which he had published in various forms, shows the fossil assemblages that identify his strata, the names of the strata on the shelves of the geological collection, the colours of the strata on his map, the names and their "peculiarities" as given in his memoir to the map and finally economic uses of the strata. Interestingly Smith included this note at the foot of the table: "From the reexamination of the Authors numerous Specimens in the arrangement of his Geological Collection in the British Museum and his subsequent observation this list of Strata has been improved and his future exertions will be in proportion to the encouragement which he receives from the public".

The only other chart included by Smith was *Stratigraphical Table of Echini* (pages 110-111), the chart shows the stratigraphic ranges of various echinoids, together with their classification and description. In his introduction (iv) Smith refers to the fact that, in addition to echinoids, he has also constructed similar tables for ammonites, terebratulids and zoophites. In total he says he charted the ranges of more than a hundred species. Included in the current publication is a copy of Smith's *Table of the Distribution of Ammonites* (pages 112-113). The chart published in 1860 (*Quart. Journ. Geol. Soc.* vol. xvi) was drawn up by John Phillips "under the direction of William Smith in 1817" and is similar in format to the echinoid chart. To date, no trace has ever been found of the charts for Terebratula and Zoophites. What is so remarkable about these charts is that they demonstrate that Smith was aware of the stratigraphic ranges of various fossils and hence could judge their individual importance in identifying particular strata.

Like *Strata Identified by Organized Fossils*, *A Stratigraphical System of Organized Fossils* was also unfinished. The table of contents for Part I records coverage down to the Marlstone (No 24). For the rest of the succession Smith stated "Part II; which completed the Work, will be speedily published".

Although never published, a draft MS of Part II is held in the William Smith Archive at OUMNH. The draft lists and describes genera and species from the Blue Marl, the rest of the Lias, the Redland Limestone and the Mountain Limestone (Cox, L.R., 1930). The draft is probably not in Smith's handwriting (for instance it does not show his distinctive curled lower case "d"). Kate Diston (Head of Print and Digital Collections, OUMNH, pers. comm.) believes it may be in John Phillips' hand, for although unlike later examples of his handwriting, he would probably only have been fifteen at the time. In total more that 140 additional specimens are described and located in the MS. The date of the MS is not known precisely, but the paper on which it is printed bears a Britannia watermark similar to that used by James Simmons after 1814.

Even though Part II was never published there is evidence that Smith had made four revisions of Part I before it was printed (Eyles, J.M., 1967 p.198). Also, Hugh Torrens has found evidence of later revision, in Smith's own hand on an annotated copy of *A Stratigraphical System of Organized Fossils* (W. Smith Volume with DeGolyer Bookplate 551.7 Sm68s at the University of Oklahoma). The annotations clearly show that Smith planned to introduce two more of his strata into the publication. These included Sand and Calc Grit (No 13) between the Coral Rag and the Clunch Clay and Sand and Sandstone (No 17) between the Cornbrash and the Forest Marble. He also planned to abandon the term Brick Earth and instead use the term Golt. Similarly Coraline Oolite was to be substituted for Coral Rag and Pisolite. Many of the corrections concerned additional localities, missing specimen numbers on plates and some new species and are relatively minor. However, other changes are more significant, particularly the many additions of the word "Diluvial" after particular fossils. These additions indicated that Smith considered the specimens to be "gravel" or "alluvial" fossils and therefore not in situ. This has particular relevance in regard to two such fossils, *Ammonites communis* and *Tellina* both from Happisburg cliff in Norfolk and figured mistakenly in the London Clay Plate of *Strata Identified by Organized Fossils*. This led Smith to note:

"NB It may be remarked that in Norfolk and Suffolk there are scarcely any London Clay Fossils – The above two are wrong – S. Woodward has only 8 in a numerous list of Norfolk Clay fossils – this confirms my early opinion that <u>London</u> clay extends not into these counties".

The same specimen of *Ammonites communis* is also shown on *the Table of the Distribution of Ammonites* where a footnote (b) marks it "as of a doubtful occurrence; it was probably a drifted specimen". Smith's difficulties in correlating the post-Chalk strata in East Anglia have been described by Peter Riches (Riches, P., 2016-17).

Smith also corrected an error he made in the Whitby area of Yorkshire, where he had previously assigned some fossils to the Clunch, in his corrections he reassigned them to the Liassic Marlstone.

A listing of all fossils, including names, locations and strata in Part I and Part II (MS) shows that in total there are 1,345 specimens listed in the two parts with 472 different species which is less than the "near 700 species" from 2,657 specimens quoted by Smith (Eyles J.M., 1967, p.195). These numbers imply that the catalogue, as listed in *A Stratigraphical System of Organized Fossils Part I-II,* is not a complete listing of all specimens. It is likely that included in the 2,657 specimens are a number of duplicates from the same locality. In Part II duplicates are represented by numbers (often between 1 and 4) appended after localities.

In this discussion of Smith publications and the sale of his fossils to the British Museum it is important to recognize the contribution made by Smith's nephew, John Phillips, whose life and times has been described in Jack Morrell's excellent book, *John Phillips and the business of Victorian science* (Morrell, J., 2005). Phillips (b. 1800) had been orphaned, together with his sister Anne, in 1808. Initially John and Anne lived with William's brother John, and William paid for Phillips to be educated at Holt in Wiltshire. Phillips was clearly an able student and in 1814, after five years at Holt, he spent a year with the Rev. Benjamin Richardson at Farleigh Hungerford were he learned more of geology and taxonomy. In 1815, Smith brought the boy to London where he immediately started assisting Smith prepare his fossil collection for sale. Phillips' precocious talent was soon employed in cataloguing and organising the specimens and preparing tables, and he may also have helped Smith in the preparation of *Strata Identified* (Morrell, J., 2005, p.19). For the best part of a decade Phillips was with Smith learning from the master and in later life went on to become one of the pre-eminent geologists of Victorian times.

Reprinting of Strata Identified by Organized Fossils, including photographs of Smith's original plate fossils and Stratigraphical System of Organized Fossils, with Part II transcribed from Smith's manuscript

In this reprinted version of *Strata Identified* plates containing photographs of Smith's fossils are presented on facing pages each corresponding to its original engraved plate. The fossil photographs are shown to scale mostly at life-size in the same layout as the engraved plates. Occasionally, a figured specimen could not be found in his catalogue, possibly implying that the fossil may never have arrived at the British Museum. Where an exact match could not be found, a specimen of the same species from the Smith collection has been substituted where possible, usually from the same location. The Appendix lists the fossils illustrated with their locations, revised or re-identified names, NHM registration numbers, Smith codes and notes. Where a substitution is included a note has been appended. On the photographic plates of fossil, the revised names of the fossils have been used. Where no fossil could be found its silhouette (derived from the engraved plate) has been included. The engraved and fossil photo plates have been interposed within the relevant original text describing each plate. The overall appearance of the text has been matched to the original printed text, where possible, with only small formatting changes being made.

For unpublished plates where only a MS sketch is available, the sketch has been reproduced facing the corresponding fossil photographs. In *A Stratigraphical System of Organized Fossils* Smith gives his selection of further specimens for new plates. At the end of the description of the Under Oolite (p. 110, two plates), the Sand and Sandstone (p. 111), and the Marlstone (p. 113) Smith designated specimens that he intended to illustrate. Since there are no sketches and specimens may often be from a variety of locations, precise identification of Smith's chosen specimen is difficult. In most cases the best represented specimen has been photographed. The arrangement on the plates follows that adopted in *Strata Identified* with fossils shown according to the systematic approach Smith used in *A Stratigraphical System of Organized Fossils.*

Although Smith would have originally intended the MS sketches and fossils listed for other plates to form part of *Strata Identified by Organized Fossils,* it has been considered more appropriate in this reprint to show them with the relevant fossil descriptions given in *A Stratigraphical System of Organized Fossils.*

Although *A Stratigraphical System of Organized Fossils* was reprinted in 2010 by Cambridge University Press as part of the Cambridge Library Collection, a new digital version is reproduced in the current publication. The original text runs to over 120 pages but here it is reprinted in a smaller font size and in a three column format with Smith's annotated MS corrections (from Hugh Torrens) marked in a blue text.

Three tables are also shown, Smith's *Geological Table of British Organized Fossils, Stratigraphic Table of Echini* and *Table of the Distribution of Ammonites.* (Phillips, J., 1860). Each of these tables has been redrawn from original copies and coloured using an approximation of Smith stratigraphic tints. The version of *Geological Table of British Organized Fossils* used shows Smith's numbers for each stratum. It is known that Smith intended to use this version in a corrected edition. Similarly, Smith's MS corrections to the *Stratigraphic Table of Echini* have been used and added in a blue text.

Part II has been transcribed from Smith's MS notes (probably in his nephew, John Phillips' hand) and reproduced with a typeface similar to that used in Part I.

In all his work, Smith was very particular to record the exact location of each of his fossils; at the time of original publication he did not show localities on his maps. However, in the current publication, a short section with a discussion of Smith's fossil locations and his maps follows *A Stratigraphical System of Organized Fossils.* A map of fossil locations is shown with the size of the location marker representing the number of specimens at each locality. This is followed by a series of larger scale maps showing locations on several Smith geological maps, including a facsimile of his first geological map around Bath which he made in 1799.

STRATA

IDENTIFIED BY

ORGANIZED FOSSILS,

CONTAINING

𝕻rints on 𝕮olored 𝕻aper

OF THE MOST

CHARACTERISTIC SPECIMENS

IN EACH

STRATUM

BY WILLIAM SMITH,

MINERAL SURVEYOR,

AUTHOR OF "MAP OF THE STRATA OF ENGLAND AND WALES," AND
"A TREATISE ON IRRIGATION."

𝕷ondon:

Printed by W. Arding, 21, *Old Boswell Court, Carey Street;*

And sold by the AUTHOR, 15, Buckingham Street, Strand; J. SOWERBY, 2, Mead Place,

Lambeth; SHERWOOD, NEELY, and JONES, and LONGMAN, HURST,

REES, ORME and BROWN, Paternoster Row;

And by all Booksellers.

JUNE 1, 1816-1819.

JUNE 1, 1816.

No. 1.
STRATA

IDENTIFIED BY

ORGANIZED FOSSILS,

CONTAINING

Four Plates:

Frontispiece---Large Fossil Tooth opalized.

London Clay Fossils.

Crag   Do.

Upper Chalk   Do.

The Work will be comprised in Seven Numbers, quarto, price 7s. 6d.; highly finished copies 10s. 6d. each.

To be continued Monthly, in the order of Strata, until complete.

Five Plates, engraved by SOWERBY, will be given in the next Number.

All the Figures will be printed on coloured paper, to represent that of the Stratum in which the Specimens were found; and with reference to Mr. SMITH's Map of the Strata of England and Wales; which may be had of Mr. CARY, Map Engraver, 181, Strand. References are likewise made to SOWERBY's Mineral Conchology of Great Britain

OCTOBER 1, 1816.

No. 2.
STRATA

IDENTIFIED BY

ORGANIZED FOSSILS,

CONTAINING

Five Plates:

Lower or Hard Chalk, frequently called Grey Chalk.

Class of Strata beneath the Chalk.

Green or Chlorite Sand.

Micaceous Brick Earth.

Portland Stone.

The Work will be comprised in Seven Numbers, quarto, price 7s. 6d.; highly finished copies 10s. 6d. each.

To be continued Monthly, in the order of Strata, until complete.

Five Plates, engraved by SOWERBY, will be given in the next Number.

All the Figures will be printed on coloured paper, to represent that of the Stratum in which the Specimens were found; and with reference to Mr. SMITH's Map of the Strata of England and Wales; which may be had of Mr. CARY, Map Engraver, 181, Strand.

References are likewise made to SOWERBY's Mineral Conchology of Great Britain, and British Mineralogy.

SEPTEMBER 1, 1817.

No. 3.
STRATA

IDENTIFIED BY

ORGANIZED FOSSILS,

CONTAINING

Five Plates:

Oak Tree Clay.

Coral Rag and Pisolite.

Clunch Clay and Shale.

Kelloways Stone.

The Work will be comprised in Seven Numbers, quarto, price 7s. 6d.; highly finished copies 10s. 6d. each.

All the Figures will be printed on coloured paper, to represent that of the Stratum in which the Specimens were found; and with reference to Mr. SMITH's Map of the Strata of England and Wales; which may be had of Mr. CARY, Map Engraver, 181, Strand.

References are likewise made to SOWERBY's Mineral Conchology of Great Britain, and British Mineralogy.

The Subscribers to this Work, by reference to Mr. Smith's Section of the Strata and Geological Table, published by Mr. Cary, may now perceive the plan and extent of this Work, and be satisfied that it will not exceed the seven Numbers proposed.

No. I. comprises	PLAINS	London Clay	1	Number of Colour
		Crag	3	on the Section and
	CHALK HILLS	Upper Chalk } Lower ditto	5	Table.
No. II.		Green Sand	6	
		Brickearth	7	
		Portland Rock	9	
	CLAY VALES	Oak-tree Clay	11	
		Coral Rag and Pisolite	12	
No. III.		Clunch Clay and Shale	14	
		Kelloways Stone	15	

No. 4.
STRATA

IDENTIFIED BY

ORGANIZED FOSSILS,

CONTAINING

Five Plates:

Cornbrash.

Forest Marble.

Clay over the Oolite.

Upper Oolite.

Fuller's Earth Rock.

The Subscribers to this Work, by reference to Mr. Smith's Sections of the Strata and Geological Table, published by Mr. Cary, may now perceive the plan and extent of this Work, and be satisfied that it will not exceed the seven Numbers proposed.

No. I. comprises	PLAINS	London Clay	1	Nos. of Colour on the
		Crag	3	Sections and Tables.
	Chalk Hills	Upper Chalk } Lower ditto }	5	
		Green Sand	6	
No II.		Brickearth	7	
		Portland Rock	9	
	Clay Vales	Oaktree Clay	11	
		Coral Rag and Pisolite	12	
No. III.		Clunch Clay and Shale	14	
		Kelloway's Stone	15	
		Cornbrash	16	
		Forest Marble	18	
No. IV.	Stonebrash Hills	Clay over the Upper Oolite	19	
		Upper Oolite	20	
		Fuller's Earth Rock	21	

INTRODUCTION

The present age is distinguished by many of the most extraordinary discoveries that were ever unfolded to the human mind; and amongst them the discoveries in Chemistry stand pre-eminent. The most extensively useful part of this science has, however, been long before the Public, and contributed greatly to the improvement of various branches of manufacture; but the benefits of Chemistry have not yet been extended to the soil.

Agriculture in this, as in most other instances, is the last to profit by any thing new. That easy analysis of the soil, which seemed to promise great advantages to the Farmer, by telling him correctly the component parts of the materials he has to work upon, has not been spread through the country, or even yet become an object of attention with many of the best informed Farmers, by whom the advantages of this science must be carried into effect; and while the theory is in the possession of one class of men, and the practice in another, who have little or no connexion, it is greatly to be feared, that the culture of land may long remain without its expected benefits from Chemistry.

In a similar way, also, the benefits resulting from the science of Botany, have been equally limited, and likely to remain so, until those who grow the grasses shall take the trouble to distinguish one from another, or until those who know them scientifically shall condescend to become the cultivators.

Nature furnishes the clue to each of these sciences, and to the most extensive application of their benefits.

She has also given the Farmer other more easy helps, to much of the useful knowledge he requires.

The method of knowing the Substrata from each other by their various substances imbedded, will consequently shew the difference in their soils. – All this is attainable by rules the most correct, and easily learnt, and also the simplest and most extensive that can well be devised; for by the help of organized Fossils alone, a science is established with character on which all must agree, as to the extent of the Strata in which they are imbedded, those characters are universal; and a knowledge of them opens the most extensive sources of information, without the necessity of deep reading, or the previous acquirement of difficult arts.

The organized Fossils (which might be called the antiquities of Nature,) and their localities also, may be understood by all, even the most illiterate: for they are fixed in the earth as not to be mistaken or misplaced; and may be as readily referred to in any part of the course of the Stratum which contains them, as in the cabinets of the curious; and, consequently, they furnish the best of all clues to a knowledge of the Soil and Substrata.

INTRODUCTION

The practicability of thus distinguishing so great a variety of materials in the earth, as successively terminate at the surface being admitted; and their courses delineated in a large map of the Strata just published; I may now confidently proceed with a general account of those organized Fossils, which I found imbedded in each Stratum, and which first enabled me more particularly to distinguish one Stratum from another.

Fossil Shells had long been known amongst the curious, collected with care, and preserved in their cabinets, along with other rarities of nature, without any apparent use. That to which I have applied them is new, and my attention was first drawn to them, by a previous discovery of regularity in the direction and dip of the various Strata in the hills around Bath; for it was the nice distinction which those similar rocks required, which led me to the discovery of organic remains peculiar to each Stratum. Their perfect state of preservation, and most tender structure, raised a doubt respecting their diluvian origin, and a close attention to the Gravel Fossils, clearly proved *two distinct operations of water.*

The Fossils of the former deposit being all finely preserved, while those of the latter, (which are chiefly superficial,) are all greatly rounded by attrition. Those of the first class are never found but in their respective sites in the Strata; – those of the latter, by their promiscuous mixture, superficial situation, and other circumstances, most strongly confirm the previous deposit, and complete induration of the Strata which contain the former. Conceiving, therefore, the Gravel Fossils to be the most indubitable effects of a great body of water passing over the surface of the earth, with violence sufficient to tear up fragments of the Strata, round them by attrition, and drive them many miles from their regular beds to the promiscuous situations which they now occupy. These have been called *alluvial Fossils,* and the Gravel which contains them being thus clearly distinguished from the regular Strata beneath, much of the mystery in which Fossil Shells, and other materials of the earth were involved, seemed to be removed by this distinction.

Thus far it may be necessary to apprise the reader of the meaning here attached to the word alluvial.

The organized Fossils which come under that head, being as various as the Strata from whence they have been dislodged, an account of them will most properly be given in the last number.

Under the same head, also, will be given, further particulars of the Frontispiece, or annexed Engraving of a singular Fossil Tooth, of some extinct monstrous unknown animal, which is opalized;---found in Norfolk.

Fossil Tooth, "of some extinct monstrous unknown animal found in Norfolk" *Tab: I.*

FRONTISPIECE PLATE (AND FACING PAGE)

Mastodon tooth: *Anancus arvernensis*

0 cm 1 2 3 4 5 6 7 8 9 10

STRATA

WITH ORGANIZED FOSSILS

THE eastern and south-eastern half of England, as far inland as a curved line from Exeter to Teesmouth, abounds with organized Fossils, regularly imbedded in the Strata. The vast expanse of red Marl and its Sandstone, has none of them, but they are very abundant in the Limestones which accompany it.

These, however, occupy but a small portion of the island, compared to the great extent of Strata before-mentioned, and when it is considered that in the remainder of the Strata, Red and Dunstone, Killas and Granite, organized Fossils are not found, or very rare; they seem chiefly confined to the district before described, and to the Coalmeasures, the former nearly all animal, and the latter chiefly vegetable. The Muscles and Ammonites found in Ironstone of the Coalmeasures, and the bituminized wood of blue clays, in the other district, being trifling exceptions to general rules so extensive.

The eastern side of the island is, therefore, best for the commencement of regular observations on the organized Fossils which are illustrative of its Geology. It is also necessary that the series of British Strata, for the simplification of science, should be considered in classes. The part above the Chalk is one, and the principal divisions of which it is susceptible, are reducible to two---a great Sand and a great Clay, with a general parting of Crag; but each of these is subject to considerable variations.

The Sand lies next the Chalk, and the clay over that forms insular hills.

The great Sand is in many places interspersed with Clay, or Brickearth, and the Clay as frequently with Sand and Loam. Pebbles are common to both, but to what depth beneath the surface may be difficult to determine.

The chief partition Strata have not always the same appearance. The Crag being, in some parts of its course, composed of shells and sand, in some places of shells and clay, and in others of shells and coral, united in a soft stoney rock, which about Orford is used in building. In other places the shells are filled with, and imbedded in a hard blue grey Sandstone, and in some parts of their course they appear to be deficient, or found only thinly interspersed with a blue grey concreted loam, or indurated Brickearth. The alluvial Pebbles, Clay, and Sand spread over great breadths of the plains formed by the surface of these thin partition Strata, much increases the difficulty of tracing their outcrops.

The greatest breadth of the Clay is in Essex, and the vicinity of London, as described in my delineation of the Strata by the dun or dark blue colour, and the localities of the most remarkable sites of its organized Fossils, are noted in a list which accompanies the explanation of the plate.

The other great division of Sand and Brickearth, is represented on the map by yellowish brown, and the sites of its peculiar Fossils under the head of Crag, similarly described---but the partition Strata which produce these shells, vary so much in hardness, colour, consistence, and uses, as to render a local description of one part, almost unintelligible to those who are acquainted with it in another. For on a cursory view of these shelly Strata in their course through the three north-eastern counties, from the banks of the Thames, some miles below London, it is singular that a considerable distinction in the site or accompaniments of the shells should be peculiar to each of the counties.

The shells in Essex are lodged in a strong blue Clay which makes a tenacious soil.

All through Suffolk in a light or blowing Sand, which, in many parts of the course of Crag, is some of the worst land in the county.

Through Norfolk the shells lie much nearer to, or in contact with the top of the Chalk, and under a loamy soil, on or near some of the best land in Fleg and the Vale of Aylesham.

In the present state of our knowledge of these Strata, and the shells they contain, any attempt at a minute division of them, seems, therefore, more likely to perplex, than instruct the reader.

The strong features only of the country, will therefore, first be noticed. The order of nature which is shown by my discoveries, suggests the outline of the work, and the different Strata serving like chapters for the principal divisions, the subject will be so treated; taking each of their outcrops in succession, from East to West. The figures of organized Fossils in each Stratum are printed on coloured paper, to correspond with the most general colour of the matter in which they are imbedded, and also with that by which their courses are represented on the Map; where otherwise, as in the Chalk, it will be particularly noticed under each head.

It may be necessary to remark, that the Strata over Chalk, occupy much of the eastern, south, and south-eastern coast of England, and seem to be only parts of much larger districts of corresponding Strata on the Continent.

In England this class is separated into three portions, by vacancies on the heights of Hampshire, and in the sea by the Wash. The mouth of the Humber makes also a lesser division – but for these, the class might be said to extend from Dorsetshire to Yorkshire, for Pool Harbour is in one extremity, and Bridlington Bay in the other.

The northern-most of the three principal portions, North and South of the Humber, is small, long, and narrow, lying· low, and as yet little noticed for organized Fossils, except large bones washed out of the crumbly cliffs of Holderness, which correspond with those washed out of similar cliffs on the coast of East Norfolk, Suffolk, Essex, East Kent, and South Hants.

The middle and principal portion extends north-eastward from the Hampshire Hills to the coast of Norfolk; it flanks the Chalk through Surrey and Kent, on the south side of the Thames; the Buckinghamshire and Hertfordshire Chalk Hills on the north side. It embraces the whole Estuary of the Thames; spreads over nearly all Essex, three-fourths of Suffolk, and all the eastern half of Norfolk, except the Vales about Norwich and Aylesham.

The southern portion, chiefly in Hampshire and Dorsetshire, narrows both ways from its widest part about the new Forest, to its western extremity, near Dorchester, and its eastern, near Brighton. Its widest part is from Newport in the Isle of Wight, to the similar elevations of Chalk and down lands, between Salisbury and Winchester. Each of these districts is abundantly stored with organized Fossils. Large teeth and bones, greatly resembling those on the Continent, have been most frequently collected from the shores of the middle portion, and large vertebrae further inland, at Whitlingham, Leiston old Abbey, Diss, Hoxney, and Hawkedon.

3

LONDON CLAY.

SOIL.--*Colour,* Orange brown, Y. R. B. 2, of Sowerby's Chromatic Scale, varying when wet.
  Consistence, Tenacious; free from Stone; dries clotty; cracks in drying; surface
  frequently covered with alluvial Pebbles.
SUBSOIL and Ditches, Retentive.
EXCAVATIONS, Hold Water.
STRATUM, Dry, of a dun colour. Darker when wet.
WATER, Rarely any; the little which it produces of a bad quality.

THIS thick Stratum, from its being the site of the Metropolis, and most abundant in its environs, has been called the London Clay. Its course north-eastward to the sea is described in the Map by the same colour as the plate annexed.

The greatest length, from S. W. to N. E. is in a line passing from Richmond, through London to Harwich.

The greatest breadths, from Norwood Hill to Enfield Chase, and from Langdon Hills to the extremity of Epping Forest. It thence occupies the heights in the hundreds of Essex, and east of Chelmsford and Colchester; extends through the Sokens to the sea side at Walton Nase and Harwich.

The soil is of a mellow brown or umber colour, and the subsoil generally the same, although the Stratum deeper (as lately shown by the tunnels under London,) is of the colour by which I have endeavoured to represent it.

The exact boundaries of soft Strata are generally difficult to define, but particularly so in this district, where they alternate with no hard materials in the form of Rock.

Outcrops also of such loose Strata, are too confused for the Geologist to avail himself of the distinctive advantages to be derived from their peculiar imbedded Fossils, as throughout the district over Chalk, they are found only in deep excavations.

The shelly part of the London Clay bears but a small proportion to the thickness of the mass. The shells, therefore, should rather be considered as Indices to the site of that particular part, than to a knowledge of the whole. They lie near the bottom of the Stratum, and in some instances are difficult to be distinguished from those of the Crag, which accompanies the sand.

ORGANIZED FOSSILS.

FIG.
1 Vivipara fluviorum — Well at Brixton Causeway. Hordwell Cliff.
2 Tellina, &c. — Sheppey. Happisburgh.
3 Arca Linn. Pectunculus *Lam.* — Bognor.
4. Chama — Hordwell Cliff.

FIG.

5 Voluta spinosa	Barton.	
6 Voluta	Bognor.	
7 Cerithium	Woolwich.	Bracklesham Bay.
8 Large Shark's tooth	Sheppey.	Highgate.
9 Small do.	Highgate.	
10 Pectunculus decussatus	Highgate.	
11 Ammonites communis	Happisburgh.	
12 Calyptrea, *Lam.*	Barton Cliff.	
13 Crab	Highgate. Sheppey.	

SITES OF LONDON CLAY. *FOSSILS.*

Bognor	Newhaven Castle.
Selsea Bill	Harwich.
Stubbington	Sheppey.
Ryde, Isle of Wight	Bexley Heath.
Muddiford	Woolwich.
Barton and Hordwell Cliffs	Highgate.
Alum Bay	Brentford.
Emsworth	Richmond.
Pagham	

LONDON CLAY.—*Sowerby's Mineral Conchology.*
Fusus Longrevus, Tab. 63. Barton and Hordwell Cliffs. Muddiford.
Vivipara lenta, Tab. 31. Fig. 3. Barton and Hordwell Cliffs.
Nautilus Imperialis, Tab. I. Highgate. Brentford. Minster Cliff, Isle of Sheppey.
Modiola elegans, Tab. 9. Bognor. Highgate. Richmond.
Venericardia planicosta, Tab. 50. Bracklesham Bay.
Teredo antenautæ   Sheppey.
                     Highgate.
                     Regent's Canal.
                     Croydon Canal.
Sowerby's Mineralogy.—Tab. 14. Pag. 33.
Argilla Marga, containing shells. Streatham, in Surry.
The Fossil shells of the Southern portion of this Clay, were first regularly described by Brander.

Those of the district round London, many years since excited much curiosity, from the great quantity turned up in digging the foundation of a house in Hanging Wood, near Woolwich.

They have, also, been found in sinking various wells around the Metropolis, but the recent excavations for a tunnel through Highgate Hill, brought them most into notice.

LONDON CLAY. Brit. Min: 246.

Tab. 2

Nº 1. Viripara fluviorum Min: Con: t. 31. f. 1.

2. Tellina &c.

3. Pectunculus Brit: Min: t. 35.

4. Chama.

5. Voluta spinosa Min: Con: t. 115. f. 2.

Nº 6. Voluta.

7. Cerithium. Lamarck.

8. Large Sharks Tooth.

9. Small Dº.

10. Pectunculus decussatus Min: Con: t. 27. f. 1.

Nº 11. Ammonites communis Min: Con: t. 107. f. 2. 3.

12. Calyptrea. Lamarck.

13 Shell of a Crab. Sheppy.

PLATE 1 (AND FACING PAGE)

EOCENE (MOSTLY), INCLUDING LONDON CLAY

1. Gastropod (clipped from block): *Viviparus suessoniensis*
2. Bivalves (clipped from block): *Abra splendens*
3. Bivalve: *Glycymeris brevirostris*
4. Bivalve: *Chama squamosa*
5. Gastropod: *Volutospina luctator*

6. Gastropod: *Volutospina denudata*
7. Gastropod: *Brotia melanioides*
8. Shark's tooth: *Otodus obliquus*
9. Shark's tooth indet.
10. Bivalve: *Striarca wrigleyi*

11. Ammonite: *Dactylioceras commune*
probably from glacial till (extinct by Eocene)
12. Gastropod: *Sigapatella aperta*
13. Crab: *Zanthopsis* sp. *

0 cm 1 2 3 4 5

Fossils in silhouette have not been found
* *similar fossil substituted from Smith's collection*

CRAG.

CRAG is a local term for shells mixed with sand, overlaying the Chalk, in the counties of
Norfolk and Suffolk.

It is best known and most in use for agricultural purposes in the latter county.

It extends from Tattingstone Park south of Ipswich, through the East Sands or Flock district, to Henham
Park west of Southwold.

Re-appears South and North of the Yare, below Norwich, at Bramerton and Thorpe, and has been found
at Marsham in the vale of Aylesham, in its course to the sea side west of Cromer.

Crag is but a small proportion in thickness of the sandy Strata overlaying chalk.

ORGANIZED FOSSILS.

FIG.

1 Murex contrarius	Thorpe Common, Harwich. Alderton, Suffolk. Holywell near Ipswich. Tattingstone Park.
2 M. striatus	Bramerton, Holywell, Alderton, Aldborough.
3 Turbo littoreus	Bramerton. Trimingsby. Thorpe Common. Leis--ton old Abbey, between Norwich & Yarmouth.
4 Turbo *Linn.* Turritella *Lam.*	Thorpe Common.
5 Patella Fissura *Linn.* Emarginula *Lam.*	Bramerton. Harwich. Holywell.
6 Balanus tesselatus	Bramerton.
7 Arca *Linn.* Pectunculus *Lam.*	Tattingstone Park. Thorpe Common.
8 Cardium *Linn.*	Bramerton, Happisburgh (or Hasbro'). Tatting-stone. Trimingsby.
9 Mya lata	Bramerton. Trimingsby.
10 11 12 13 14 } Vertebrae	Thorpe Common.
15 Palate	Tattingstone Park
16 Tooth	Stoke Hill.
17 18 19 } Teeth	Reading. Ipswich.
20 Quadruped's Bone	Tattingstone Park.
21 Stalactite	Burgh Castle.

CRAG. *Sowerby's Min. Conch.*
Scalaria similis, *Tab.* 16. Bramerton. Holywell. Also at Newhaven Castle.
Murex corneus, *Tab.* 35. Aldborough. Holywell. Walton Nase.

Several Fossil shells of this and the Stratum preceding, greatly resemble some which are recent. In the Clay they are generally white, but some in the Crag, as Turbo littoreus, often retain their natural colour.

Oysters, of various sorts, found plentifully in the Strata over Chalk, seem to define the course of Crag at the following places: – Headley, Reading, Woolwich, Blackheath, and in stone at Stifford, in a valley one mile south of Hertford, at Beckingham and Damerham, and in stone at New Cross, and Addington Hills, near Croydon.

Crabs and Lobsters are more numerous in these than in any of the inferior Strata.

Horns of very large animals are also found in low places, where these Strata approach the Marshes, which are considered to be alluvial.

Ivory has been collected from the sandy Crag; teeth, vertebrae, and other bones are numerous in it, some of these, and the shells being rounded and mixed with fragments of numerous imperfect shells, lead to an opinion that this part of the Crag may be alluvial. It is, however, traced through the same course of country, and if not connected with the stoney Crag, is so very contiguous thereto, as not to be separated in a general account.

The stoney calcareous Crag is in more regular layers than the sandy. In some places it appears to be covered with Brickearth. Shells are found perfect in this sort, which are probably only fragments in the other, and some perfect in that, are only casts in this, as the murex striatus of Sowerby.

CRAIG.

Nº 1. *Murex contrarius*, Reversed Whelk. Min:Con:t.25.

2. *Murex striatus*, Striated Whelk. Min:Con:t.22.

3. *Turbo littoreus*, (Perriwincle) Bramerton.

4. *Turbo*, Linn. Turritella Lam.

5. *Patella fissura* Linn. Emarginula Lam.M.C:t.55.

6. *Balanus tessellatus* M.C:t.84.

7. *Arca* Linn. Pectunculus Lam.

Nº 8. *Cardium* Linn.

9. *Mya lata* M.C:t.81.

10. Short vertebra of a Fish.

11. Elongated or Hourglass vertebra.

12. Another, worn.

13. }
14. } Dº showing the six costa forming a sort of star.

Nº 15. Palate Bone of a Fish.

16. Large Sharks tooth worn.

17. } Three others; such are found in the Lon-
18. } don Clay in a more perfect state but they
19. } are characteristic here from being worn very smooth.

20. Quadrupeds bone.

21. An angular stalactite.

PLATE 2 (AND FACING PAGE)

PLIO-PLEISTOCENE CRAG

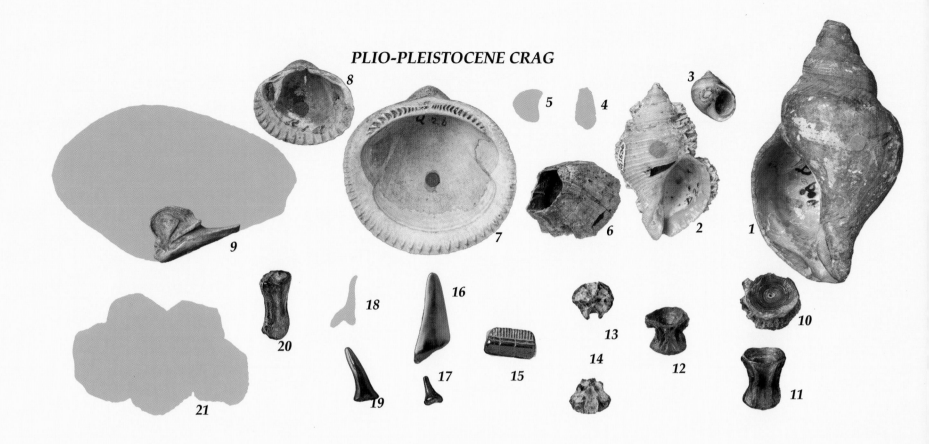

1. Gastropod: *Neptunea angulata*
2. Gastropod: *Nucella incrassata* with encrusting barnacles
3. Gastropod: *Littorina littorea*
4. Gastropod: *Potamides tricinctus*
5. Gastropod: *Emarginula fissura*
6. Barnacle: *Balanus* sp.
7. Bivalve: *Glycymeris variabilis*

8. Bivalve: *Cerarstoderma hostei*
9. Bivalve: *Mya arenaria* (hinge only) *
10. Fish vertebra, teleost indet.
11. Vertebra: *Platax woodwardi*
12. Vertebra, teleost indet. (worn)
13. Vertebra: half a teleost indet.
14. Vertebra indet, as above

15. Tooth palate of an Eagle Ray: *?Aetobatus* sp.
16. Shark's tooth: '*Isurus*'sp.
17. Shark's tooth: ? Lamnid
18. Shark's tooth: ?Lamnid
19. Shark's tooth. 'Odontaspid' type probably all re-worked from the London Clay
20. Toe phalange, possibly gazelle
21. Stalactite (not fossil animal)

0 cm 1 2 3 4 5

Fossils in silhouette have not been found
* similar fossil subsituted from Smith's collection

UPPER CHALK.

SOIL.---*Colour*, generally brown, but by the sides of hills of various mellow tints, from that to brownish white.

Consistence, loose, crumbly, thickly interspersed with Flints, absorbent.

SUBSOIL, and Ditches, white, dry.

EXCAVATIONS ditto ditto.

STRATUM, dry to a great depth.

WATER, remarkably bright and clear, in chalk roads and rivulets white in hasty rains.

The chalk Stratum is generally known by the feature which it gives to our Island, in the white cliffs of Britain, and long ranges of interior hills.

For want of colour in the Stratum, it is defined in my map by a green line.

Its course through the Island from the English Channel to the German Ocean, is from S. W. to N. E. from a point on the western extremity of Dorsetshire, to Flambro'head in Yorkshire, with a considerable curve to the eastward. It has two singular branches from Hampshire, one through Sussex, and the other through Surry and Kent, which approach the sea in their respective cliffs at Beachy head and Dover. These are the chains of hills which it forms; its greatest plains are in Wiltshire and Hampshire.

Insular parts occur in the Isle of Thanet, and the Isle of Wight, and on the western extremities of the Stratum in Dorsetshire.

The Flints which constantly accompany the upper part of this Stratum in abundance, furnish materials for its identification, far superior to those of the laxer Strata above it.

Our fields and highways are frequently strewed with Zoophites, Echini, and other fine Fossils of this Stratum, turned up by the plough, or brought in Gravel for repairing the roads.

The upper part of the Chalk is particularly distinguished by numerous Zoophites, and other marine remains, so that in some parts there are but few of those innumerable knotty and irregular Flints, but owe their form to a nucleus of some such organization.

ORGANIZED FOSSILS.

FIG.

1 Alcyonium Flint, others in Chalk	Wighton. Wilts.
2 Ditto	Wighton.
3 Serpula	Norwich.
4 Valves of Lepas, *Linn.*	Norwich.
5 Hollow Valve of Ostrea	Norwich.
6 Flatter Valve of Ditto	Norwich.
7 Ditto attached to a Belemnite	Norwich.
8 Pecten	Norwich.
9 Terebratula subundata, (long variety)	Norwich.
10 Echinus	N. of Norwich. Croydon. Taverham, Wilts.
11 Palate of a Fish	Warminster.

12	Part of Echinus	N. of Norwich.
13	Echinus Spine	N. of Norwich.
14	Shark's Tooth with 2 ridges	N. of Norwich.
15	Shark's Tooth serrated	N. of Norwich.
16	Vertebræ	N. of Norwich.

Ovate Echini and Zoophites, without enumerating localities, may be found any where on the surface of Upper Chalk.

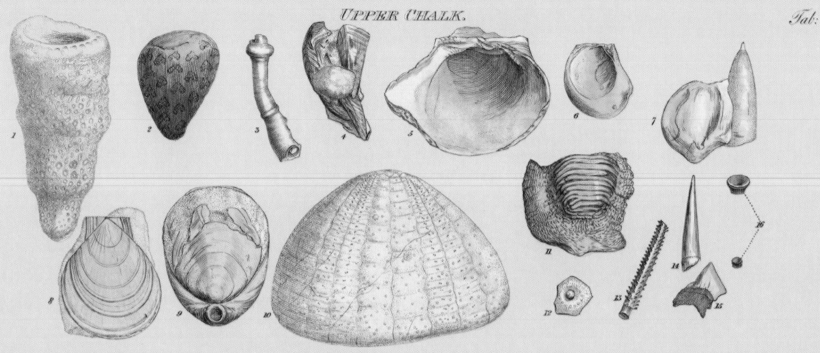

UPPER CHALK.

Tab: 3

Nº 1. Flint Alcyonite.

2. Flint Alcyonite.

3. Serpula.

4. Fragments of a Lepas. Linn.

5. Hollow valve of a Shell allied to Ostrea.

6. Flatter valve of Dº.

Nº 7. Dº attached to a Belemnite.

8. Pecten.

9. Terebratula subundata. Min: Con: t. 15. f. 7.

10. Echinus. Linn.

11. Fishes palate.

12. Part of an Echinus.

Nº 13. Muricated Echinus spine.

14. Sharks tooth with two sharp ridges.

15. Sharks tooth serrated.

16. Vertebræ.

PLATE 3 (AND FACING PAGE)

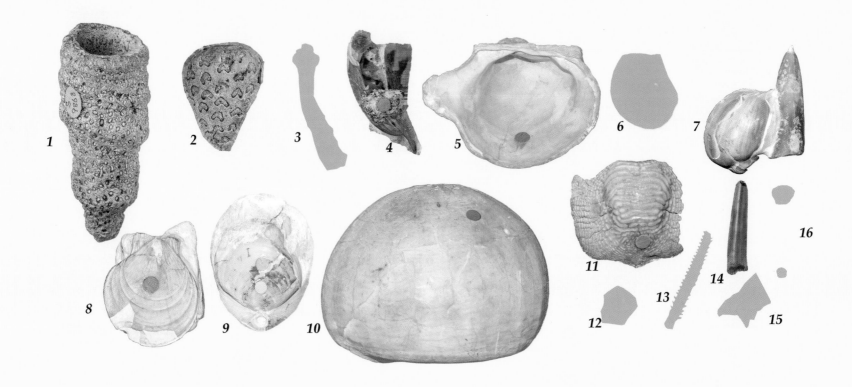

1. Sponge: *Sporadoscinia alcyonoides*
2. Sponge: *Toulminia catenifer*
3. Tube worm: *?Filogranula sp.*
4. Barnacle fragment: *Regioscalpellum maximum*
5. Oyster (interior): *Pycnodonte vesicularis*
6. Oyster (interior): *Pycnodonte vesicularis*

7. Belemnite: *Belemnitella mucronata* attached to oyster
8. Bivalve: *Mimachlamys mantelliana*
9. Brachiopod: *Concinnithyris subundata*
10. Echinoid: *Echinocorys scutata* *
11. Fish palate: *Ptychodus mammillaris*
12. Echinoid: basal plate of a cideroid with boss for spine

13. Echinoid: spine of a cideroid
14. Fish tooth: *Enchodus* sp.
15. Shark tooth: 'Corax' tooth
16. Vertebra: indet. (possibly shark)

0 cm 1 2 3 4 5 6 7 8 9 10

Fossils in silhouette have not been found
* *similar fossil substituted from Smith's collection*

LOWER or HARD CHALK,

Frequently called GREY CHALK.

SOIL.-- *Colour,*   Light brown, frequently grey, with small fragments of stoney Chalk, and in some places almost white.

In several places Chalk is exposed by cutting away the turf, in the form of a horse.*

    On the White or Malm Land, at the foot of the hills, of a dirty grey, called *White Land.*

Consistence,   Crumbly, with a mixture of whitish grey Flints :—Lower on the sides of steep hills, chiefly small rubble stoney Chalk, thinly interspersed with some browner fragments of soil—all very dry—at the foot of the hills mouldering when dry; smeary when wet.

SUBSOIL - *Colour,*   White, greyish white, or blue grey, small rubbly Chalk—pulverizable Malm, dry.

EXCAVATIONS,
HOLLOW-WAYS, } Grey or bluish white, dry.
STRATUM, White, bluish white, or light grey; soft stone, which moulders with frost.
WATER, Bright, transparent.

THE bottom part of the Chalk, now under consideration, defines the boundary of that thick Stratum, which, though here divided into upper and under, has no distinct separation. It is the escarpment of this lower part of the Stratum, which forms in the west and midland counties the abrupt edge of the Chalk hills. Its course is the same as that of upper Chalk, before described. The chain of hills which extend in a north-easterly direction, from Dorsetshire to the fens, though they gradually diminish in height north-eastward, may be viewed distinctly from the similar and parallel escarpment of the Oolite rocks, as well from the heights near Sherborne, Bath, and Cheltenham, and the whole range of Cotswold hills; as also from the similar eminences in Oxfordshire and Northamptonshire.

    The more northern part of this chalky range is likewise conspicuous from the Lincolnshire ridge of Oolite.

    In Yorkshire, the escarpment of Chalk seems to form the western limits of the great vale of York. In the vicinity of New Malton, its dry surface, as at Swaffham in Norfolk, and on the Downs of Wiltshire, is equally famed for coursing and the sports of the field.

*The original white horse, which gives name to the hill and rich vale adjoining, 5 miles from Wantage, is thought to have been cut in honour of Alfred the Great, who was born in the neighbourhood: a white horse being the arms of Saxony.

Two others have since been cut in the turf near Calne and Westbury, and one lately near Marlborough.

The short turf of the Chalk hills, the site of ancient British sports, the seats of Druidism and ancient Kings, will ever continue to be favourite places of amusement: Gentlemen of *the Turf* having found this to be the best for ascertaining the comparative speed of British horses; the races of Newmarket, Epsom, Salisbury, Brighton, and several other places being on this Stratum. These open hills are also the sites of many large fairs and rustic sports. The Chalk hills have the purest air, and the clearest water flows in abundance from almost every part of their base.

This under part of the Stratum is much less chalky than the upper, it being scarcely anywhere soft enough for writing. It is in some places sufficiently indurated for building, in many burnt to lime, and in some parts used on the roads combined with flints, or, for want of better materials, alone; as at Market-Weighton, Marlborough, and the vicinity of Warminster.

Sharp ridges terminating in prominencies, are formed of this under part of the Chalk Stratum, as that between Dorchester and Weymouth, which extends through the Isle of Purbeck, to the remarkable promontory at its east end, which recommences in a still more remarkable one called the Needles, and extends in a ridge through the Isle of Wight. The promontory of Beachyhead is formed by the termination of a ridge of Chalk, called the South Downs; and that between Folkstone and Dover, of the ridge of Chalk which extends from thence through Kent and Surrey, to the Hogsback.

The chain of hills formed by the escarpment of this part of the Stratum, toward the south, and of the South Downs toward the north, are called, by the inhabitants of the interior weald district, the north and south Chalk hills. These, and other part of the Chalk, from the abrupt ascent occasioned by it on every road south-west and north of London, are well known to travellers; as Beachy-head, Flamborough-head, and the north Foreland and cliffs of Dover, are known to mariners.

A singular variety, at least in the appearance, of this under part of the Chalk, occurs in Lincolnshire, which, from a tinge of red oxyde of iron, is there called red caulk. The same, very highly tinged with red, reappears on the opposite side of the Wash, under the cliff exposed to the sea, at the north-western point of Norfolk. Various beds towards the bottom of the Chalk sandy, and fine grained, seem to indicate the change to the coarser Strata of Sand which lie beneath. Considerable protrusions of the lower part of the Stratum of Chalk, Hurlock, Malm, and Firestone, greatly inferior in altitude to the general range of high downland, occur in several parts of the interior course of the Strata. Dunstable stands on the plain of one of these protrusions.

Other such projections, shown on the map by a second shade of green, about Watlington, spread westward to Tetsworth, which is on the extremity of the white or malm land.

South-west of the Thames, and similarly spread far west of the general line of Chalk hills this kind of white land may be traced parallel to the river, half way from Wallingford to Abingdon.

The vale of Pewsey, and other vales which deeply indent the line of Chalk outcrop in Wiltshire, have some of the same kind of land. Some white land also spreads wide from the general range of Chalk, north-eastward of Dunstable, in different places thence to Cambridge.

ORGANIZED FOSSILS

1 Inoceramus Cuvieri	Knook Castle and Barrow, Heytesbury. Hunstanton Cliff.
2 Inoceramus	Wilts (Warminster).
3 Cast of a Trochus	Mazen Hill.
4 Ammonites	Mazen Hill. Norton Bevant.
5 Cirrus depressus.	Warminster.
6 Terebratula	Heytesbury.
7 Terebratula	Heytesbury. Warminster. Mazen Hill.
8 Terebratula subundata	Heytesbury. Mazen Hill. Warminster.
9 Shark's teeth	Warminster.

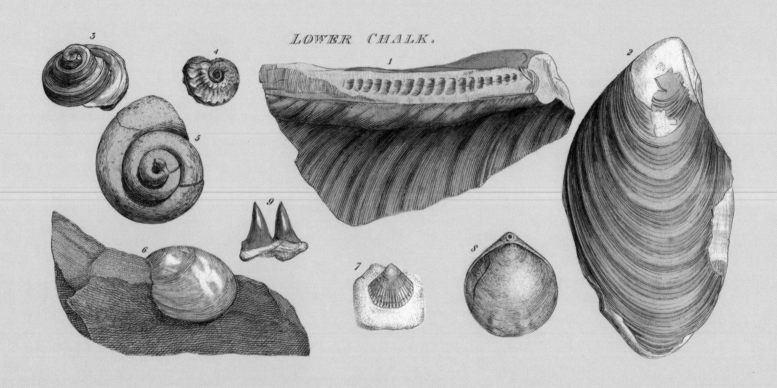

LOWER CHALK.

1. *Inoceramus Cuvieri*. Thoms. Annals X. 4 p.448.   4. *Ammonites*.   7. *Terebratula*.

2. *Inoceramus*.   5. *Cirrus depressus*. Sowerby. M.S.   8. *Terebratula subundata*. M.C.15.f.7.

3. *Cast of the inside of a Trochus*.   6. *Terebratula*.   9. *Sharks teeth*.

PLATE 4 (AND FACING PAGE)

UPPER CRETACEOUS, LOWER CHALK

1. Bivalve: *Volviceramus involutus*
2. Bivalve: *Mytiloides labiatus*
3. Gastropod: *Bathrotomaria* sp.

4. Ammonite: *Schloenbachia subtuberculata* *
5. Gastropod: *Bathrotomaria* sp.
6. Brachiopod: *Gibbithyris semiglobosa*

7. Brachiopod: *Orbirhynchia cuvieri* *
8. Brachiopod: *Gibbithyris semiglobosa*
9. Shark's tooth: indet. *

* similar fossil substituted from Smith's collection

CLASS of STRATA beneath the CHALK.

The preceding description having ended with the Chalk hills, which form the boldest feature of all the eastern and southern parts of England, it may here be necessary to make some observations on the class of Strata beneath.

Soils and Sub-strata as different as the appearance in the two surfaces, commence at the termination of Chalk: this difference is most striking in the northern and western parts. The most unobserving can scarcely pass without notice, in either of these, or a north-east direction out of London, this remarkable change in the country, which occurs on their descent from the Chalk hills.

In most parts a vale of considerable breadth appears to the extent of vision, parallel to the hills, which gives generally a correct notion of the country, as none of the Strata compared within the class, which must necessarily be considered together, rise to great altitude, or at least but rarely without some sort of intermediate valley. There are, however, some instances where the Sand (which is the next Stratum beneath the Chalk) rises to a greater height than the contiguous Chalk hills. Leith hill, and the hills about Longleat, Stourton, and Fonthill are remarkable instances. These little hills show by their immediate connexion with the Chalk, that the greater sandy heights in the interior of Sussex and Kent, and those of Black Down and North York Moors, are formed of the same Strata. The materials of these vast spaces, and of those more inland; the vales of Blackmore, Wardour, Warminster, Pewsey, Whitehorse and Aylesbury, and a similar vale extending through Bedfordshire to Cambridge, (with the Strata which compose the margin of those vales) form the class to be considered together, and which in many instances will be sub-divided with difficulty.

The districts enumerated consist of a great variety of Strata, which in the map are all represented by three colours, —two blues, with a dark brown and its shades, representing the Oaktree Clay, Purbeck and Portland stone, and the Carstone. The green sand being considered to occupy the white space on the map parallel to the termination of the Chalk, which is represented by green. The following is a more particular division of those districts of Strata:-

Three Sands, two Rocks, and two Clays.—Green or Chlorite Sand is the first, which contains Burstone, Fuller's earth, and Firestone. Indurated Brick earth succeeds, which is rather sandy and micacious. Sand and Rock, which produces the Portland and Swindon stone. —The other lower divisions come not within the present number.

Chlorite which gives the green tint, from which the name of Green sand has been taken, is repeated in the stony or concreted beds of land herein enumerated, and from these repetitions, the different courses of it, in different parts of the district, are liable to be mistaken or confounded.

The Oak-tree Clay also may be mistaken or confounded with the Brick earth, which in several parts produces good oak. It appears, however, on further investigation, that the Clay beneath the Portland stone, was the one generally so called by Mr. Davis in his Wiltshire report; and which in this, and the succeeding parts of the work, will be called by that name.

The green sand Stratum properly so called, which produces the extraordinary good land, is very limited in breadth and is quickly succeeded by other sands, producing soil of an opposite quality.

GREEN or CHLORITE SAND.

SOIL.– *Colour,* dark grey, dries whiter—another part so dark when wet and fresh plowed, as to be called *black land,* but dries much whiter.

Consistence, Dry, a fine mellow loam-where wet rather sticky.

SUBSOIL, Sandy, cohesive, absorbent.

EXCAVATIONS, } Sides stand perpendicular, cohesive sand, dry; blue grey or greyish green,
HOLLOW-WAYS, occasioned by small blackish specks of Chlorite—small Mica in some beds.

STRATUM, Sand and incompact Sand stone, with layers of more concrete lumps or nodules from some of which Burs or scythe stones are made.

WATER, very bright, copious, and of a high temperature, where that of the Chalk and Sand flows all from this Stratum. In the west much used in irrigation.

No road stone along the course of this Stratum, and its white land boundary, but partakes either of Chalk, Malm, Greensand, or soft Freestone, or Sand concreted by a ferruginons cement; many of the roads (as in Sussex) are consequently bad.

Much of the first breadth of Sand from the Chalk hills in Sussex and Kent, is now, or till lately, was uninclosed heath.

ORGANIZED FOSSILS.

FIG.

1 Alcyonite (funnel form)	Pewsey. Warminster. Devizes. Dinton Park
2 Alcyonite (doliform)	Pewsey. Warminster.
3 Venus angulata	Blackdown.
4 Murex *Linn.*	Blackdown.
5 Turritella *Lam.*	Blackdown.
6 Pectunculus *Lam.*	Blackdown.
7 Cardium	
8 Rostellaria *Lam*	
9 Trigonia alæformis.	In a mass from Blackdown
10 Cucullæa. *Lam.*	

FIG.

1 Vermicularia (chambered)	Horningsham, Wilts.
2 Solarium *Lam.*	Rundaway.
3 Pecten (echinated)	Chute Farm. Rundaway.
4 Terebratula pectinata	Chute Farm. Warminster.
5 Terebratula lyra	Chute Farm.
6 Terebratula	Warminster. Chute Farm.
7 Chama haliotoidea	Dilton. Black Dog hill, Teffon. Evershot. Stourton. Alfred's Tower. Blackdown.
8 Pecten quadricostata	Chute Farm. Warminster. Blackdown.
9 Pecten	Chute Farm.
10 Ostrea (Gryphea *Lam.)*	Stourton. Dinton Park. Tinhead.
11 Echinus with a singular anal appendage	Chute Farm. Warminster.
12 Echinites *Leske*	Warminster. Chute Farm.
13 E. lapis cancri	Chute Farm, &c.
14 Spatangus *Leske*	Warmimter. Chute. Rundaway.
15 Cyclolites *Lam.*	Chute. Puddle hill, near Dunstable.
16 Madreporite	Chute Farm.
17 Alcyonite	Chute Farm.

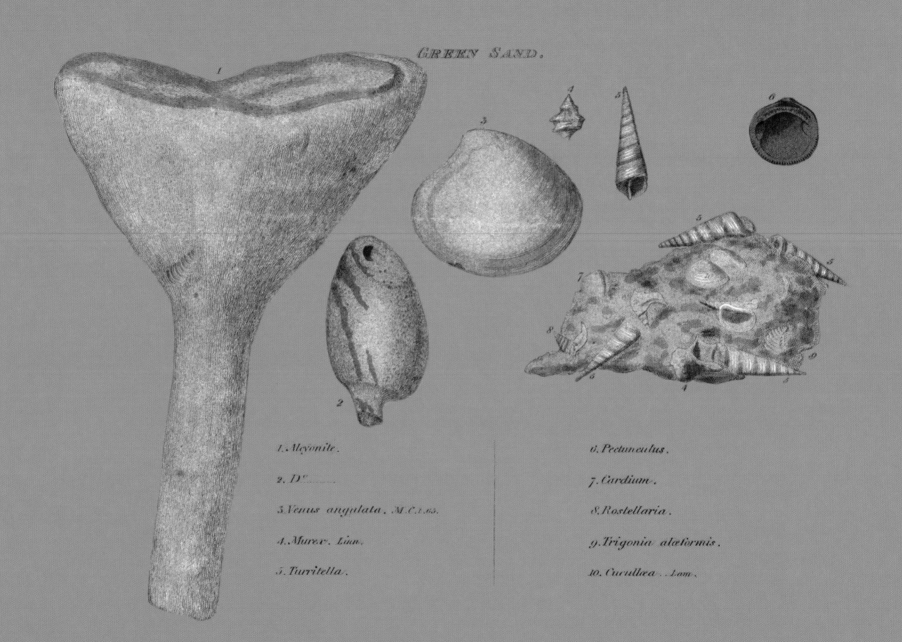

GREEN SAND.

1. Alcyonite.

2. D°........

3. Venus angulata. M.C.1.65.

4. Murex. Linn.

5. Turritella.

6. Pectunculus.

7. Cardium.

8. Rostellaria.

9. Trigonia alœformis.

10. Cucullœa. Lam.

PLATE 5 (AND FACING PAGE)

LWR-UPP CRETACEOUS, UPPER GREENSAND

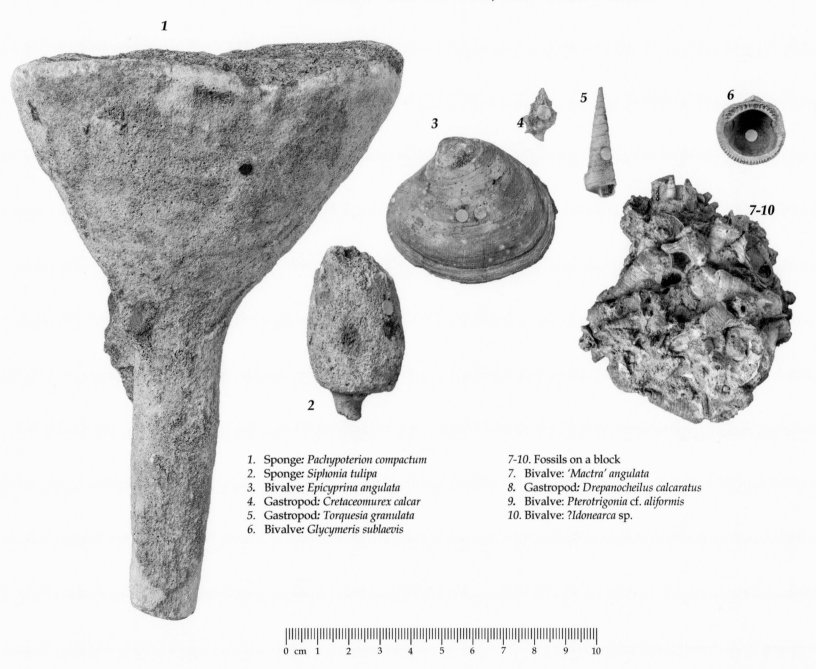

1. Sponge: *Pachypoterion compactum*
2. Sponge: *Siphonia tulipa*
3. Bivalve: *Epicyprina angulata*
4. Gastropod: *Cretaceomurex calcar*
5. Gastropod: *Torquesia granulata*
6. Bivalve: *Glycymeris sublaevis*

7-10. Fossils on a block
7. Bivalve: *'Mactra' angulata*
8. Gastropod: *Drepanocheilus calcaratus*
9. Bivalve: *Pterotrigonia* cf. *aliformis*
10. Bivalve: ?*Idonearca* sp.

GREEN SAND.

1. Serpula.

2. Solarium.

3. Pecten.

4. Terebratula pectinata. Min.Con.t.138.f.1.

5. Lyra. Min:Con.t.138,f.2.

6. Terebratula.

7. Chama haliotoidea. M.C.t.25.

8. Pecten 4 costata. Brit: Min.t.183.

9. Pecten.

10. Ostrea.

11. Echinus.

12. Echinites.

13. Echinus lapis cancri.

14. Spatangus.

15. Cyclolites. Lam.

16. Madreporite.

17. Alcyonite.

PLATE 6 (AND FACING PAGE)

1. Tube worm: *Rotularia concava*
2. Gastropod: *Nummogaultina fittoni*
3. Brachiopod: *Merklinia scabra*
4. Brachiopod: *Dereta pectita*
5. Brachiopod: *Terebrirostra lyra*
6. Brachiopod: *Cyclothyris latissima*

7. Bivalve: *Amphidonte obliquatum*
8. Bivalve: *Neithea gibbosa*
9. Bivalve: *'Chalmys'* aff. *subacuta*
10. Bivalve: *Amphidonte obliquatum*
11. Echinoid: *Salenia petalifera*
12. Echinoid: *Discoidea subuculus*

13. Echinoid: *Catopygus columbarius*
14. Echinoid: *Holaster laevis*
15. Coral: *Microbacia* sp.
16. Coral: indet.
17. Sponge: *Barroisia* sp.

0 cm 1 2 3 4 5 6 7 8 9 10

Fossils in silhouette have not been found

MICACEOUS BRICK EARTH.

SOIL.—*Colour,* blackish brown.
          Consistence, kneadable, tenacious or sticky when wet, mouldering when dry.
SUBSOIL, yellower than the soil, retentive, good brick earth, some of it works freely into tiles
          and coarse pottery.
EXCAVATIONS, retain water, browner or bluer, digs hard, falls in large lumps of a conchoidal
          fracture.
STRATUM,   indurated micaceous clay, yellowish brown to dun blue; cuts smooth; returns
          earthy smell.

————————

The surface of this stratum is frequently so obscured by the loose incumbent stratum of Sand, that in some parts its outcrop may be passed without notice, and its course traced with difficulty.

It often constitutes the base of some of the highest western promontories of chalk; seldom quits the chalk hills far enough to occasion any great breadths of clay land: is often covered with small woods, chiefly of oak, in tolerable state of luxuriance. As this clay keeps up the water of the chalk and green sand, and occasions the first springs at the foot of those hills; the course of it may thus be traced: also, by rushes and other indications of a clay surface, especially in a district so generally abounding in sand.

————————

ORGANIZED FOSSILS.

FIG.

1 Ammonites	Near Godstone. Steppingley Park. Prisley Farm Bedfordshire.
2 Hamites	N . West part of Norfolk.
3 Echinus *Linn.* Spatangus *Leske*	Near Devizes.
4 5 }Belemnites	North of Riegate, near Godstone. Norfolk (N. W . part). Steppingley Park. Prisley Farm.

PLATE 7 BRICK EARTH (OVERLEAF)

BRICK-EARTH.

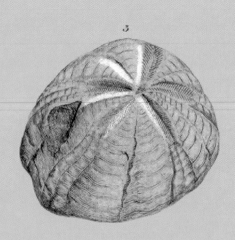

1. *Ammonites.*
2. *Hamites.*
3. *Echinus.*
4. } *Belemnites.*
5. }

PLATE 7 (AND FACING PAGE)

LOWER CRETACEOUS, GAULT CLAY

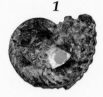

1. Ammonite *: Hoplites dentatus* *
2. Ammonite: *Idiohamites* sp.
3. Echinoid: *Pliotoxaster* sp.
4. Belemnite: *Neohibilites minimus* *
5. Belemnite: *Neohibilites minimus*

0 cm 1 2 3 4 5

similar fossil substituted from Smith's collection

PORTLAND STONE.

SOIL.—*Colour,* Brown.
        Consistence, absorbent, sandy loam; much intermixed with stones, which vary in quantity, size, and hardness, as the different beds of rock occupy the surface, commonly called Stonebrash.

SUBSOIL, Orange brown, all stone, or sand and stone alternating, absorbent.

EXCAVATIONS, all dry; in sand and stone; some made down to the water.

STRATUM, masses of stone in thick beds or layers; bluish white, brownish white, and some hard blue or blue grey.
        Disintegration, Few persons who have not made observations on this subject can be aware, how a rock nearer and nearer to the surface, gradually divides into building stone, wall stone, rubble stone, and soil. This should be particularly attended to in tracing the terminations or outcrops of rocky Strata.

WATER.—Copious springs flow from the bottom of the rock.

The Swindon stone, unlike many other great rocks, forms not of itself, any elevated or distinct ranges of hills, except at particular places, and then only, too frequently in conjunction with the lower Strata, by which those of the stone are hidden or much obscured. The rock is also subject to great change in appearance and quality, yet the Portland stone can be easily identified at particular places, along the course of the Stratum which produces it, to as great an extent as some of the other Strata with which it alternates. Portland Isle is one extremity, and Hambledon hills, in Yorkshire, the other. The rock, however, it is evident from various causes, cannot, in a connected line of outcrop, ever be traced from one of these points to the other, which is a space of 300 miles, but the Strata above and below, which seem to inclose the rock, if not the identical beds of stone, may be recognized for a considerable part of the distance. It is best known in Portland, Purbeck, Wiltshire, the vale of Aylesbury, and in Kent and the vale of Pickering. Hambledon hills also produce the Portland variety. The stony land on the western border of Dorsetshire, appears to be the same. It has long been worked for building, equal in quality to that of the noted island, in the vale of Wardour. Sand is much blended with it at Swindon.

This rock, though long worked to a great extent in several places, in others would be discovered with difficulty. Its site is in many parts near the foot of the Chalk hills, and in others so widely distant from them as to leave the intermediate course doubtful with a skilful Geologist.

It contains some very thin beds of chert or flint, and some thick beds of Freestone, as soft as Chalk.

Large flinty nodules are sometimes enclosed in the Freestone, the beds of which vary much in different quarries. The organized fossils vary less. They are therefore in this instance, remarkably useful in identifying the Strata.

In passing over the Strata from east to west, and noticing their successive terminations, it may be remarked, that this Stratum, in a large portion of the island, is the first beneath the Chalk which produces quarry stone hard enough to be used on the roads. In the space between the course of this Stratum and the green sand, a very hard material is sometimes found, consisting of thin beds of coarse flint or chert, which, in layers about three inches thick, is used in building at Haslemere, Warminster, and Chard.

No flint below this Stratum. The organized fossil shells preserved in chert, are the finest in the kingdom.

————————

ORGANIZED FOSSILS.

FIG.
1 Cast of Natica *Lam.* Swindon.
2 Turritella inside cast Swindon. Portland.
3 Cast of Venus *Linn.* Swindon.
4 Trigonia Swindon. Chicksgrove. Fonthill. Teffont.
5 Venus, inside cast Swindon. Chicksgrove.
6 Pecten Swindon Portland. Chicksgrove. Thame
7. Fossil Wood Woburn. Fonthill.

PORTLAND STONE.

1. Cast of a Natica Lam.
2. Turritella, inside Cast.
3. Cast of Cyclas.
4. Trigonia.
5. Venus, inside cast.
6. Pecten.
7. Fossil Wood.

PLATE 8 (AND FACING PAGE)

UPPER JURASSIC, PORTLAND STONE

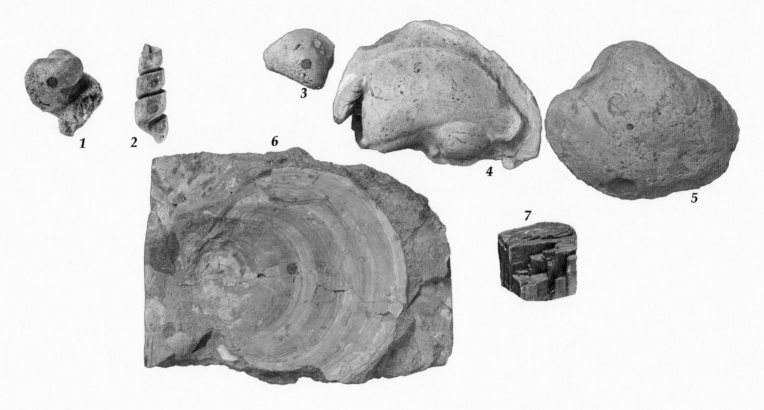

1. Gastropod: *Neritoma sinuosa*
2. Gastropod: *Aptyxiella portlandica*
3. Bivalve: *Eomiodon* sp.

4. Bivalve: *Myophorella incurva* *
5. Bivalve: *Protocardia dissimilis*
6. Bivalve: *Camptonectes lamellosus*

7. Wood: Section of larger piece of conifer

0 cm 1 2 3 4 5 6 7 8 9 10

Fossils in silhouette have not been found
* *similar fossil substituted from Smith's collection*

OAK TREE CLAY.

SOIL—*Colour,* Brown, yellowish, bluish.
   Consistence, Tenacious, unabsorbent Clay; cracks in dry summers.
SUBSOIL.—Scarcely anywise different from the thick mass of the Stratum.
   Colour, Sometimes yellowish tenacious Clay, varying to blue and yellow mixed, and
   deeper to the regular blue of the Stratum.
EXCAVATION, and Ditches, hold Water.
STRATUM, Hard blue Clay, interlaminated with stony nodules of indurated Marl, and layers of
      Fossil shells; some blacker, laminated, splits like Clay slate; some bitumenized wood.
WATER,   In every pit and ditch, and through the winter in the foot-marks of every heavy
      animal. In summer short of water, and that in the wells generally of a bad quality.

SOIL, very different from that of the Stratum, is in this district common to a Subsoil of Gravel, which abounds with calcareous matter. This will be described at the end of the work, as such Fossils vary not according to their sites, but according to the nature of the Strata, from whence the fragments of the compound appear to have been torn, and rounded in water.

This is the second Stratum of the Clay vales, or those within the lowland class, at the foot of the Chalk hills. In some parts of the course of this Stratum it would appear to be properly the first thick blue Clay Stratum, descending in the series of British Strata; the Clays above the Chalk being generally brown or dun coloured, or rarely exposed so blue as those below the Chalk, which form the two great interior Clay and Marl vale districts: that nearer the Chalk is more of a Brick-earth. As deep as the plough goes, the Clays in Essex are generally brown, but here the plough frequently exposes the native blue colour of the Stratum. Where the subsoil partakes thus much of the nature of the Stratum, this kind of land is little cultivated. Amongst these Clays a subsoil of a lightish brown yellow is exposed by the plough.

Widely-extended parts of this Stratum, and also insular and widely-detached hills of it rise upon a base of sand and stone, to considerable altitudes between the vales of White-Horse and Isis, and also between the vales of Aylesbury and Ottmoor. Badbury and Faringdon Hills, Bagley Wood and Shotover, on opposite sides of the Thames, below Oxford, and Brill Hill, are some of the most remarkable.

The surface composed of this Clay is of great breadth between Swindon and Wotton Basset. Thence eastward it connects with the vale of White-Horse, where it extends wide and long, and lies so flat as to give name to Standford in the Plain; and in the space before mentioned, the names of Morton and Even-Swindon, are evidently taken from low, level, and watery parts on the surface of this Stratum.

It appears to be this Clay which forms the deepest part of the Strata, exposed by the vast rising in the under-Strata between the fork of the Chalk hills, in Kent and Sussex.

It is here, as in other parts, thickly covered with Oak; and here also, as in other parts of its course through the interior, it seems to be distinguished by considerable plains, which in this district are most remarkable on each side of the Forest Ridge, between the sands of that hill and those nearer the Chalk hills, and constitutes what may be called the deepest parts of the Wealds of Kent and Sussex.

Organized Fossils contained in the Septaria of a thick Stratum of Clay, incumbent on rock, are frequently the same as in the top of the rock itself; therefore, figures of these need not be repeated. The Melania of the Oak-tree Clay is the same species as M. Heddingtonensis, which, is common to the top of the Coral Rag rock.

Cockscomb Oysters are also common both to that rock, and to the Septaria above; in fact those large Clay-balls found plentifully in the deep cutting of the north Wilts Canal seemed to partake both of the inhabitants of the rock above, and of that below the Clay; the Trigonia of the Clay-balls being the same species as those large ones which compose the chief part of some beds of stone, about four feet thick, near the bottom of the Swindon rock.

It may at first appear that the identification of Strata, by the organized Fossils they contain, would in such cases be somewhat doubtful; but in the course of the work I shall make further remarks on such apparent repetitions, which will rather show the great utility of them, to well-sinkers and others, concerned in deep excavations in these thick Strata of Clay, abounding with alternations of stony matter and organized Fossils.

The flat Oyster, fig. 6, in a layer, is so common in the ditches of this land, as to be called *Clay Shells.*

None other of the organized Fossils are found but in deep excavations.

ORGANIZED FOSSILS

FIG.

I Melania Heddingtonensis	North Wilts Canal.
2 Turbo	North Wilts Canal.
3 Trochus	North Wilts Canal.
4 Ampullaria	North Wilts Canal.
5 Chama	Bagley Wood Pit. North Wilts Canal. Well near Swindon, Wilts and Berks Canal.
6 Ostrea delta	Canal at Seend. Well near Swindon, Wilts and Berks Canal. North Wilts Canal. Bagley. Wood Pit. Near Shrivenham. Even Swindon Wotton Basset.
7 Ammonites	North Wilts Canal. Well near Swindon, Wilts and Berks Canal.
8 Venus	North Wilts Canal.
9 Terebratula	Bagley Wood Pit. Well near Swindon, Wilts and Berks Canal. North Wilts Canal.

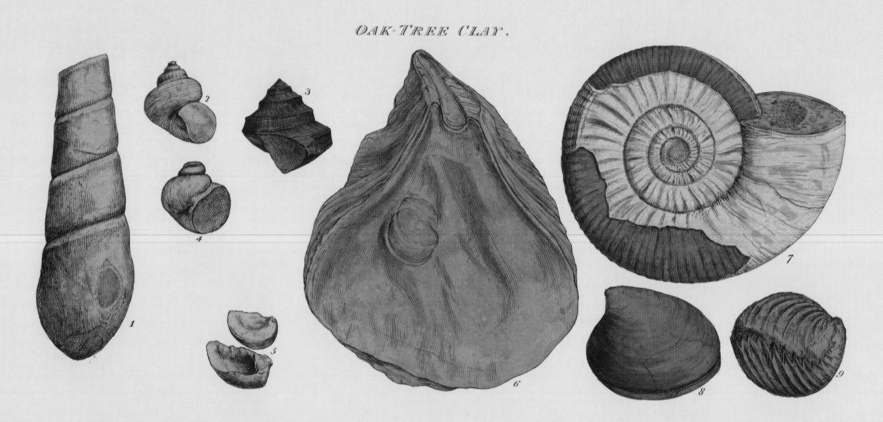

OAK-TREE CLAY.

Fig: 1 Melania Heddingtonensis *Min: Con: t.39.*

2 Turbo ?

3 Trochus

4 Ampullaria

Fig: 5 Chama

6 Ostrea delta *Min: Con: t 148.*

7 Ammonites

8 Venus

Fig: 9 Terebratula

PLATE 9 (AND FACING PAGE)

UPPER JURASSIC, KIMMERIDGE CLAY

1. Gastropod: *Pseudomelania heddingtonensis*
2. Gastropod: indet.
3. Gastropod: *Bathrotomaria reticulata*
4. Gastropod: *Ampullina* sp.

5. Bivalve: *Nannogyra nana*
6. Bivalve: *Deltoideum delta*
7. Ammonite: *Pictonia baylei*
8. Bivalve: *Neocrassina ovata*

9. Brachiopod: *Torquirhynchia inconstans* *

0 cm 1 2 3 4 5 6 7 8 9 10

Fossils in silhouette have not been found
* similar fossil substituted from Smith's collection

CORAL RAG and PISOLITE.

SOIL.—*Colour*, Dark brown.
　　　Consistence,　Loose when dry; rather tenacious or kneadable when wet; thickly strewed
　　　　　　　with small stones, roundish or irregularly shaped, which in roads wear
　　　　　　　white.
SUBSOIL.—Moist Clay and a rough irregular Limestone.
EXCAVATIONS, Shallow, on outcrop of the rock; stone whitish; where mixed with Clay, hold water; where
　　　　　　sandy, dry.
STRATUM, Lightish blue in deep pits; where the Stratum is entire, beneath its incumbent Clay
　　　　　hard and solid, except the cavities occasioned by stems of Madrepores.
　　　　　The Pisolite part of the rock beneath has a dryer, stony, and less adhesive soil,
　　　　　of the sort usually called Stonebrash. The stone in some of its beds, is white,
　　　　　and composed of unequal sized ova. Loose ova may be seen at the sides of banks
　　　　　and other bare places.
WATER, flows in abundance from this rock, and the Sand and Sandstone, which is the
　　　　　bottom of the Stratum.

My Geological Table of organized Fossils shows that this rock and the Sands have been represented on my map by the same colour; but now, by the better arrangement of my fossils in the British Museum, and my subsequent observations, these Strata are more distinctly divided.

The Coral Rag consists chiefly of lumps of coralline Limestone, which in the quarry are very rough, irregular, and dirty; but where roads cross the outcrop, or where this stone is used as a road material, it wears to a smooth surface, which is whiter and harder than any other stone in the vicinity.

The Pisolite Freestone beneath is softer. In some parts it being an Oolite of fine grain, is used in building, and in specimens without organized Fossils, is scarcely to be distinguished from Portland Stone.

Coral Rag and Pisolite, with the Sand and Sandstone beneath, make a surface of dry land, which, within a generally moist surface of Clay land, is very desirable for tillage, and is commonly thus appropriated.

Among the stones turned up by the plough, most of its organized Fossils may be found, but the quarries generally produce sharper and better specimens.

The greatest breadth of surface formed by the outcrop of this Stratum is in Wiltshire, Berkshire, and Oxfordshire: its course north-eastward becomes obscure, or is covered with alluvial matter before it reaches Buckinghamshire.

From Steeple Ashton, Wiltshire, the south-western course is indistinct, or the stone is deeply covered in the high hills of Sand, and forms part of their altitude; as in this direction it re-appears in the low part of Longleat park; and beyond the high Sand hills of Stourton, the outcrop of this rock again occupies a considerable surface of ploughed land, extending from Penselwood through the vale of Blackmoor to Stourminster Newton.

The greatest surface of this stony land is about Calne, by Bremhill, Lyneham, and Tokenham, to Wotton Basset; thence by Lydiard, Blunsdon, Stanton, Stratton, and Sevenhampton, to Highworth; Coleshill, Shrivenham, &c. to Faringdon, and thence by the great road to Oxford, and spreading eastward, almost to Abingdon, where it is covered with gravel.

Over the Thames it again expands from Sandford, westward by Cowley, Heddington Common, and all the elevated plain between the foot of Shotover Hill and Oxford, to Stanton St. John's, &c. contracting in the width of its course northward, till it becomes indistinct in the great breadth of clay land.

The sand which lies beneath this rock is scarcely known in some places; in others it occupies a great breadth of surface, and in others is highly tinged with the red oxyd of Iron, which gives it a very different appearance.

Between the limestone rocks, containing the Fossils herein described, and the sand beneath, lies a floor of stone, which preserves the escarpment of the stony ridge, by which the great clay vale district might be said to be divided into two ranges of vales; the vales of White-Horse and Aylesbury being to the east, and the vales of Bedford, Ottmoor, Isis, and Avon or north Wilts to the west of this ridge.

ORGANIZED FOSSILS.

FIG.

1 Madrepora — Stanton near Highworth. Shippon. Bagley Wood Pit. Banner's Ash. Well near Swindon, Wilts and Berks Canal. Steeple Ashton. South of Bayford.

2 Madrepora — Steeple Ashton.

3 Madrepora — Steeple Ashton. Longleat Park. Stratton. Wotton Basset. Banner's-Ash. Well near Swindon, Wilts and Berks Canal. Shippon. Bagley Wood Pit. Stanton. Ensham Bridge

---

FIG.

1 Turbo — Longleat Park. Derry Hill. Steeple Ashton. Banner's Ash. Wotton Basset. Bagley Wood Pit

2 Ampullaria — Longleat Park. Marcham. Kennington. Silton Farm. South of Bayford. Hinton Waldrish.

3 Melania striata — Calne. Steeple Ashton. Silton Farm. Banner's Ash. Well near Swindon, Wilts and Berks Canal. South of Bayford.

4 Ostrea crista galli — Derry Hill. Shotover Hill. Westbrook. Longleat Park. South of Bayford. Wotton Basset.

5 Cidaris — Hilmarton. Well near Swindon, Wilts and Berks Canal.

6 Clypeus — Meggot's Mill, Coleshill. Longleat Park. Hinton Waldrish.

This latter specimen, as shown in my "Stratigraphical Table of Echini" is one of the characteristic distinctions of the Pisolite part of the rock.

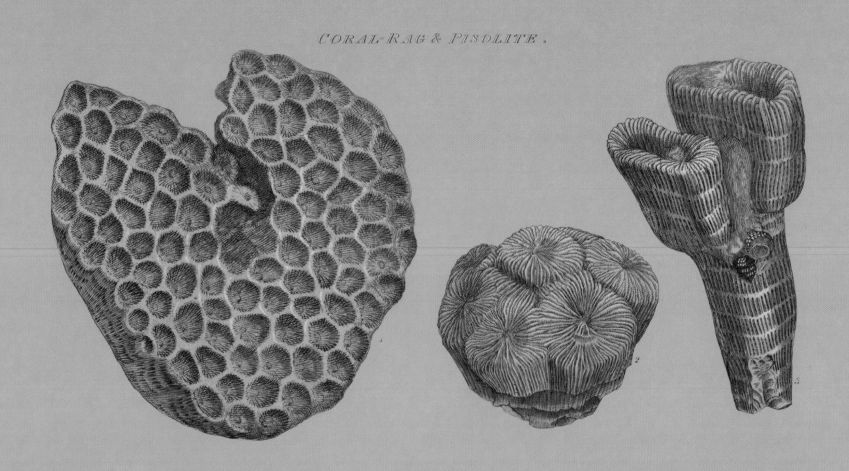

CORAL-RAG & PISOLITE.

Fig: 1. Madrepora.

2. Ditto

3. D.º

PLATE 10 (AND FACING PAGE)

UPPER JURASSIC, CORALLINE OOLITE

1. Coral: *Isastrea explanata*
2. Coral: *Complexastrea depressa*
3. Coral: *Thecosmilia annularis*

0 cm 1 2 3 4 5 6 7 8 9 10

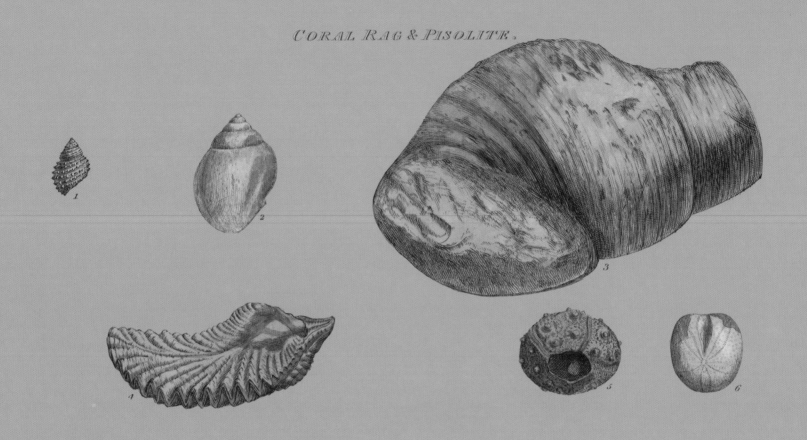

CORAL RAG & PISOLITE.

Fig. 1. Turbo

2. Ampullaria

3. Melania striata   Min. Con. tab. 47.

Fig. 4 Ostrea crista-galli

5 Cidaris

6 Clypeus

PLATE 11 (AND FACING PAGE)

UPPER JURASSIC, CORALLINE OOLITE (2)

1. Gastropod: *Ooliticia muricata*
2. Gastropod: *Ampullospira sp.*
3. Gastropod: *Bourguetia saemanni* *

4. Bivalve: *Actinostreon gregarium* *
5. Echinoid: *Paracidaris smithii* *
6. Echinoid: *Nucleolites clunicularis*

0 cm   1   2   3   4   5

* *similar fossil substituted from Smith's collection*

CLUNCH CLAY and SHALE.

***

SOIL.—*Colour,* Brown, darker and bluer wet.
　　　　Consistence, unabsorbent, adhesive, and tenacious clay; dries in hard lumps; cracks
　　　　　　in dry summers.
SUBSOIL—Much the same as the Stratum, in some places yellowish; deeper, gradually changing·
　　　　　　to blue.
EXCAVATIONS and Ditches, hold Water.
STRATUM, hard clay rising in lumps, called Clunch; deeper in the Stratum, blacker and laminated,
　　　　　called Shale.
WATER, The remarks on water in the Oak-tree Clay are applicable to this Stratum.
　　　　The best water in the clay vale district lies in gravel, or in the rocks beneath the clays.

***

Clunch Clay forms the base of the hills which are surmounted by the rocks and sands before described, appearing chiefly, if not wholly on the escarpment side of those eminences, and in the lower grounds of the several wide vales adjoining. Where the last mentioned and the Portland rock, and their accompanying sands also, become deficient, the absence of such partitions in these clays, which altogether form the broad district parallel to the chalk before-mentioned, renders the distinction between the thick clays and the Brickearth above them very difficult. And which of them keeps possession of the low surface, wherein they ought all to be found, must ultimately be determined by further and more accurate observations on these and other of their respective distinguishing characters.

　　The Stratum of the Clunch Clay, and the other clay on the confines of the, stony district, terminate in some parts of their course in rounded low hills, which are called knolls or knowls. A small hill by the Worcester road, two miles out of Oxford, and Lew-hill, near Bampton, are some of these. Other such occur between Malmsbury and Chippenham, and further westward along the courses of these Strata, through the vale of Blackmoor.

　　The general course of these very thick Strata of clay, through the interior of England, may be known as the site of the broadest vales before enumerated, and likewise of the lowest land in the island, and of that most frequently subject to inundation; but they also rise like other soft Strata, into hills of moderate elevation.

　　The outcrop or basset edge of the thick Stratum of Clunch Clay, from its N. E. course, through Buckinghamshire, enters Bedfordshire, between Olney and Bedford, and is protruded on the heights, into the great bend of the river Ouse, between these two places. The extreme continuation of the Clunch northward, seems to form the summit of drainage, through the remainder of Bedfordshire, north of the Ouse, and so continues to form the boundary between Northampton and Huntingdonshires, into the fens below Peterborough, and continues northward through Lincolnshire, under and parallel to the low land.

Proceeding south-westward, from the well defined part in North Wilts, its course, in or near the same high ground as the Stratum before described, narrows much, but like that stone spreads again in the broad vale of Blackmoor, following the outcrop of the Coral Rag and Pisolite Rock, past the River Stour; further westward, where the stony land is deficient, the course of the Clunch Clay is less distinct, and here, as in the north, is not likely to be identified, or clearly distinguished from the other Clays above it, but by the organized Fossils in wells and other excavations.

But for these, and the numerous experiments for coal, the nature and contents of these clayey Strata deep in the earth could not have been known.

By some of the perforations in Wiltshire, &c. it appears that the lower part of this thick Stratum is considerably laminated, and ribs in large flat pieces, which when dried are slightly inflammable.

Thus as the best and most delicate fossils of this Stratum will not bear exposure, they can be found only by persons employed in excavations, or those who overlook such works; hence it would be fruitless to search for any but in those places; and there being little inducement to make deep excavations in these strata, and no canals or other public works in hand, specimens of these fossils can not be multiplied for collections, or will be obtained with difficulty.

The lower part of this thick clay, like that of the one preceding, contains septaria stored with organized fossils, greatly resembling those of the stony Stratum beneath.

Ammonites Calloviensis in mass are inclosed in these septaria, remarkably sharp and fine, with a whitish exterior, but are liable to decomposition from the oxydation of the Sulphuret of Iron they contain.

The beautiful specimens many years since dug up from my good friend Mr. T. Crook's estate, in a large septarium lying in clay, are omitted in this Stratum, the same species being figured as characteristic of the rock beneath.

In this as in several other instances where the bottom of the clay contains the same fossils as the rock which it covers, it is difficult to determine to which Stratum they belong.

―――――――

ORGANIZED FOSSILS.

FIG.

1 Belemnites		Dudgrove Farm.
2 3 } Gryphrea-dilatata		Derry Hill. Meggot's Mill, Coleshill. Tytherton Lucas. Dudgrove Farm.
4 Ammonites		Tytherton Lucas. Thames and Severn Canal.
5 6 } Serpula		Wilts and Berks Canal, near Chippenham.

The upper part of this thick Stratum contains large incurved oysters or Gryphæa, so much resembling others I have collected from remote parts, of a clay which now appears to be Oak-tree clay, as to be distinguished with difficulty; but this is only one of the many instances of the general resemblances of organized Fossils, where the Strata are similar.

CLUNCH CLAY & SHALE.

Fig:1 Large Belemnite

2 Gryphœa dilatata Min:Con.tab. 149.
lower valve.

Fig:3 Gryphœa dilatata upper valve.

4 Ammonites armatus? Min:Con.t.95.

5 Serpula

6 Serpula

PLATE 12 (AND FACING PAGE)

MID-UPP JURASSIC, OXFORD CLAY

1. Belemnite: *Cylindroteuthis puzosiana*
2. Bivalve: *Gryphaea dilatata* *

3. Bivalve: *Gryphaea dilatata* *
4. Ammonite: *Kosmoceras spinosum*
5. Serpulid worm: *Genicularia vertebralis*
6. Serpulid worm: *Genicularia vertebralis*

0 cm 1 2 3 4 5 6 7 8 9 10

Fossils in silhouette have not been found
* *similar fossil substituted from Smith's collection*

KELLOWAYS STONE.

SOIL.—*Colour*, yellowish brown.
Consistence, over the stone dry sandy loam, above and below approaching to clay; kneadable clay loam intermediate.
SUBSOIL, yellower than the soil, sandy with rubbly stone; where wet, and the stone deficient, kneadable, or very sticky and tenacious.
EXCAVATIONS, rare, shallow, hold water; in some places a clay covering to the stone, abounding with Selenite.
HOLLOW-WAYS, in roads across the course of this Stratum but little sunk beneath the surface of the adjoining lands, seem to indicate its site.
STRATUM, brown rubbly stone, with sandy exterior; irregular lumps, bluer and harder within, composed chiefly of organized Fossils; used only on the roads.

In most parts the surface and soil of this stratum differs but little from that of the clay courses on each side, and that little distinction is still further partially obscured by the soil of the calcareous alluvium which is common to the clay vale district.

This extraordinary stone, which neither from its thickness or consistence can properly be called a rock, should be considered like the two preceding rocks and sands, only as one of the divisions in the great clay district before described; there being beneath this stone another stratum of clay, which is the boundary of the great stony district called the Stonebrash Hills.

The course of the Kelloways Stone is known only by the few excavations in it, chiefly for road materials, which in a country abounding so much with clay are very scarce. It no where forms any characteristic surface, or rarely a hill or other feature which is distinguishable to any but those who know where to look for the Stratum.

Several small commons in North Wilts, rather sandy and springy, seem to be of the soil formed by the outcrop of this Stratum, whose course is but partially defined.

Good bricks are made of earth dug near the course of this stone and its sand.

Selenite is very abundant in the clay above it: bituminous wood, and a brown aluminous earth below it. There is great reason to believe, that the mineral waters of the lower part of the clay vale series are from this stone, or some contiguous part of the clay above or below it.

Rarely as this stone appears by outcrop, the recent excavation for coal at Bruham proved it to be perfect in the deep, and there to contain the lobate Oyster, or Gryphus, *(b* in the British Museum,) and the other organized Fossils by which it is most distinctly characterised.

The excavations of the Kennet and Avon, and Wilts and Berks Canals, exposed new outcrops of this stone, which I afterwards found on the Thames and Severn Canal, near South Cerney.

From the great obscurity in the course of the Kelloways Stone, the organized Fossils of the Stratum can only be found in excavations, and in the stone used on the roads. Some of the larger Ammonites polished, exhibit the same beautiful arrangement of colours as the septa of the large Septaria, which in Dorsetshire are cut and polished for slabs and chimney-pieces.

24

ORGANIZED FOSSILS.

FIG.

1 Rostellaria	Kelloways. Wilts and Berks Canal, near Chippenham.
2 Ammonites sublævis	Christian Malford. Ladydown Farm. Kelloways.
3 Ammonites Calloviensis	Wilts and Berks Canal, near Chippenham. Kelloways.
4 Ammonites	Dauntsey House. Kelloways. Wilts and Berks Canal near Chippenham. Kennet and Avon Canal, near Trowbridge.
5 Gryphæa incurva	Kelloways. Wilts and Berks Canal, near Chippenham. Ladydown. Bruham Pit.
6 Terebratula ornithocephala	Kelloways. Dauntsey House. Thames and Severn Canal. Wilts and Berks Canal, near Chippenham.

From these and other organized Fossils, it is impossible to mistake the Kelloways Stone; and but for the course of this Stratum, the limits of the clays above and below it would be ill defined.

Strata Identified by Organized Fossils | 65

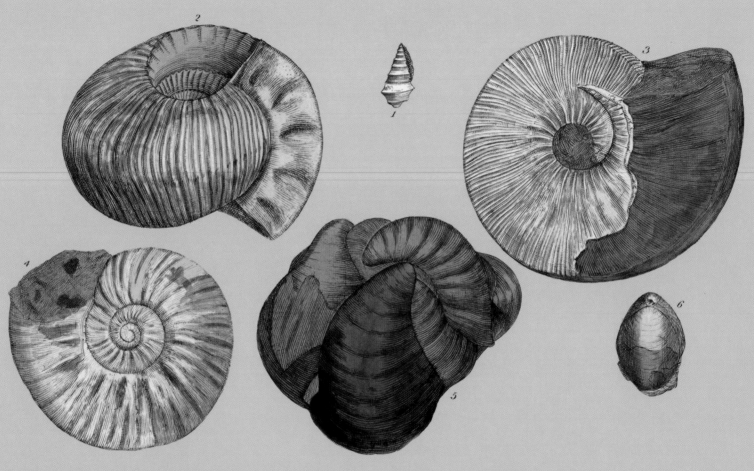

KELLOWAYS STONE.

Fig. 1 Rostellaria

2 Ammonites sublævis Min: Con: t. 54.

3 A. Calloviensis Min: Con: t. 104.

Fig. 4 Ammonites

5 Gryphæa incurva Min: Con: t. 112.

6 Terebratula ornithocephala Min: Con: t. 101.

PLATE 13 (AND FACING PAGE)

MIDDLE JURASSIC, KELLAWAYS ROCK

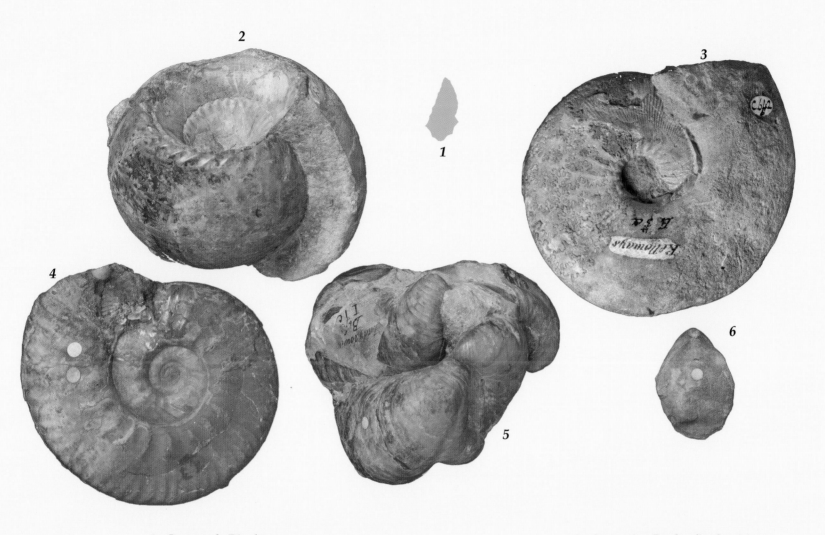

1. Gastropod: *Dicroloma* sp.
2. Ammonite: *Cadoceras sublaevis*
3. Ammonite: *Sigaloceras calloviense*

4. Ammonite: *Proplanulites koenigi*
5. Bivalve: *Gryphaea dilobotes*
6. Brachiopod: *Ornithella ornithocephala*

0 cm 1   2   3   4   5   6   7   8   9   10

Fossils in silhouette have not been found

CORNBRASH.

SOIL--*Colour*, reddish. brown, more remarkable on the outcrop of the upper, than of the lower part of the rock.

> *Consistence,* rather tenacious when wet; but like other Stonebrash soils on the rubbly subsoil of a Limestone rock, it is kept loose enough for cultivation by the small rubble stones thickly strewed on the surface of its ploughed fields, but which disappear when laid down to pasture. In some fields these are mostly organized fossils.

SUBSOIL, Rubble or roadstones, rather flat, and so little intermixed with soil or earth, as to be used on the roads as they are shovelled up from the quarries.

STRATUM, the same. The bluer, thicker, and larger stones in deep quarries are rarely more than six inches thick in the beds: outsides brown and earthy, darker and harder within. The rock generally grey or blue under its incumbent stratum of clay.

WATER, in the winter too commonly fills every crevice in the stratum of rock, the subsoil and soil; dry in the summer.

EXCAVATIONS, hold water in winter,--not deep,--made for the use of the roads, to the extent of some acres, and if well levelled, resoiled, and drained, taking out the stone in some instances, rather improves than injures the land.

In a distinct arrangement of British Geology into assemblages of Strata, which collectively form distinguishing features of the Earth's surface, and each class described by an appropriate name, the Stratum under consideration must form the boundary of one of those important divisions. It is the decided limit of the *Clay Vale District,* and the commencement of the stony surface, which gradually rises to the Stonebrash Hills. It rarely ascends to the highest of those hills, but occurs more generally on the confines of the low ground formed by the incumbent Stratum of clay. As the hills of this stratum are not high, so its vallies are not deep: in some parts they are merely slight undulations of surface, which correspond to similar undulations in the Stratum, and crossing its general course, produce many small springs and rivulets, frequently dry in the summer.

Like some other Limestones, the Cornbrash forms small insular knolls, or caps of hills, on the sloping side of the great series of Stonebrash Hills, of which it forms a part. Such detached parts occur near Charterhouse Hinton, south of Bath. That of Addington, Woodford, and Wold Farm, north of the river Nen, in Northamptonshire, appears to be so.

It is remarkable for regularly sloping planes on its surface, as near Witney, Campsfield near Woodstock, and near Bicester in Oxfordshire, and also near Peterborough. It is chiefly in arable, superior in quality to much of the similar soils of the Stonebrash Hills, and when otherwise appropriated to pasture, produces grass of a good quality.

The Cornbrash, though altogether but a thin rock, has not its organized fossils equally diffused, or promiscuously distributed. The upper beds of stone which compose the rock, contain fossils materially different from those in the under. The clusters of small oyster-shells, and the stems of the pentacrinus, lie near together, and not many other fossils occur toward the bottom of the rock. Both these sorts are found about the clay which lies beneath the stone; and in a detached piece of the Cornbrash Stratum, (not ten acres,) near Pipe-house, south of Bath, the encrini are found above the springs, in the brownish clay turned up by the plough.

ORGANIZED FOSSILS.

FIG.

1 Natica?	Road, Sleaford. Wick Farm.
2 Ammonites discus	Closworth. Road. S. W. of Wincanton. Chillington.
3 Modiola	Closworth. Wick Farm. Holt.
4 Trigonia costata	North side of Wincanton. Wick Farm.
5 Venus *Linn* .	Trowle. Sheldon. S. W. of Wincanton. Norton.
6 Cardium.	Road. Elmcross. Wick Farm. Sleaford. Woodford. Near Peterborough. Near Stilton.
7 Unio ?	North Cheriton. Road. Draycote. Maisey Hampton. Sleaford. S. W. of Tellisford. Sattyford. S. W. of Wincanton.
8 Avicula echinata	Closworth. North Cheriton. Lullington. Trowle. Sheldon. Draycot. Norton. Stony Stratford. S. W. of Tellisford. North side of Wincanton. S. W. of Wincanton
9 Terebratula digona *(var.* gibbosa, rotunda)	Closworth. Redlynch. Trowle. Wick Farm. Sheldon. Latton. Woodford.

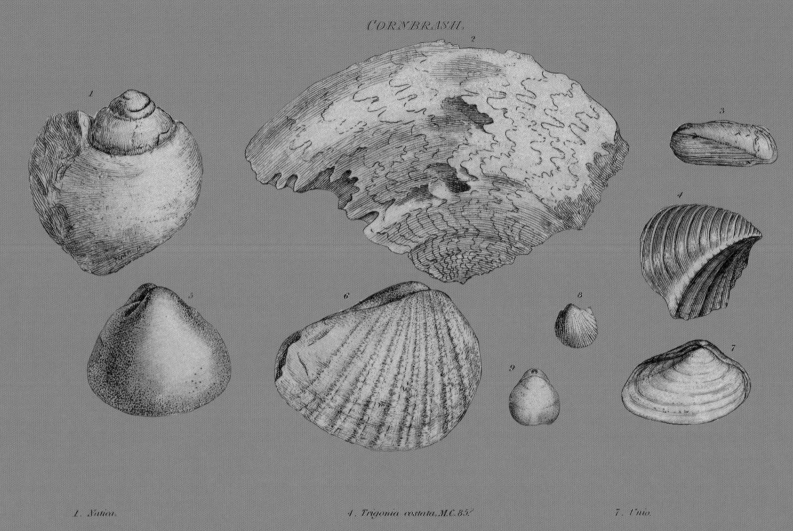

CORNBRASH.

1. Natica.

2. Ammonites discus. M.C.12.

3. Modiola.

4. Trigonia costata. M.C.85.

5. Venus.

6. Cardium.

7. Unio.

8. Avicula echinata. Strat. Syst. P.67.

9. Terebratula digona v. globosa.

PLATE 14 (AND FACING PAGE)

MIDDLE JURASSIC, CORNBRASH

1. Gastropod: cf. *Ampullospira* sp.
2. Ammonite: *Clydoniceras discus*
3. Bivalve: *Modiolus imbricatus*

4. Bivalve: *Trigonia crucis*
5. Bivalve: *Protocardia buckmani*
6. Bivalve: *Pholadomya deltoidea*

7. Bivalve: *Pleuromya uniformis*
8. Bivalve: *Meleagrinella echinata*
9. Brachiopod: *Digonella siddingtonensis*

0 cm 1 2 3 4 5 6 7 8 9 10

FOREST MARBLE.

SOIL —*Colour*, dull dark brown.
  Consistence, tenacious, sticky, or adhesive, and difficult to plough when wet; when
    dry loose or dusty; thinly strewed with flat stones.
SUBSOIL, gray; broad flat stones, with clay or tenacious earth between: in some parts a whitish
    blue indurated marl between.
STRATUM, gray coarse grained stone, some of which on closer inspection appears to he composed
    of dark coloured shells, interspersed with whiter grains of ova. Bivalve shells most
    common to the thick beds; univalve to the thin. Decomposed pyritical wood often gives
    a partial redness; and some of the joints have a reddish tinge.
    Some of the most solid beds in different parts of its course are raised and polished for
    marble. Much of the stone is brown on the outside, and gray or blue within.
EXCAVATIONS, not very deep; sometimes dry, but more commonly in low ground hold water,
    particularly in winter.

This rock is distinctly separated from the preceding by a course of clay, below which a sand and sandstone, alternating with some of these shelly beds, renders the top of this rock less distinct. The bottom of it rests upon clay, which is the covering of the upper Oolite rock, and which occasionally contains thin gray lamina of stone, like some of the forest marble beds, composed of ova, and small turbinated shells compact enough to receive a polish. The beds of the rock which rise large and sound enough for slabs and marble chimney pieces, lie generally in clay, or in pits which hold water. Where the separating clay is thin, the water of this rock sinks into the more capacious joints of the Oolite rock beneath, by apertures called swallow-holes, which are very numerous in the course of this Stratum, from Bath by Tetbury, and other parts of the Cotswold Hills, to the forest of Whichwood, from which place and its adjacent quarries it has received the name of Forest Marble.

In some dry quarries the stone is so soft and porous, so much lighter in colour, and thickly interspersed with ova, as to be scarcely distinguished by specimens from the Barnack rag or top of the upper Oolite, which is equally stored with small turbinated shells. In such cases there is but little clay between the two rocks.

The Forest Marble might thus be considered as a rider to the great Oolite rock, and where both crop out in the same hills, south of Bath, and thence westward, the former is the well defined summit edge of the escarpment.

Its general course through the Cotswold district may be distinguished by the prevalence of timber trees, woods and pasture, and by more numerous sites of population than on the Oolite, where water is obtainable only by deep wells, at a great expense. Coarse roofing slates are in general use, and flagstones also, in the houses, courts, and streets of the towns and villages in the course of this rock. Though its various beds of stone are composed of little else but a mass of shells, loose and whole specimens are rare, and extracted with great difficulty.

The organized fossils which are visible in every bed of stone, are rarely or ever obtained but from quarries, and other excavations: a few are occasionally found in the clay between the stone. Bones teeth, and wood, firmly imbedded in the stone, are some of its most characteristic identifications. This is the third rock downwards, in the British series, which contains any ova. These little globular interpersions seem to indicate its contiguity and relationship to the greater and more perfect rocks of Oolite beneath. Through a great extent of country it is generally used on the roads.

Amongst the fossils of this Stratum, teeth and bones are the most remarkable. The teeth found in the stone quarries about Pickwick and Atford, are by the quarrymen called "bird's eyes" to which they bear some resemblance. They are all of a dark chocolate colour, which, with their high polish, and being set in the light coloured stone, renders them very conspicuous. Pickwick and Atford quarries used to be most noted for them; but since it has been generally understood that the same Stratum may uniformly be expected to produce the same organized fossils throughout its course, other quarries of the same stone have been searched, and found to contain them.

ORGANIZED FOSSILS.

FIG.

1 Patella rugosa	Hinton. Minching Hampton Common.
2 Ancilla	Farley Castle.
3 Rostellaria ?	Poulton. Farley Castle.
4 Ostrea	Wincanton. Road Coal experiment.
5 Pecten	Siddington. Foss Cross.
6 Pecten	Farley Castle.
7 Oval Bufonite	Stunsfield. Pickwick.
8 Round Bufonite	Stunsfield. Pickwick. Didmarton.
9 Fish Palate	Pickwick.
10 Cap-formed Palate	Pickwick.
11 Shark's Teeth	Stunsfield. Pickwick. Farley Castle.

FOREST MARBLE.

1. *Patella rugosa, M.C.*

2. *Ancilla,*

3. *Rostellaria, imperfect Specimens. Strat. Syst. P. 72.*

4. *Ostrea,*

5. *Pecten,*

6. *Pecten,*

7. *Oval Bufonitæ, or Teeth,*

8. *Round Bufonitæ,*

9. *Palate of a Fish,*

10. *Do.*

11. *Teeth of Fishes,*

PLATE 15 (AND FACING PAGE)

MIDDLE JURASSIC, FOREST MARBLE

1. Gastropod: *Symmetrocapulus tessoni*
2. Gastropod: *Cylindrites archiaci*
3. Gastropod: *Rostellaria* in block
4. Bivalve: *Catinula* sp.

5. Bivalve: *Plagiostoma subcardiiformis*
6. Bivalve: *Camptonectes auritus*
7. Fish tooth: *?Eomesodon* (splenial bone)
8. Fish tooth: *?Lepidotes* sp.

9. Fish palate:*?Asteracanthus magnus*
10. Fish palate: *Asteracanthus tenuis*
11. Fish teeth: probably 1 x shark, 1 x teleost

0 cm 1 2 3 4 5

Fossils in silhouette have not been found

CLAY over the UPPER OOLITE.

As the bottom part only of this Clay contains organized fossils, and most of these being Zoophites, attached to the rock by their roots; and apparently extended up into the Clay by their growth, they need not be considered as the products of a separate Stratum, but rather as the appendages to the top of the upper Oolite rock, which is thus covered with Clay. The organized fossils being all filled with stone, further confirms their relationship to the rock. Lying in Clay they are all loose, and easily collected and cleaned. The stony matter contained in the shells, which are entire, has few or no marks of ova; nor is there much of this general characteristic of the rock in the first four or five feet beneath the Clay. Many of these fossils can only be found in excavations which expose the top of the rock. Corals, tubipora, fig. 4, and fragments of millepora, fig. 5, may be collected from some of the ploughed fields south of Bath, which are on the plane of the upper Oolite rock. The tenacious and adhesive nature of this soil readily distinguishes it from that of the Stratum beneath, and accurately defines the boundary of the stony land.

UPPER OOLITE, or Calcareous Freestone.

SOIL—*Colour*, yellowish brown.
    Consistence, loose, crumbly, stony, with a large proportion of small stony fragments;
      over the Freestone some loose ova; over other parts of the rock some large flat
      stones, commonly called Stonebrash.
    State of moisture, absorbent; where sufficiently free from small stones may be kneaded.
SUBSOIL, small stones with a little soil, and fragments of the rubble stone which lies over the rock.
EXCAVATIONS, always dry.
STRATUM, masses of rock in beds, divided by large open vertical joints.
    Colour. The Freestone part yellowish white; other beds, some gray, and some
      almost blue in the middle. Freestone, calcareous, soft, oviform; cuts easily with
      a toothed saw or any edge tool; used in the repair of Westminster Abbey; alternates
      in the rock with other harder calcareous beds, but little interspersed with ova.
    Disintegration. See remark on the Portland rock, page 15, applicable to this.
WATER, hard, transparent: springs copious and numerous, in roads, ditches, and brooks;
    white from hasty rains.

This is the thickest of the calcareous rocks which form the great pile of Strata called the Stonebrash Hills. Where it occurs it forms the greatest breadth of their dry surface, and occasions many deep excavations for water. In these perforations, and in numerous deep quarries for the fine soft Freestone, which is imbedded between very thick beds of different sorts of stone, the nature and properties of the whole rock are ascertained.

This most valuable part of it varies much even in quarries of the same neighbourhood, south of Bath. The other sorts of stone are rarely used but are rough walls around the fields, and in the stone buildings common to its surface. The length of this Stratum, from unconformableness or other causes, is more deficient than either of the other rocks on the Stonebrash Hills. This might be adduced as one of the many instances of the necessity of attending to the course and full extent of every Stratum, before any geologist can decide upon the number contained in the British series; and hence also it must be evident, that those who have taken only partial views of the subject must be perpetually liable to error. Until the clay was removed from its top by the recent excavation of canals, &c. this rock was thought to contain but few fossils, and thus to be sufficiently distinguished from the under Oolite, which is most abundantly stored with them; and considering these fossils as appendages to the top of the Stratum, the remark still applies as to the rock itself. That extraordinary fossil zoophite, the pear encrinus, was first discovered most perfect with its root attached to the top of the rock, in a field belonging to my truly good friend, the Rev. Benjamin Richardson, at Berfield, near Bradford; and thence for some time afterwards was called the Berfield fossil. Several species of zoophites, with five or six species of inequivalved Bivalves and Echini, are the most numerous identifications. Between the beds of stone deeper in the rock, oysters and a few inside casts of equivalved bivalves occur: very small univalves, similar to those in Forest Marble, are numerously blended with ova and minute corals, in some of the upper beds, which are very indifferent Freestone.

On account of the scarcity of fossils in the rock, and the rare exposure of those on its top, and the great variation it is subject to, this seems the most difficult to trace to its extremities of any of the rocks which compose the Stonebrash Hills.

ORGANIZED FOSSILS *of the Clay over the Upper Oolite.*

FIG.
1 Pear Encrinite   Bradford. Berfield.
2 Vertebrae ditto   Farley Castle. Hinton.
3 Stems ditto   Winsley. Pickwick.
4 Tubipora   Broadfield Farm. Farley Castle.
5 Millepora   Broadfield Farm. Farley Castle. Hinton, Pickwick.
                                                                 Westwood.
6 Chama crassa   Stoford.
7 Plagiostoma   Bradford.
8 Avicula costata   Bradford. Hinton. Winsley.
9 Terebratula digona: the long variety   Farley Castle. Stoford. Bradford. Winsley. Pickwick.
10 Terebratula reticulata   Farley Castle. Bradford. Stoford. Hinton. Winsley
                                                                 Pickwick.

ORGANIZED FOSSILS *of the Upper Oolite Rock*

FIG.
1 Tubipora   Broadfield Farm. Combe Down. Westwood.
2 Tubipora   Combe Down.
3 Madrepora turbinata   Farley Castle. Broadfield Farm.
4 Madrepora porpites   Broadfield Farm.
5 Madrepora flexuosa   Castle Combe.

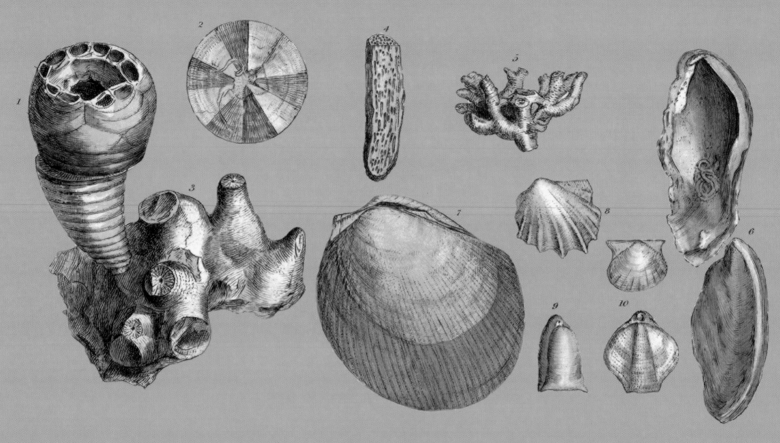

CLAY OVER THE UPPER OOLITE.

1.2.3. *Pear Encrinus.* 2. *The Clavicle.*

3. *The Root and Stems.*

4. *Tubipora.*

5. *Millepora.*

6. *Chama crassa. Strat. Syst. P. 80.*

7. *Plagiostoma.*

8. *Avicula costata. Strat. Syst. P. 81.*

9. *Terebratula digona, M.C. 96.*

10. *Terebratula reticulata. Strat. Syst. P. 83.*

PLATE 16 (AND FACING PAGE)

MIDDLE JURASSIC, BRADFORD CLAY

1. Crinoid: *Apiocrinus elegans*
2. Crinoid: *Apiocrinus elegans* *
3. Crinoid: *Apiocrinus elegans*
4. Serpulid worm: *Filograna* sp.

5. Bryozoan: *Terebellaria ramosissima*
6. Bivalve: *Praeoxygyra crassa*
7. Bivalve: *Plagiostoma cardiiformis* *

8. Bivalve: *Oxytoma costata*
9. Brachiopod: *Digonella digona*
10. Brachiopod: *Dictyothyris coarctata*

Fossils in silhouette have not been found
* similar fossil substituted from Smith's collection

0 cm 1 2 3 4 5 6 7 8 9 10

UPPER OOLITE.

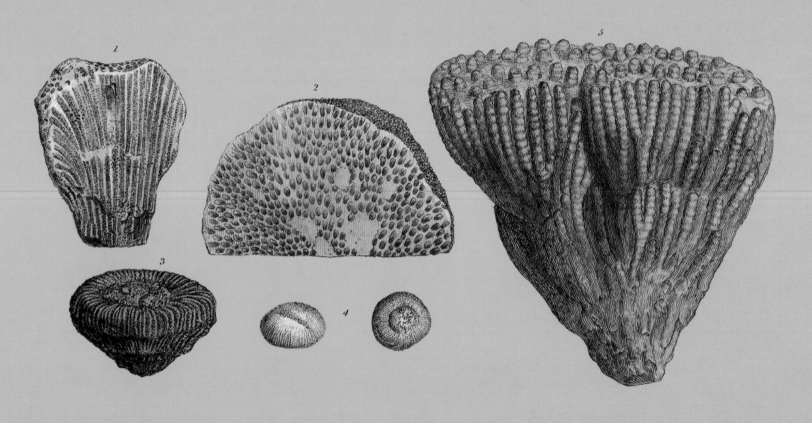

1. *Tubipora; Strat. Syst. P. 85.*

2. *Tubipora;*

3. *Madrepora turbinata. Linn. Strat. Syst. P. 84.*

4. *Madrepora porpites.*

5. *Madrepora flexuosa, Linn.*

PLATE 17 (AND FACING PAGE)

MIDDLE JURASSIC, GREAT OOLITE

1. Coral: *Lochmaeosmilia radiata*
2. Coral: *Lochmaeosmilia radiata*
3. Coral: *Montlivaltia* sp.
4. Coral: *Chomatoseris porpites*

5. Coral: *Cladophyllia babeana*

0 cm 1 2 3 4 5 6 7 8 9 10

Fossils in silhouette have not been found

FULLER'S EARTH ROCK.

———

SOIL—*Colour*. This soil is rather distinguished by its being of a lighter brown than that of the rocks above and below; but in side-lying ground it is generally mixed with the rubblestone of the rock above. When less mixed is very tenacious, slippery, and retentive of moisture. The fragments of its included rock, blended with the soil, are chiefly organized fossils.

SUBSOIL.—*Colour*, lightish blue, yellowish white, &c. varying much in the more clayey parts to dark blue.

Consistence, soft rubblestone, mixed with indurated marl, clay, and fuller's earth.

STRATUM, soft, whitish, yellowish, or light brown rock, and courses of rubblestone, generally too irregular and too slightly indurated for any use. The mass consists of this alternating with indurated marl, blue clay, and fuller's earth. The hardest bed of this stone is blue in the middle.

EXCAVATIONS, some hold water; others not.

———

The Fuller's Earth Rock, which in many places is so soft and imperfectly lapidified as scarcely to deserve the name of stone, with the indurated marl and clay in which it is inclosed; occupies the midway slope of many of the steep hills around. Bath. Its course is more distinctly definable around the sides of those steep hills than upon the more level parts of the Stonebrash district. Its clayey soil is in some degree distinguishable by less cultivation than upon the dryer soils of the Oolite rocks, above and below it, which are more genial to the growth of corn. Woods and timber trees are also common to it, on the slopes of the hills of which it so often forms a part. Little round insular hills in the vicinity of Bath, as Duncomb, Kelweston Round hill, and Monmouth's hill, seen from Pulteney-street, Bath, are also characteristic.

This Stratum of stone, with its accompaniments, may be traced from the high ground, six miles N. E. of Bath to Northleach, through the forest of Whichwood to Ditchley, in Oxfordshire, and through Northamptonshire to the ploughed fields on the north side of Stamford, and thence through the district of Kesteven, in Lincolnshire. It may be easily identified westward to a chasm in the hill south of Sherborn, in Dorsetshire. Every where it produces a very poor soil, distinguishable by its crops, whether in grass or tillage, unless greatly assisted by art.

The colour and nature of the subsoil materially assists the identification, which some of its numerous organized fossils readily confirm. They may be collected from the ploughed lands without the trouble of breaking them out of the stone, and consequently require but little cleaning. In this, as in some other respects, its organized fossils resemble those in the Cornbrash rock.

A small species of oyster, thin, smooth, and flat, is so abundant and so strongly contrasted by its dark colour with the whitish subsoil, turned up by the plough, or exposed in wheelruts, as to be highly characteristic of the outcrop of this Stratum.

Some parts of the, course of the Fuller's Earth, and inferior Fuller's Earth and its rock distinguishable chiefly by their organized fossils, long remained doubtful, as the boundaries of these and other subdivisions of the rocky Strata which compose the Cotswold Hills, and great breadths of stony land adjoining, are not there so well defined as in the more abrupt slopes of the hills round Bath. The indistinctness of these intermediate Strata renders it difficult in many parts to ascertain the division of the two Oolites, and the great similarity of colour in all these Strata contributes to the obscurity. The organized fossils are, therefore, in some cases essential to the decision. The inferior Fuller's Earth, and the indurated clay which accompanies it has none of the long turbinated shells, but is distinguished by a peculiar nautilus, and some very thick Ammonites; yet Ammonites agreeing with the more general form are not common. Most of the fossils are casts, at least such are most numerous: all the large bivalves are so, except the great rough oyster, and Ostrea diluviana, *Linn.* (Marshii, *Min. Conch.)* These, like most of the species of oysters in other Strata, have their shells preserved. All the smaller fossils in these Strata, as the little hooked oyster, and all the terebratulæ, which are very numerous, have their shells entire.

ORGANIZED FOSSILS.

FIG.

1 Nautilus	Lansdown.
2 Ammonites modiolaris	Dundry. Rowley Bottom.
3 Modiola anatina	Avoncliff.
4 Cardita	Grip Wood. Hardington.
5 Cardium	Charlton Horethorn. Near Gagenwell. Near Redlynch
6 Tellina	Avoncliff. Hardington
7 Ostrea acuminata	Orchardleigh. Avoncliff. Below Combe Down Caisson. North of Stamford
8 Ostrea Marshii	Monkton Combe. Cotswold Hills.
9 Terebratula media	Near Bath. Charlton Horethorn. Orchardleigh.

FULLERS EARTH ROCK.

1. *Nautilus. Strat. Syst. P. 87.*

2. *Ammonites modiolaris. Strat. Syst. P. 88.*

3. *Modiola anatina. Strat. Syst. P. 89.*

4. *Cardita.*

5. *Cardium.*

6. *Tellina.*

7. *Ostrea acuminata M.C.135.*

8. *Ostrea Marshii. M.C.48.*

9. *Terebratula media. M.C. 83.f.5.*

PLATE 18 (AND FACING PAGE)

MIDDLE JURASSIC, FULLER'S EARTH

1. Nautiloid: indet.
2. Ammonite: *Tulites modiolaris*
3. Bivalve: *Modiolus anatinus*

4. Bivalve: *Ceratomya* aff. *striata*
5. Bivalve: *Pholadomya* aff. *lirata*
6. Bivalve: *Cercomya* aff. *pinguis*

7. Bivalve: *Praeexogyra acuminata*
8. Bivalve: *Actinostreon marshii*
9. Brachiopod: *Rhynchonelloidella media* *

0 cm 1 2 3 4 5

Fossils in silhouette have not been found
* *similar fossil substituted from Smith's collection*

STRATIGRAPHICAL SYSTEM

OF

ORGANIZED FOSSILS,

WITH
REFERENCE TO THE SPECIMENS
OF

THE ORIGINAL GEOLOGICAL COLLECTION
IN THE
BRITISH MUSEUM :
EXPLAINING
THEIR STATE OF PRESERVATION
AND
THEIR USE IN IDENTIFYING
THE
BRITISH STRATA.

BY
WILLIAM SMITH,
CIVIL ENGINEER AND MINERAL SURVEYOR;

Author of a " Treatise on Irrigation," a "Map and Delineation of the Strata of England and Wales," with a Memoir,"Strata identified by organized Fossils," "Geological Section" and "Table."

LONDON:

Printed for E. WILLIAMS, Bookseller to the PRINCE REGENT, and to the DUKE and DUCHESS of York, No. 11, Strand, near Charing Cross; and sold by all other Booksellers in the Kingdom.

1817.

PART I.

CONTENTS.

Introduction.

Geological Table of British Organized Fossils.

Stratigraphical Table of Echini.

Observations on Echini.

Indexes to Genera and Species and to their Localities will be given in the succeeding part of the work; and the Characters of the Genera will be explained.

Part II., which completes the Work, will be speedily published.

INTRODUCTION.

This novel and interesting description of near seven hundred species of Fossil Shells, Zoophites, and other organized Fossils, found in England and Wales, and collected in identification of the Strata, refers particularly to the specimens of a geological collection deposited in the British Museum. On the specimens, Roman capitals mark the genus,—the figures, 1, 2, 3, &c. refer to the species,—and the small letters, a, b, c, &c. to the localities or sites in the Strata.

This copious reference to the stratum which contains the Fossils, to the particular site therein whence obtained, and to the individual specimens of the collection, which is intended to be publicly exhibited in the British Museum, seemed to render figures of them unnecessary; especially as reference is constantly made to another work of the Author's now publishing by Mr. Sowerby, which consists chiefly of engravings; and as further reference is likewise made to the numerous figures of Sowerby's *Mineral Conchology*.

It is hoped, and confidently expected, that this method of combining the stratified and systematic arrangement of Fossil Shells, &c. will comprise all the information respecting them which can be required, either by the curious Conchologist or by the most attentive investigator of the Strata. Lamarck's system, which is an extension and improvement of that of Linnæus, has been preferred, as most applicable to the arrangement of organized Fossils; of which the species and even genera are sometimes not without difficulty determined. His more particular attention to the form, muscular attachment, and other striking characters apparent in Fossils where the hinge cannot often be observed, better enables the Mineral *Conchologist* to distinguish the generic and specific characters of those numerous organized Fossils which are merely casts of the inside of the shell, or of the animal which inhabited it. As this country abounds with numerous species which cannot be arranged under any of the genera given by M. Lamarck, new genera have been formed by Sowerby, Parkinson, and others, which are herein adopted and referred to: reference is likewise made to most of old authors on the subject.

In the arrangement of Echini, I have followed *Leske* in his comment on Klein.[a2]

[iv] Four of the most copious divisions, Echini, Ammonites, Terebratula, and Zoophites, to the extent of more than a hundred species, have been arranged in a tabular form, which shows by inspection their relative situation in the Strata, and gives the effect of collating the specimens.

By the tables it will be seen which Fossils are peculiar to any Stratum, and which are repeated in others.

The order naturally suggested by the situations of the organized Fossils themselves, Zoophites, Testacea, Echini, Crustacea, Bones of large Animals, is uniformly observed in each Stratum throughout the work: so that this book naturally divided by the Strata, admits of easy reference to the innumerable specimens of this extensive branch of Natural. History. In addition to these several references, to the Stratum in which any particular kind of Fossil is found, to the particular site in its course where it was collected, to the identical specimen in the British Museum, and to the Authors who have written on them, I have, for the convenience of those who have not the opportunity of visiting remote parts, given other reference to my map of the Strata of England and Wales, by colours corresponding to the coloured lines on that map, by which the courses of the Strata are represented.

My method of arranging Fossils generally, according to the Strata which contain them, having long since been adopted by all to whom my early discoveries were communicated, such connoisseurs will make by the help of this work the material improvement in their collections which is now offered to them; by which the stratified and systematic ·arrangements are most usefully combined. All the localities of each Species in each Stratum are enumerated in succession, showing, as the specimens would if placed together, their use in identifying the Strata.

The following works have been consulted, for the purpose of giving to the specimens the most appropriate and descriptive names:

LATIN.

Linnæus . . . . .Systema Naturæ.
Llwyd . . . . .Lithophylacii Brittanici Ichnographia. 8vo.
Klein with Leske . . . . .Echinodermata. 4to.
Brander and Solander . . . . .Fossilia Hantoniensia. 4to.

FRENCH

Cuvier . . . . . . .Géographie Minéralogique des Environs de Paris. 4to.
Les Annales du Muséum d'Histoire Naturelle, containing Lamarck's
Description of the Fossils of Grignon, Courtagon, &c. 4to.
[v]

ENGLISH.

Plot . . . . Natural History of Oxfordshire. fol. pl.
Morton . . . . .Natural History of Northamptonshire. fol. pl.
Woodward . . . . Catalogue. 8vo. 2 vol.
Walcot . . . . Petrifactions in the neighbourhood of Bath. pl.
Ellis and Solander . . . . Zoophites. 4to. with Plates.
Martin . . . . .Derbyshire Petrifactions. 4to. with Plates.
Parkinson . . Organic Remains of a former World. 4to. 3 vols with Plates.
Townsend . . Credibility of the Mosaic History established, &c. 4to. with Plates.
Sowerby . . . . . Mineral Conchology of Great Britain. 8vo. with Plates.

My original method of tracing the Strata by the organized Fossils imbedded therein, is thus reduced to a science not difficult to learn. Ever since the first written account of this discovery was circulated in 1799 it has been closely investigated by my scientific acquaintance in the vicinity of Bath; some of whom search the quarries of different Strata in that district with as much certainty of finding the characteristic Fossils of the respective rocks, as if they were on the shelves of their cabinets. By this new method of searching for organized Fossils with the regularity with which they are imbedded in such a variety of Strata, many new species have been discovered. The Geologist is thus enabled to fix the locality of those previously found; to direct the attentive investigator in his pursuits; and to find in all former cabinets and catalogues numerous proofs of accuracy in this mode of identifying the Strata.

The virtuoso will therefore now enter upon the study and selection of organized Fossils with the twofold advantage of amusement and utility. The various component parts of the soil, and all the subterraneous productions of his estate, become interesting objects of research; the contents of quarries, pits, wells, and other excavations, hitherto thought unworthy of notice, will be scrupulously examined.

The organized Fossils which may be found, will enable him to identify the Strata of his own estate with those of others: thus his lands may be drained with more certainty of success, his buildings substantially improved, and his private and public roads better made, and repaired at less expense.

To possess such general knowledge of the Soil, Subsoil, and Strata, on every road he travels and in every field he traverses, with their respective Fossils stratigraphically arranged in his cabinet, must furnish an endless source of gratification to every inquisitive mind. His own house will be the best school of Natural History[vi] for all the younger branches of the family, and a source of amusement to all his scientific acquaintance;— science will become more general;—all will lend assistance;—no time will be idly lost: nor with such resources can a country gentleman be (as Pope says) "a prisoner in his own house every rainy day." Rural amusements, to those who can enjoy them are the most healthful; and the search for a Fossil may be considered at least as rational as the pursuit of a hare,—one the sport of infants, the other of adults; one squanders time and property, the other improves the mind and may afterwards extend such infant knowledge to the improvement of the estates he may enjoy. No study, like that of the organized Fossils, can be so well calculated for the healthful and rational amusement of youth; and nothing can more effectually lead to general improvement than the early diffusion of science. That of Natural History should be the first object of every country gentleman; and if it be not an insult to nature to pass unnoticed her various productions, which are superior far to the nicest workmanship, it will sometime be an insult to the understanding to be considered totally ignorant of these things.

The Author is aware that for want of proper and settled terms there may be some mistakes in his arrangement of the Fossils; but if a *Venus* should be mistaken for a *Cyclas*, or a *Mactra* for a *Mya*, it cannot be of more importance (in the present state of the science) than the misspelling of a word which alters not the sense; —errors of *misnomer* in the work or in the tables may be easily corrected with a pen as more perfect specimens are obtained, or as the science improves, but errors in their stratified arrangement can be corrected by those only who are locally acquainted with the Strata, and the numerous organized Fossils they contain. On this principle I have ventured, without much knowledge of Conchology, and with weak aids in that science, to give the outlines of a systematic arrangement combined with the stratified, it being much easier to learn the useful than to unlearn the useless; and finding myself pressed to the task by others who are proceeding with such works with but imperfect knowledge of the Strata, I may therefore hope that my imperfections in the systematic arrangement placed against their's in the Strata, the balance will be in favour of this work.

A combination of the stratified with the systematic arrangement will always have the advantage of showing the locality of specimens, and from the simplicity of form, errors in genera and species may be readily corrected and the species hereafter discovered as readily added.

My observations on this and on other branches of the subject are entirely original, and unincumbered with theories for I have none to support: nor do I refer my reader to foreign countries to prove what I advance: but I have drawn [vii] and described the face of a country whose internal contents are more deeply explored than any other part of the earth's surface; and in which every one, to the extent of his local knowledge, is a critic on my work. With such a host of critics as might rise up against me in the extensive districts I describe, it may reasonably be supposed that accuracy claimed my utmost attention, and that in the collection and arrangement of the numerous Fossils, and in the determination of the facts which they support, the mind would frequently hesitate, and doubts have remained some time for want of specimens or an opportunity of visiting the site of any dubious part. Rules, however, have arisen out of the research, which wonderfully assist the investigation of Strata; these will be described in the course of my works, if the encouragement which I expect from the public should enable me to publish all my manuscript. The extent and accuracy of the observations which I have made and recorded will excuse me for any apparent procrastination, and encouragement only is wanting in this important branch of natural History to unravel the mystery and simplify our knowledge of all the terrene part of the creation; for enough is already discovered to render the subject familiar and extensively useful. Geologists are also aiding greatly an improvement in the science by their minute examination of the materials of Strata, and by the modern adoption of a settled plan of observing and recording natural facts.

This particular branch of Geology has already proved that a large portion of the earth once teemed with animation, and that the animals and plants thus finely preserved in the solid parts of the earth's interior, are so materially different from those now in existence, that they may be considered as a new creation, or rather as an undiscovered part of an older creation. They are chiefly submarine, and as they vary generally from the present inhabitants of the sea, so at separate periods of the earth's formation they vary as much from each other; insomuch that each layer of these fossil organized bodies must be considered as a separate creation; or how could the earth be formed *stratum super stratum*, and each abundantly stored with a different race of animals and plants ? Surely these innumerable and finely organized fossils are not the sports of nature placed there to excite the attention of the idly curious, but they must, like the other works of the Great Creator, have their use. The miner has long thus identified his local sinkings of shafts, and why should not the virtuoso, the owner and occupier of the soil, quarry-men and workers of stone, do the same more extensively ? The result of my labours is a settled plan for doing this, and therefore the identification of Strata by the help of organized Fossils, becomes one of the most important modern discoveries in Geology. It enables the Geologist clearly to distinguish one Stratum [viii] from another in Britain, and also to trace their connexion with the same Strata on the continent. Thus it is capable of the most extensive or of the most local use.

Strata, when identified by organized Fossils, with the localities of each Stratum accurately delineated, will also define on maps of the country the limits of districts in which they are most prevalent. Thus it appears by this work, and by the map of the Strata, that three principal families of organized Fossils occupy nearly three equal portions of the English and Welsh parts of Britain;

Echini are most common to the superior Strata;

Ammonites to those beneath;

Producti with numerous Encrini to the inferior; or at least to the lowest of those which are most abundantly stored with the animal class.

This order in the section gives the following order on the map;

Echini most abundant in the eastern and south-eastern districts;

Ammonites in the interior, or in the course of those Strata which occupy the midland counties in a north-easterly direction, from Char-mouth to Whitby;

The species of Anomia. *Linn.* now called Productus, occur no higher in the series than in the limestones which are the boundaries of coal.

Taking another extensive view of a singular division of the animal class, it appears by the peculiar localities of certain species, and even several genera of these organized fossils peculiar to certain Strata, that many of them occur not throughout large districts of the country. Thus, the Corals, which accompany the Pisolite and the two Oolites in the greatest abundance, are not found within the denudation, a district which is composed of large portions of Kent, Surry, Sussex, and Hampshire; and more locally known as the Forest Ridge and the Wealds of Kent and Sussex. Two similar expansions of the same Strata occasion a similar deficiency of the numerous species of these extensive genera, on North York Moors, and on Blackdown, which embraces a considerable portion of the counties of Somerset, Dorset, and Devon.

So far the deficiency arises from a want of exposure in those Strata which contain them; but another cause of the deficiency arises from defects in the courses of those Strata: two of the three rocks before mentioned are not discovered north of the Humber, or south west of the borders of Somerset, and the other is but partially seen to the south west of these limits; consequently a still larger portion of Yorkshire in the north east and of the parts beforementioned in the south west (wherein these fossils might have been expected) is deficient in them.

These deficiencies arise from the *unconformableness* of some of the other Strata.

Other deficiencies of organized Fossils, to a considerable extent, on many parts of [ix] the surface where they should, according to the course of their out-cropping strata, be found, are occasioned by a thick covering of alluvial matter; this, in the rounded fragments or nodules of the different Strata, contains entire many of the specimens herein described, or loose ones which have been detached from their original beds in the Strata, much rounded by attrition in water: these will be described under the head of *Alluvial Fossils.*

Fortunately for the science which these investigations must establish, many Strata are entirely deficient in organized Fossils, some of these so thick as to occupy of themselves large portions of the island, and some much thinner, which alternate with others that contain them.

How far these facts tend to establish a certain theory, which pretends to give the relative ages of Strata according to the presence or absence of organized Fossils, others may determine.

Many Strata being entirely without organized Fossils, the investigation is much facilitated, by rendering the courses of those Strata which contain

them more distinct; and the courses of all the Strata being known, the name of the place where any specimen is found is sufficient to mark its locality in the Strata, and the specimens being filled with the matter in which they are imbedded materially assist in identifying the Stratum to which they belong. In this respect Mineral Conchology has much the advantage of recent; the matter of the Stratum fully compensating in a geological point of view, for any defect in the specimen. Shells are generally without the animals, which are mostly incapable of preservation; fossils frequently represent the animals without the shells (*i. e.* the interior conformation of the shell). In general, fossil shells are so effectually closed and filled with stony matter, that the hinge, opening, and other characters, cannot he observed.

Numerous Zoophites naturally too tender for preservation, have in their fossil state their shape and most minute organization beautifully retained in limestone, flint, and other solid matter. Thus not only in clays, sands, and rocks, but in the hardest stones, are displayed all the treasures of an ancient deep, which prove the high antiquity and watery origin of the earth; for nothing can more plainly than the Zoophites evince the once fine fluidity of the stony matter in which they are enveloped, no fluid grosser than water being capable of pervading their pores. The process which converted them and their element into stone seems to have been similar to that of freezing water, which would suddenly fix all the inhabitants of the ocean, each in its place, with all the original form and character. Organized Fossils are to the naturalist as coins to the antiquary; they are the antiquities of [b][x]the earth; and very distinctly show its gradual regular formation, with the various changes of inhabitants in the watery element.

Thus endless gratification may be derived from mountains of ancient animated nature, wherein extinct animals and plants innumerable, with characters and habits distinctly preserved, have transmitted to eternity their own history, and the clearest and best evidence of the earth's formation.

As the section of a tree shows its increase by annual rings of growth, so the Strata seem to show the earth's lamellar increase.

The interior of the earth therefore, like other better investigated works of nature, is formed upon the wisest and best principles, incomprehensible in their extent, but to the limits of our capacity exceedingly useful.

The angle of declination in the Strata towards the horizon, and their consequent successive terminations in the surface of the earth, is one of the most wonderful dispositions of Providence that could be devised for the benefit of man. Without such an angle of the Strata with the surface of the earth, coals and other useful minerals could not be worked; nor could the edges of the Strata have been thus identified by the organized Fossils imbedded. They are therefore of great use in tracing the outcrops of open-jointed Strata, which alternate with clays, and produce springs; as also in identifying the Strata of deep wells sunk to those subterraneous reservoirs in the cavities of rocks: and the vegetable impressions particularly define in the collier's shaft the approach to coal. They are found in their respective Strata at the greatest depths, as well as at the greatest heights. Hence the consideration of such an immensity of animal and vegetable matter, the time required for its perfection and subsequent consolidation in the Strata, evidently in deep and quiet water, may at first seem incomprehensible to many, but further investigation leads to further admiration of the great unerring cause. In this, as in every other part of the creation, there seems to have been one grand line of succession, a wonderful series of organization successively proceeding in the same train towards perfection.

Zoophites and shell fish appear to have been the first of the animal creation, and to have been in existence prior to the completion of dry land, as they have entered into the composition of a large proportion of the solid parts of the earth. Many Strata of considerable extent are little else but an accumulation of their remains, which have been quietly entombed in the Strata, with all the form, characters, and habits of life, in the places where they are; there being no appearance of their having been disturbed or drifted about. The change of the watery element in [xi].which they lived, from a fluid to a solid state, has been the cause of their destruction and the means of their fine preservation; and that change seems in most instances to have been produced without violence: the form of the tenderest substance is as finely preserved in the hardest stone as in the original state.

These numberless appearances of an animated origin in Strata of such immense thickness and extent, must strike the admirers of nature with a degree of reverential awe and grateful adoration of the Almighty Creator. And though the mysterious cause which placed them there comes not within our comprehension, these remains of animal and vegetable life are the clearest evidence of the boundless extent of creation; that one

destroying and reanimating power has ever existed, and that nothing is done in vain. If these animals and vegetables had only to live and die, and mark respectively the sites of their existence in the mass of matter which now forms the earth, they have had their use, and will for ever remain indefaceable monuments of that wonderful creative power which formed them and all things.

The position in which these organized Fossils are arranged seems to be the most useful part of the knowledge to be derived from them; is it not therefore better to profit by that which is in our power, than to waste our time about that which is incomprehensible? not that there is reason to fear any result from man's deepest investigation of the works of nature, which must end in the acknowledgement of an omnipotent, incomprehensible, allwise, directing agent.

The chief object of this work being to show the utility of organized Fossils in identifying the Strata, nothing further will be attempted in the systematic arrangement than is necessary to make the subject intelligible; and the numerous useful and interesting deductions thence resulting will more appropriately follow than precede the regular description of them in the order of the strata.

The term "Organized Fossils" *is generally applied to all fossil matter that has a relation to the form of any organized body, either animal or vegetable.*

These substances are also called "*Fossils,*" "*Petrifactions,*" and " *Organic Remains.*"

EDITOR'S NOTE: *lower case Roman numerals in square brackets in the Introduction are original page numbers, other letters are printers marks.*

LONDON CLAY.
TESTACEA.
UNIVALVIA.
VOLUTA.

Voluta spinosa. *Sowerby's Mineral Conchology.*

Fig. 5 and 6, London Clay Plate, Strata identified, &c.

A cast of the inside of the shell; oblong, with a short spire and not many volutions, a few longitudinal undulations on the upper part of each.

Bognor.

FUSUS.

Fusus longaevus. *Min. Conch.*

Ventricose, smooth, spire turreted with a few large knobs upon the upper part of the latter whorls; beak as long as the spire, slightly curved near the end.

Muddiford.

CERITHIUM.
SPECIES 1.

Cerithium melanioides. *Min. Conch.*

Fig. 7, London Clay Plate.

Turreted, volutions convex, with one spiral largely tuberculated carina above the middle, and several tuberculated carinæ beneath it; obscurely undulated longitudinally: beak very short.

a. Woolwich. *b.* Bracklesham bay.

SPECIES 2

Cerithium intermedium. *Min. Conch.*

Pyramidal, sides straight: volutions many, the upper edge distinctly crenated, and several small crenulated threads beneath a concavity at the meeting of the volutions: mouth squarish.

a. Woolwich. *b.* near May Place. in an angle of Bexleyheath b specimens were filled with sand stone

B

2

SPECIES 3.

Cerithium funatum. *Min. Conch.*

Conical, elongated, with two obtuse crenulated transverse ridges upon each whorl; upper part of each whorl thickened and tuberculated; mouth squarish; base smooth, with two transverse ridges .

Newhaven Castle Hill.

This species has fewer volutions than species 2 the row of tubercles on the upper edge is larger, nor has it so many spiral threads beneath.

VIVIPARA.

Vivipara fluviorum. *Min. Conch.*

Fig. 1, London Clay Plate.

Volutions four to six convex, shell about twice the length of the aperture; lines of growth rather sharply conspicuous, giving the shell a finely striated appearance.

Brixton Causeway, out of a deep well.

MULTILOCULAR or CHAMBERED UNIVALVES.
NAUTILUS.

Nautilus imperialis. *Min. Conch.*

Involute, umbilicate; aperture lunate; septa entire, concave, broadest in the middle, truncated and slightly recurved at their ends; siphunculus nearest to the inside.

Isle of Sheppey, a small specimen.

AMMONITES.

Ammonites communis. *Min. Conch.* Lias Fossil Diluvial

Fig. 11, London Clay, Plate.

Involute; volutions six or more exposed; radii numerous, prominent, bifurcating over the front; aperture nearly circular, equal to about one-fifth of the diameter of the shell.

Happisburgh cliff.

There are two varieties of this species, one of them has a flattish spire, with an oval aperture; the other a rounder spire, with a nearly circular aperture.

This specimen is of the first variety.

BIVALVIA
EQUIVALVED BIVALVES.
MODIOLA.

Modiola depressa. *Min. Conch.*

Much depressed, ovate, narrowing toward the posterior side; surface smooth.

Bognor.

3
PECTUNCULUS.
SPECIES 1.

Pectunculus decussatus. *Min Conch.*

Fig.10, London Clay Plate.

Transversely obovate; sides rather straight; surface covered with numerous longitudinal striæ: hinge teeth twenty-five to thirty: margin thick, plain.

Highgate archway.

SPECIES 2

Pectunculus.

Fig. 3, London Clay Plate.

Orbicular, rather depressed, thickest near the beaks; longitudinally undulated; undulations indistinct, alternately wider and narrower many concentric rugæ.

Bognor.

CYCLAS.
SPECIES 1.

Cyclas deperdita, *Lam.*

Ovato-triangular, depressed, beaks acute, anterior side subtruncated; surface with sharp transverse lines of growth.

Woolwich.

The middle tooth is frequently bifid, and the lateral ones crenulated.

SPECIES 2.

Suborbicular or transverse, beaks acute, the anterior side straightest; surface with acute transverse elevations.

a. Woolwich. *b.* Newhaven Castle Hill.

Differs from the last species in the more central position of the beaks.

VENERICARDIA.
SPECIES 1.

Venericardia planicosta. *Min. Conch.*

Subcordate, very thick, smooth; ribs broad and flat about twenty, expanding into each other toward the margin; a few large teeth within the posterior edge.

Bracklesham Bay.

SPECIES 2

Subcordate, oblique, beaks lying toward the less produced side; many longitudinal flattened undulations indenting the margin, and crossed by transverse rugæ; inner edge of the shell furnished with undulations equal in number to those on the outside:-shell thick.

Bognor.

This species resembles venericardia senilis but the undulations are much flatter and more numerous.

B 2

4
TELLINA.

Fig 2, London Clay Plate.

Ovate, wider than long; transversely striated.

a. Sheppey. *b.* Happisburgh cliff. Diluvial

MYA.

Mya intermedia. *Min. Conch.*

Depressed, smooth, twice as wide as long, sides rounded; anterior side expanded, gaping a little; posterior side small; front nearly straight.

Bognor.

INEQUIVALVED BIVALVES.
CHAMA.

Chama squamosa *Brander.*

Fig. 4, London Clay Plate.

Subrotund, valves convex, with transverse squamous furrows; beak of the lower valve most projecting.

Hordel cliff.

OSTREA

Oblong, a little oblique, rather smooth; lower valve gibbous in the middle, depressed at the margin; pit oblong, narrow.

Woolwich.

CRUSTACEA.
CRAB.

Several species of Crabs have been found at Sheppey, but I have not the opportunity of distinguishing them.

BONES.
TEETH.

Fig. 8, London Clay Plate.

Large, conical, one side flat, smooth; with two fangs or small teeth, one on each side.

Isle of Sheppey.

Fig. 9, London Clay Plate, Diluvial

Thin or much depressed, the point oblique, with two fangs or small teeth, one on each side.

Happisburgh cliff.

NB It may be remarked that in Norfolk and Suffolk there are scarcely any London Clay Fossils – The above two are wrong – S. Woodward has only 8 amongst in a numerous list of Norfolk Clay fossils – this confirms my early opinion that London clay extends not into these counties

---

5

CRAG.
ZOOPHITA.

Spheroidal or depressed, with concentric cavities or cells; surface with numerous angular depressions, covered by the points of very small aggregated tubes; no stem appears.

Aldborough.

Orbicular; with numerous fasciculi of small tubes radiating from the stem; the upper surface covered by the aggregated points of tubes.

Aldborough.

FLUSTRA.

Surface undulated; with minute openings placed on small elevations, radiating from the root or place of attachment in a quincuncial order.

Aldborough.

TESTACEA.
UNIVALVIA.
EMARGINULA.

Emarginula reticulata. *Min. Conch.*

Fig. 5, Crag Plate, Strata identified &c.

Shell oval, reticulato-striated, vertex rather acute, principal radii twenty four or more.

Bramerton.

VOLUTA.

Voluta Lamberti. *Min. Conch.*

Fusiform, short, smooth; base elongated, obscurely truncated; columella with three or four plaits; aperture acute above; outer lip sharp, not expanded toward the base.

Aldborough—cast of the inside.

MUREX.
SPECIES 1.

Murex striatus. *Min. Conch.*

Shell ventricose, with many spiral rounded projections, and from three to five parallel striæ between each, crossed by longitudinal sutures: volutions from three to six; beak nearly straight; mouth oval.

a. Alderton. *c.* Bramerton.

6
SPECIES 2

Fig 2, Crag Plate.

Oblong or ovate; volutions five or six, ventricose; with many spiral threads, (alternately larger and smaller); longitudinal sutures distinct, aperture oblong, wide in its upper part, ending below in a short deep canal; the right lip grooved at the edge.

These grooves correspond in number and in size to the threads on the outside, the lip generally acute. In most of the specimens two of the larger threads in the upper part of the volution are more conspicuous than the others, and continue to the apex; the upper one of the two forms a slight angle in the contour; the alternation of larger and smaller threads is not always regular.

a. Between Norwich and Yarmouth. *b.* In the parish of Leiston. *c.* Thorpe Common. *d.* Tattingstone Park. e Bramerton. A specimen from this place is nearly covered with small Balani. Foxhole. One from this place is covered with larger Balani.

Playford. Sutton. These specimens have the upper larger thread very distinct.

A VARIETY approaching Murex latus. *Min.Conch.*

a. Trimingsby. *b.* Bramerton. *c.* Thorpe Common.

SPECIES 3.

Oblong, obtuse, volutions about five, with eight or more spiral ridges, two of which in the upper part are larger than the others, and are continued to the apex: longitudinal sutures distinct, aperture oblong, straightened on the inner side, wide in the upper part; canal short, broad.

Of the two projecting ridges the upper is the largest and there is a considerable hollow between them, with two or more parallel striæ. A small ridge on the upper edge of the volution.

a. Bramerton. *b.* Thorpe Common. Sutton.

This species may be distinguished from the others by its large and few ridges.

SPECIES 4

Murex contrarius. *Linn. Min. Conch.*

Fig. 1, Crag Plate.

Spire reversed, volutions five or six, slightly expanded at the upper part, and contracted toward the beak: surface either smooth or with many rounded projections: mouth irregularly ovate; beak rather short.

7

a. Alderton. *b.* Suffolk. *c.* Tattingstone Park. Foxhole. Playford. Sutton. Newborn. Brightwell.

SPECIES 5.

Murex rugosus. ? *Min. Conch.*

Suburreted or oblong; volutions rather flattened, and suddenly contracted into a short beak, with several large longitudinal undulations crossing many deepish spiral striæ.

Foxhole.

The inside of the shell is undulated in the same manner as the outside.

SPECIES 6.

Murex antiquus. *Linn.*

Ovate, wide at the base; volutions about seven, expanded, with many spiral projections, which are crossed by longitudinal undulations in the upper part: aperture oblong; right lip sharp, with internal undulations corresponding with the external projections:

Surface reticulated; aperture expanded at the base; left lip spread.

Playford.

GEOLOGICAL TABLE OF BRITISH ORGANIZED FOSSILS,

WHICH IDENTIFY THE COURSES AND CONTINUITY OF **THE STRATA** IN THEIR ORDER OF SUPERPOSITION;
AS ORIGINALLY DISCOVERED BY **W. SMITH**, Civil Engineer; WITH REFERENCE TO HIS
GEOLOGICAL MAP OF ENGLAND AND WALES.

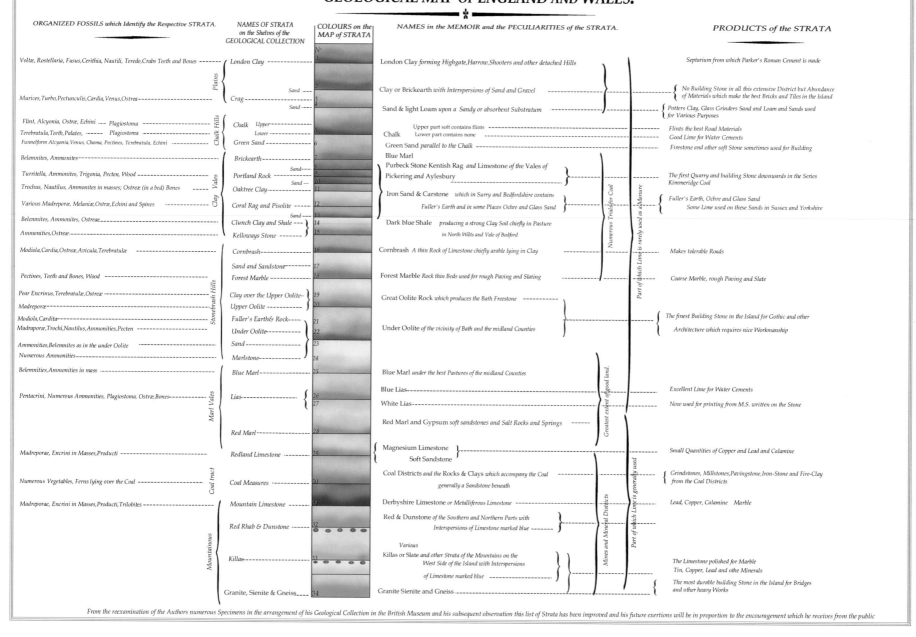

ORGANIZED FOSSILS which Identify the Respective STRATA.		NAMES OF STRATA on the Shelves of the GEOLOGICAL COLLECTION	COLOURS on the MAP of STRATA	NAMES in the MEMOIR and the PECULIARITIES OF THE STRATA.			PRODUCTS of the STRATA
Voltæ, Rostellaria, Fusus, Cerithia, Nautili, Teredo, Crabs Teeth and Bones	Plains	London Clay	1	London Clay forming Highgate, Harrow, Shooters and other detached Hills			Septarium from which Parker's Roman Cement is made
Murices, Turbo, Pectunculis, Cardia, Venus, Ostrea		Crag — Sand 2, Sand 3, 4	2 3 4	Clay or Brickearth with Interspersions of Sand and Gravel; Sand & light Loam upon a Sandy or absorbent Substratum			No Building Stone in all this extensive District but Abundance of Materials which make the best Bricks and Tiles in the Island; Potters Clay, Glass Grinders Sand and Loam and Sands used for Various Purposes
Flint, Alcyonia, Ostræ, Echini — Plagiostoma; Terebratula, Teeth, Palates — Plagiostoma; Funnelform Alcyonia, Venus, Chama, Pectines, Terebratula, Echini	Chalk Hills	Chalk Upper, Lower; Green Sand	5 6	Chalk Upper part soft contains flints; Lower part contains none; Green Sand parallel to the Chalk			Flints the best Road Materials; Good Lime for Water Cements; Firestone and other soft Stone sometimes used for Building
Belemnites, Ammonites		Brickearth	7	Blue Marl			
Turritella, Ammonites, Trigonia, Pecten, Wood	Clay Vales	Portland Rock — Sand 8, 9	8 9	Purbeck Stone Kentish Rag and Limestone of the Vales of Pickering and Aylesbury			The first Quarry and building Stone downwards in the Series Kimmeridge Coal
Trochus, Nautilus, Ammonites in masses; Ostreæ (in a bed) Bones		Oaktree Clay — Sand 10	10 11				
Various Madreporæ, Melaniæ, Ostræ, Echini and Spines		Coral Rag and Pisolite — Sand 12, 13	12 13	Iron Sand & Carstone which in Surry and Bedfordshire contains Fuller's Earth and in some Places Ochre and Glass Sand			Fuller's Earth, Ochre and Glass Sand; Some Lime used on these Sands in Sussex and Yorkshire
Belemnites, Ammonites, Ostreae		Clunch Clay and Shale	14	Dark blue Shale producing a strong Clay Soil chiefly in Pasture in North Wilts and Vale of Bedford			
Ammonities, Ostreæ		Kelloways Stone	15				
Modiola, Cardia, Ostreæ, Avicula, Terebratulæ	Stonebrash Hills	Cornbrash	16	Cornbrash A thin Rock of Limestone chiefly arable lying in Clay			Makes tolerable Roads
Pectines, Teeth and Bones, Wood		Sand and Sandstone; Forest Marble	17 18	Forest Marble Rock thin Beds used for rough Paving and Slating			Coarse Marble, rough Paving and Slate
Pear Encrinus, Terebratulæ, Ostreæ; Madreporæ		Clay over the Upper Oolite; Upper Oolite	19 20	Great Oolite Rock which produces the Bath Freestone			
Modiola, Cardita; Madraporæ, Trochi, Nautilus, Ammonities, Pecten		Fuller's Earth & Rock; Under Oolite	21 22	Under Oolite of the vicinity of Bath and the midland Counties			The finest Building Stone in the Island for Gothic and other Architecture which requires nice Workmanship
Ammonities, Belemnites as in the under Oolite; Numerous Ammonities		Sand; Marlstone	23 24				
Belemnites, Ammonities in mass	Marl Vales	Blue Marl	25	Blue Marl under the best Pastures of the midland Counties			
Pentacrini, Numerous Ammonities, Plagiostoma, Ostræ, Bones		Lias	26 27	Blue Lias; White Lias			Excellent Lime for Water Cements; Now used for printing from M.S. written on the Stone
		Red Marl	28	Red Marl and Gypsum soft sandstones and Salt Rocks and Springs			
Madreporae, Encrini in Masses, Producti	Coal tract	Redland Limestone	29	Magnesium Limestone; Soft Sandstone			Small Quantities of Copper and Lead and Calamine
Numerous Vegetables, Ferns lying over the Coal		Coal Measures	30	Coal Districts and the Rocks & Clays which accompany the Coal generally a Sandstone beneath			Grindstones, Millstones, Pavingstone, Iron-Stone and Fire-Clay from the Coal Districts
Madreporae, Encrini in Masses, Producti, Trilobites	Mountainous	Mountain Limestone	31	Derbyshire Limestone or Metalliferous Limestone			Lead, Copper, Calamine Marble
		Red Rhab & Dunstone	32	Red & Dunstone of the Southern and Northern Parts with Interspersions of Limestone marked blue			
		Killas	33	Various; Killas or Slate and other Strata of the Mountains on the West Side of the Island with Interspersions of Limestone marked blue			The Limestone polished for Marble; Tin, Copper, Lead and othe Minerals
		Granite, Sienite & Gneiss	34	Granite Sienite and Gneiss			The most durable building Stone in the Island for Bridges and other heavy Works

From the reexamination of the Authors numerous Specimens in the arrangement of his Geological Collection in the British Museum and his subsequent observation this list of Strata has been improved and his future exertions will be in proportion to the encouragement which he receives from the public

TABLE 1

TROCHUS.
SPECIES 1.
Conical; volutions five or six, the lower part projecting, with many finely crenulated lines; aperture rhomboidal, transverse; no umbilicus; base convex.

Trimingsby.

SPECIES 2.
Volutions four or five, the middle expanded into a keel or ridge, which continues to the apex; many spiral striæ; aperture half the length of the shell, rounded on its left side, angular on the right; no umbilicus.

Bramerton.

TURBO.
SPECIES 1.
Turbo littoreus. *Min. Conch.*

Fig. 3, Crag Plate.

Shell suboval, acute, striated; columnar margin flat: volutions about five.

a. Between Norwich and Yarmouth.

8

b Leiston, Old Abbey. *c.* Thorpe Common. *d.* Bramerton.
VARIETY.
Subglobose; volutions four or five, flat or concave at their upper edge, striated; aperture equal to more than half the length of the shell.

a. Bramerton. *b.* Thorpe Common.

SPECIES 2.
Obtuse; volutions four or five, with one spiral projection not continued to the apex; striated; aperture half the length of the shell.

Bramerton.

SPECIES 3.
Obtuse; volutions four or five, with two spiral projections, the upper one continued to the apex; striated.

Bramerton.

TURRITELLA.
SPECIES 1.
Fig. 4, Crag Plate.

Pyramidal, sides straight; with three continued crenated lines; the middle one smallest.

Thorpe Common.

SPECIES 2.
Turritella trilineata.

Volutions flattish, lower part angular, sometimes projecting, with three smooth spiral threads and obscure spiral striæ: base with several spiral striæ.

Length 1 to 2 inches, volutions about ten.

The lower part of the volution angular, with a projecting edge and a small thread above it; upper part thinned, a slight thread beneath it: a projecting thread on the middle. Base rather convex.

a. Bramerton. *b.* Trimingsby. Foxhole. Sutton. Playford [P]layford Specn [D]iluvial

SCALARIA.
Scalaria similis. *Min. Conch.*

Whorls contiguous, spire with five or six rounded transverse elevations, close to each other, and somewhat decussated, the lowest most prominent: ribs distant, circular.

Bramerton.

9
AMPULLARIA.
Subglobose, spire short, depressed; volutions four, smooth, with a canal at the upper edge; aperture oblong, a little lunate on the inner side; umbilicus often covered by the inner lip.

Trimingsby.

NATICA.
Natica glaucinoides. *Min. Conch.*

Nearly globose, spire rather elongated; umbilicus simple, partly covered; upper part of each whorl slightly depressed.

Trimingsby.

BELEMNITES.
A part of a long slender one; alluvial. Diluvial

Alderton.

The core of a belemnite with many septa: flint, transparent; alluvial. Diluvial

Aldborough.

SERPULA.
Serpula crassa. *Min Conch.*

Shell acutely conical, round within, three-sided externally, four or five times as long as the diameter of the end at the aperture.

Aldborough.

BIVALVIA.
EQUIVALVED BIVALVES.
MYTILUS.
Oval or oblong; one side straight; smooth, with transverse lines of growth; hinge with three or four small teeth at the beak; shell thin.

Brightwell.

PECTUNCULUS.
Pectunculus glycimeris.

Arca glycimeris. *Linn.*

Fig. 7, Crag Plate.

Orbicular, depressed; surface nearly smooth, with many obscure longitudinal striæ and concentric lines of growth; inner edge sharply dentated, fifteen or more teeth on each side of the arched hinge, about ten of which are large and each bent at an angle; shell strong.

a. Thorpe Common. *b.* Tattingstone Park. Foxhole. Aldborough.

c

10

Sutton. Newborn. Brightwell. Bentley.

CARDIUM.
Fig. 8, Crag Plate.

Obovate, wider than long, rather oblique, one side straightish; about twenty-five longitudinal ridges and furrows crossed by transverse risings: sulcated on the inside.

a. Tattingstone Park. *b.* Happisburgh Cliff. *c.* Bramerton. Foxhole. Sutton. Newborn. Brightwell.

The longitudinal ridges are rather wider than the furrows; the shell is often thinner than that of C. edule.

It has some resemblance to. C. Parkinsoni, *M. C. Tab. 49*, but is wider and has seldom more than twenty-five ribs; the inside appears to be more sulcated.

MACTRA. *Linn.*
Ovate, transverse, depressed, nearly equilateral; sides straightened, front margin straightish; smooth, with distinct lines of growth.

a. Between Norwich and Yarmouth. *b.* Trimingsby. *c.* Tattingstone Park. *d.* Bramerton. Sutton. Brightwell.

VENUS.
SPECIES 1.
Venus *Min.Conch.*

Uniformly convex, obcordate or nearly circular, covered with numerous transverse concentric striæ; thick, particularly in the middle; margin acute, extended, entire: cicatrix obscure.

Newborn. Foxhole. ? Foxhall on Suffolk Map Minsmere Iron Sluice.

11
SPECIES 2
Ovate, anterior side straightened; with transverse rugæ, and obscure longitudinal striæ an ovate obscure lunula on the posterior side; shell thickened at the edge.

Newborn.

ASTARTE. *Min. Conch.*
Ovate wider than long depressed; beak small, pointed with a narrow flattish space on each side of it; lineated transversely; margin denticulated on the inside. The anterior space long, narrow; the posterior ovate.

VAR. 1. Rather circular; the anterior flat space narrow; beak almost central.

Bentley.

VAR. 2. Beak almost central, and much flattened; anterior and posterior spaces large

Newborn.

VAR.3. Ovate, beak not flattened.

Newborn. Sutton.

VENERICARDIA.
Venericardia senilis.

Cordate, oblique, rather depressed, beak acute; surface with about twenty longitudinal large undulations crossed by many transverse rugæ inner edge largely dentated; shell thick.

Sutton. Newborn. Bentley.

TELLINA.
Tellina bimaculata. *Foss. Hanton. Fig. 102*

Subrotund, or ovate, wider than long, depressed, smooth, with transverse lines of growth; anterior side straightish, posterior rounded; fold of the shell slight; beak acute.

a. Bramerton. *b.* Between Norwich and Yarmouth. *c.* Trimingsby. Brightwell.

MYA.
Mya lata. *Min. Conch.*

Fig. 9, Crag Plate.

Ovate, depressed; anterior side acuminated and truncated, slightly gaping.

Aldborough, a cast of the inside. Trimingsby, hinges. Bramerton, hinges.

c 2

12
INEQUIVALVED BIVALVES.
OSTREA.
SPECIES 1.
Nearly orbicular, depressed, with obscure longitudinal ridges and many transverse squamæ; pit not large, oblong, shallow; shell smooth on the inside.

It is thinner than the shell of ostrea edulis: and is most concave near one side, the edge of which is reflected.

Sutton. Bentley. Newborn.

SPECIES 2.
Oval, oblong, depressed, one side hollowed; rough with imbricated lines of growth; pit large, oblique: shell strong.

A large irregular rough shell; one side is often hollowed.

Damerham.

PLACUNA.
Orbicular, flat; inside smooth, with a wide outer space; teeth short, diverging from the beak, and connected with the outer space; a small tubercle above the angle formed by the meeting of the teeth.

The outer surface appears to be striated and perhaps echinated; the shell is very thin. The teeth diverge at an obtuse angle, and their flat surfaces are toward each other.

AIdborough.

PECTEN.
Orbicular; depressed, two-eared; lower valve convex, with twenty or more longitudinal undulations, composed of longitudinal striæ crossed by numerous acute sutures, which give it an echinated appearance: upper valve concave, with flat risings, striated and crossed by acute sutures. Aldborough. Newborn. Sutton.

TEREBRATULA.
Terebratula spondylodes.

Oval, rather depressed, with sharp transverse lines of growth; a large circular foramen in the beak; two projecting thick teeth in the lower valve: shell thin, depressed on each side of the beak.

13
Foxhole. Near Ramholt Newborn. Aldborough, an upper valve.?

The large perforation in the beak is grooved circularly, and also the recess beneath the beak, shell thin, except at the teeth of the hinge.

MULTIVALVIA.
BALANUS.
Balanus tessellatus. *Min. Conch.*

Fig. 6, Crag Plate.

Obliquely conical, thin; valves six, obscurely ribbed, smooth; interstices finely. tessellated; aperture oval.

a. Aldborough. b. Bramerton, on a murex. c. Burgh Castle. d. Tattingstone Park. e. Keswick. Foxhole, ~~Near Ramholt~~ on a murex.

The REMAIN of LARGE UNKNOWN ANIMALS, as teeth and vertebræ, with teeth and vertebræ of many smaller species apparently marine, occur more frequently on the eastern shore and along the course of this than in any other stratum; but alluvial matter being common to large portions of the districts which produce them, and their sites in the strata being not well defined, particulars of these reliquia will be given at the end of the series with the general remarks on the alluvial Fossils.

NB The Ivory amongst Crag at Sutton Thorpe proves it there Diluvial

The Thorpe, nr Norwich, Fossils not noted nor Vale of Aylesham Ramsholt seems not to have been visited by me. Shd [be] Foxh[all] Expect my Foxh[ole] the same local[ity] (crossed out and cropped)

Have heard of shells in abundance; Lord Cobham's Park, [cropped] by a large spring near Dogkennel ? ? Crag or L[ondo]n Clay"

14
CHALK.
ZOOPHITA.
ALCYONIUM.
SPECIES 1.

Fig. 2, Upper Chalk Plate, Strata identified, &c.

Conical or pearshaped, with large openings on the sides.

The openings are often irregularly heartshaped, or with one rather acute angle and two projecting rounded ones; they, however, vary into other forms even in the same specimen; the sides of the openings appear striated.

Chittern.

SPECIES 2.

Fig. 1, Upper Chalk Plate.

Long, conical, with concentric undulations, and many unequal lateral openings; top very concave.

Wighton. Near Warminster. Guildford.

SPECIES 3.

Spreading, with small lateral openings placed in quincuncial order.

Upton.

SPECIES 4.

Long, conical, with longitudinal furrows.

a. Knook. b. Chittern.

SPECIES 5.

Oblong, clubshaped, top striated, spreading.

Warminster.

Several species of Alcyonia, minutely organized, in hydrophanous flints.

Wilts.

ENCRINUS.

Maraspite[?Marsupite – this was named by Miller 1821 pp. 134-139 from Mantell's MSS name]

A scale of the tortoise encrinite.

Near Warminster.

15
TESTACEA.
UNIVALVIA
TROCHUS.
SPECIES 1.

Volutions four or five, depressed, angular; base rounded or swelling: length more than an inch, breadth twice the length: umbilicus large.

Heytesbury.

SPECIES 2

Volutions five or six, angular, the upper part flat, the side flattish or slightly depressed in the middle; base depressed, spirally furrowed; aperture wide, umbilicus small.

a. Heytesbury. b. Mazen Hill.

SPECIES 3.

Fig. 3, Lower Chalk Plate

Depressed, volutions four or five, the upper part flat; a projecting rim on each margin of the side, the lower one rounded beneath.

Mazen Hill.

CIRRUS.

Fig. 5, Lower Chalk Plate.

Short conical, volutions about five, round, smooth; umbilicus not large. Length more than an inch.

Near Warminster.

TURBO.
SPECIES 1.

Conoidal or subturreted, volutions five or six, the upper part with two sharp carinæ beneath which are three or four lesser ones; mouth round, grooved at the edge. The spiral carinæ were probably edged with prominences on the shell, although they do not appear so on the cast of the inside.

Heytesbury.

SPECIES 2.

Conoidal, volutions five or six, round, even.

Near Warminster.

16
TUBULAR IRREGULAR UNIVALVES.
SERPULA.

Fig. 3, Upper Chalk Plate.

Cylindrical, nearly straight, smooth, with distant annular risings; opening round.

Norwich.

MULTILOCULAR UNIVALVES.
BELEMNITES.

Fusiform, apex papillary, an obscure furrow descending from it; flattened on one of the sides.

Norwich.

Slender, elongated.

Hunstanton cliff.

AMMONITES.

Ammonites tuberculatus.

Fig. 4, Lower Chalk Plate.

Involute, keeled; inner volutions half exposed, surface rough with large tubercular projections; tubercles oblong on the inner margin, furcating into two subnodose ridges; back wide, edged by large pointed knobs: keel entire.

The ridges proceeding from the knobs on the inner margin are each elevated into a smaller tubercle on the middle of the volution, and then are either obscurely united into one knob on the back, or otherwise form separate knobs: aperture oblong, about two fifths of the largest diameter, which is sometimes three inches.

Norton.

BIVALVIA.
INEQUIVALVED BIVALVES.
PLAGIOSTOMA.

Plagiostoma spinosa. *Min. Conch.*

Obovate, longitudinally furrowed, sides nearly equal, straightish; one valve spinous, spines on some half the length of the shell. The flatter valve is spinous, the number and length of the spines not constant. The angular indentation between the projecting beaks is formed in the spinous valve. Inside of the shell furrowed

a. Heytesbury. b. Near Warminster. Guildford.

17
OSTREA.

Fig. 5 and 6, Upper Chalk Plate.

Nearly circular, smooth; lower valve deep, sublobate, attached; upper valve convex externally at the beak, reflexed in the front; margins wide, crenated within near the hinge; shell thin; muscular impression roundish.

Pit of the hinge small, shallow; the upper valve sometimes irregularly striated from the beak. The lower valve often projects at the back in the manner of the Gryphites, with a narrow hinge and less oblique pit; attached sometimes by nearly the whole surface, the unattached part being in the front.

Norwich.

PECTEN.
SPECIES 1.

Fig. 8, Upper Chalk Plate.

Nearly flat, smooth; front semicircular; a few concentric flat risings, and obscure longitudinal striæ; ears two, rectangular, striated.

Norwich.

SPECIES 2.

Oblong, very depressed; valves nearly equal, with broad longitudinal ribs, and alternating furrows on which are placed one or two elevated ridges.

Mazen Hill.

TEREBRATULA.
SMOOTH OR NOT PLICATED.
SPECIES 1.

Terebratula carnea. *Min. Conch.*

Depressed, smooth, obtusely five sided, front edge short, entire; valves equally convex, slightly flattening along the middle. Front margin not undulated; sometimes a small part of the lateral margin near the beak is reflexed.

Norwich.

SPECIES 2.

Terebratula subundata. *Min. Conch.*

Nearly circular, depressed, smooth, valves equally gibbous; front margin straight or slightly depressed in the middle, with one undulation on each side.

a. Heytesbury b. Near Warminster. c. Mazen Hill. Guildford.

D

18

VAR-The under valve regularly arched, the upper considerably depressed; oval, middle of the shell flattish.

Fig. 9, Upper Chalk Plate.

Norwich.

SPECIES 3.

Terebratula semiglobosa. *Min. Conch.*

Nearly circular, gibbous, smooth; largest valve deepest and uniformly gibbous, front margin undulated, with two risings in the smaller valve.

a. Mazen Hill. b. Heytesbury. c. Near Warminster.

PLICATED.
SPECIES 4.

Fig. 7, Lower Chalk Plate.

Rather gibbous, valves almost equally convex, front margin elevated in one large wave rounding into the sides; plicæ numerous, entire; beak acute, projecting. The lateral plicæ are blended with those on the middle; width less than ¾ of an inch.

a. Near Warminster. b. Heytesbury. c. Mazen Hill. d. Norwich.

SPECIES 5.

Obscurely five sided, striated; upper valve most convex, the front sharply elevated in an angular wave with about seven distinct short plaits; sides with twelve or more distinct plaits on their edges; beak projecting, slightly incurved.

From each side of the beak of the lower valve runs a sharp angle, connecting with the lateral margin: elevation of the front sudden, with a straight upper edge, and straight subparallel sides: the plaits on the edges of the valves short, and dividing into fine striæ which continue to the beak. The plaits vary much in number.

a. Norwich. b. Heytesbury.

INOCERAMUS.
SPECIES 1.

Inoceramus Cuvieri. *Sowerby.*

Fig. 1, Lower Chalk Plate.

Heytesbury.

19

Knook Castle and Barrow. Bury St. Edmonds. Hunstanton Cliff.

SPECIES 2.

Fig. 2, Lower Chalk Plate.

Shell thin.

Near Warminster. Guildford.

MULTIVALVIA.
BALANUS.

Fig. 4, Upper Chalk Plate.

Valves long, conical, with transverse furrows, one side turned inwards.

Norwich.

ECHINI.
ANOCYSTI.
CIDARIS.
SPECIES 1.
Circular, depressed, rays biporous; twenty rows of articulated eminences, which are nearly equal on the base but unequal above, the two rows in each areola diminishing faster than those in the areæ; edges of the mouth turned inwards. Diameter about an inch

Northfleet.

SPECIES 2.
Circular, depressed; ten rows of articulated eminences, two rows in each area Diameter about an inch.

Wilts.

SPECIES 3.
Circular, depressed; shell thin, rather smooth. ?

Cidaris coronalis. *Klein. ?*

Wilts.

D 2

20
PLEUROCYSTI.
SPATANGUS.
RAYS PLACED IN FURROWS.
SPECIES 1.
Oblong, cordate, rather high, margin rounded; dorsal furrow narrow, the ray contained in it not distinct; dorsal ridge rising higher than the apex: covered with granulæ, particularly on the middle of the base.

Wilts.

SPECIES 2.
Cordate, depressed, dorsal furrow narrow; covered with granulae, particularly on the middle of the base.

a. Norwich. *b.* Wilts.

SPECIES 4.
Cordate, margin rounded, dorsal furrow large, ridge high; height of the shell two-thirds of the length.

a. Lexham. *b.* Chittem. *c.* Wilts. *d.* Smitham Bottom. *e.* Near May Place. *f.* Great Ridge. *g.* Surry. *h.* Chesterford. i Bubdown. k Pewsey. l Norwich. Guildford.

RAYS NOT PLACED IN FURROWS.
SPECIES 4.
Long-cordate, the top rounded, with a short deep groove to the mouth; rays obsolete.

Wilts.

SPECIES 5.
Cordate, base flat, top convex, dorsal furrow slight, rounded; rays ten biporous lines diverging in pairs, pores large.

a. Upton. A mass. *b.* Chittern.

21
CATOCYSTI.
CONULUS.
SPECIES 1.
E. Albogalerus. *Leske.*

a. Wilts. *b.* Burnham Overy.

SPECIES 2.
E. Vulgaris. *Leske.*

Wilts.

SPECIES 3.
Pentagonal, depressed; rays of pores ten, biporous, flexuous, depressed; the area swelling into rounded angles: mouth and vent rather large.

Lexham.

GALEA.
SPECIES 1.
Fig. 10, Upper Chalk Plate.

E. Ovatus. *Leske.*

a. Norwich. *b.* Taverham. *c.* Croydon. Guildford. Bury.

SPECIES 2.
E. Pustulosus. *Leske.*

a. Moushold. *b.* Taverham. *c.* Lexham. *d.* Carshalton. *e.* Near Norwich.

SPECIES 3.
Subelliptical, round topped, not very pointed at the end; rays biporous on the top, pustulose on the base; pustulæ smaller than in the last species.

a. Moushold. *b.* Taverham. *c.* Lexham.

22
SPECIES 4.
Oval, very pointed at one end, rounded at the other; rays biporous one third of the height downwards from the apex, very distinct on the base; ridge sharp; apex excentric towards the broad end.

Lexham.

The excentric situation of the apex, with the very pointed end, gives this species a peculiar appearance.

SPECIES 5.
Oval, pointed at one end, high; rays biporous two-thirds of the height downwards from the apex; areæ flattened.

a. Wilts. *b.* Hickling. Guildford.

SPECIES 6.
High, with flattish sides, top rounded or flattened; rays biporous downwards to the margin; height almost equal to the length.

a. Holkham Park. *b.* Lexham.

SPECIES 7.
Three-fourths elliptical, the base, forming the section, rounded, contracted.

a. Clayton Hill. *b.* Wilts.

SPECIES 8.
[In] all 19 species [of] echini

Broad-ovate, one end pointed; margin of the base undulated beneath with fourteen projections, the areolæ form five, the ridge one, and there are eight others in the areæ; a large depression on the upper part of the shell behind the apex.

Taverham.

SPINES OF ECHINI.
SPECIES 1.
Fig. 13, Upper Chalk Plate.

Long, slender, muricated.

Norwich

SPECIES 2.
Clubshaped or gibbous, granulated in lines.

Kent. Guildford.

23
SPECIES 3.
Clavicula cucumerina.

Long of nearly equal thickness, granulated quincuncial order

Surry.

BONES.
TEETH.
SPECIES 1.
Fig. 14, Upper Chalk Plate.

Long; roundish, with two sharp ridges.

a. Near Warminster. *b.* Norwich.

SPECIES 2.
One side flat, the other roundish; two-edged.

a. Wilts. *b.* Warminster.

SPECIES 3.
Fig. 15, Upper Chalk Plate.

Flattish, with serrated edges.

a. Norwich. *b.* Near Warminster.

SPECIES 4.
Triangular, flat, keen-edged.

a. Cherry Hinton. *b.* Near Warminster.

FISH PALATES.
SPECIES 1.
Fig. 11, Upper Chalk Plate.

Large, depressed; the middle elevated, deeply furrowed, the surrounding parts rough with small protuberances.

Near Warminster.

SPECIES 2.
The middle very high, deeply furrowed, the surrounding parts rough with small protuberances.

Near Warminster.

VERTEBRÆ OF FISH.
Fig. 16, Upper Chalk Plate.

Very small, concave at both ends.

North of Riegate.

24
GREEN SAND.
ZOOPHITA.
MADREPORA.
Fig. 15, Green Sand, 2d Plate.

Circular, depressed, radiated; radii very numerous on the upper surface, fewer on the under.

Chute Farm.

MILLEPORA.
Fig. 16, Green Sand 2d Plate.

Branching, surface reteporous.

Chute Farm.

ALCYONIUM.
SPECIES 1.
Fig. 1, Green Sand Plate.

Funnel shaped, top concave.

Pewsey. Warminster. Devizes.

SPECIES 2.
Fig. 2, Green Sand Plate.

Doliform, small at each end.

Pewsey.

SPECIES 3.
Fig. 17, Green Sand, 2d Plate.

Round, with a central opening, and many minute pores on the surface.

Chute Farm.

25
ENCRINUS.
SPECIES 1.
Vertebræ pentagonal, with blunt projecting angles; alternately one large and three smaller, the middle one of the three larger than the other two.

Chute Farm.

SPECIES 2 .
Vertebræ circular, alternately large and small, the large one twice as thick as the smaller. In this specimen, consisting of eight vertebræ, each terminating vertebra has five roundish oblique articulating surfaces protruded from it, probably the attachments of lateral branches.

Chute Farm.

TESTACEA.
UNIVALVIA.
TROCHUS.
SPECIES 1.
Volutions five or six, angular, the upper part flat, the side flattish or slightly depressed in the middle; base depressed, spirally furrowed; aperture wide, umbilicus small.

a. Chute Farm. *b.* Near Warminster.

SPECIES 2.
Conical, sides straightish; volutions about six, slender, flattish beneath; striated; umbilicate; height equal to the width.

a. Chute Farm. *b.* Rundaway Hill.

SOLARIUM.
Fig. 2, Green Sand, 2d Plate.

Much depressed; volutions angular, depressed, mouth wide.

Rundaway Hill.

TURRITELLA.

Fig. 5, Green Sand Plate.

Volutions about fifteen, covered by small crenulated lines; upper edge sharply crenated.

About three larger crenulated lines with several lesser ones interposed. Blackdown.

E

26
AMPULLARIA.
SPECIES 1.

Oblong, smooth; spire acute, with four or five volutions sharp at their upper edge; aperture half the length of the shell. Length three-fourths of an inch.

Rundaway Hill.

TUBULAR IRREGULAR UNIVALVES.
VERMICULARIA.
SPECIES 1.

Vermicularia concava. *Min. Conch.*

Discoid, involute, concave on one side; the last volution but slightly attached: volutions about four.

Near Warminster.

SPECIES 2.

Vermicularia umbonata. *Min. Conch.*

Discoid, involute, umbonated above, concave beneath, the smallest whorl concealed in the umbo: whorls two or three.

Near Warminster.

SPECIES 3.

Discoid, involute, volutions few, surface rough with small hollows.

SERPULA.
SPECIES 1.

Cylindrical, straightish, with distant annular risings; opening round.

a. Chute Farm. *b.* Near Warminster.

SPECIES 2.

Cylindrical, small, contorted.

Chute Farm.

MULTILOCULAR UNIVALVES .
BELEMNITES.

Elongated, with a slight furrow from the apex.

Chute Farm.

27
AMMONITES.
NO KEEL OR FURROW ON THE BACK.
SPECIES 1.

Ammonites Nutfieldiensis. *Min. Conch.*?

It seems more depressed.

Stourhead.

A KEEL ON THE BACK.
SPECIES 2.

Ammonites tuberculatus.

Involute, keeled; inner volutions half exposed, surface rough with large tubercular projections; tubercles oblong on the inner margin, furcating into two subnodose ridges; back wide, edged by large pointed knobs; keel entire.

a. Rundaway Hill. *b.* Chute Farm.

A FURROW ON THE BACK.
SPECIES 3.

Extremely depressed; back narrow, concave, with crenulated edges; inner volutions concealed.

Longest diameter half an inch.

Chute Farm.

TURRILITES.
SPECIES 1.

Turrilites costata. *Min. Conch.*

Volutions of the spire beset with short ribs on the upper part, beneath which are two rows of small tubercles.

Chute Farm.

SPECIES 2.

Volutions of the spire convex, ornamented with two rows of close and small tubercles.

Evershot.

B IVALVIA.
INEQUIVALVED BIVALVES
PECTUNCULUS

Fig.6, Green Sand Plate.

Orbicular, one side straightish, convex; beak rather prominent, acute; covered by many obscure furrows and minute transverse striæ; margin serrated within.

E 2

28

Teeth of the hinge about sixteen, rather large; the straightest side has a slight depression near the beaks, which makes it sublobate.

Blackdown.

CUCULLÆA.
SPECIES 1.

Fig. 10, Green Sand Plate.

Ovate, transverse, one side straightish; covered with numerous longitudinal decussated striæ; breadth less than three fourths of an inch.

Blackdown.

TRIGONIA.
SPECIES 1.

An inside cast of the trigonia of the Portland rock ?

Chute Farm.

SPECIES 2.

An inside cast of a small species, or perhaps of an astarte; two muscular impressions.

Rundaway Hill.

SPECIES 3.

Trigonia clavellata. *Min. Conch.*

An impression of the outside. Wrong placed – [Si]nce discovered Kelloways [Roc]k near thereto [- belon]gs to that stratum

Near Danby Beacon.

CARDIUM.

Cardium Hillanum. *Min. Conch.*

Nearly circular, a little oblique, covered with numerous concentric striæ; anterior part straightish at the edge; longitudinally furrowed.

Rather wider than long, a little gibbous.

The longitudinal furrows on the anterior side occupy about one fourth of the surface.

Blackdown.

A large transverse bivalve with unequal sides; one side produced and flattish, the other truncated and gibbous; transversely striated; beaks turned toward the produced side; length two inches, breadth three.

Blackdown.

VENUS.
SPECIES 1.

Venus plana. *Min. Conch.*

Rather depressed, subcordate, slightly angular towards the anterior side; surface smooth; edge entire: rather wider than long.

Blackdown.

29
SPECIES 2.

Venus angulata. *Min. Conch.*

Fig. 3, Green Sand Plate.

Obtusely cordate, wider than long, smooth; margin entire; an angular rising on the anterior side, which is slightly truncated; larger hinge teeth placed at a curved angle of about sixty degrees.

In the posterior side of the hinge is a roundish hollow, receiving a tooth on the opposite valve.

Blackdown.

INEQUIVALVED BIVALVES.
DIANCHORA.

Dianchora striata. *Min. Conch.*

Oblique, ovate, triangular, beak prominent, free valve obscurely ribbed; margin sharp.

The length and breadth almost equal.

Chute Farm.

CHAMA.

Chama haliotidea. *Min. Conch.*

Fig. 7, Green Sand, 2d Plate.

Oval, uneven, a deep curving hollow within the deepest valve, extending from the beaks around one side; margin thin, broad, slightly fringed, crenate within; muscular impression large; upper valve flat.

a. Dilton. *b.* Black-dog Hill, near Standerwick. *c.* Teffont. *d.* Evershot. *e.* Stourhead. *f.* Alfred's Tower. *g.* Blackdown.

OSTREA.
SPECIES 1.

Ostrea crista galli, Cockscomb oyster.

a. Chute Farm. *b.* Stourhead, *c.* Blackdown.

30
SPECIES 2.

Fig. 10, Green Sand, 2d Plate.

Oblong, gibbous, smooth; front wide, a lobe on the left side forming a short wing, right side arched; lower valve gibbous, narrowed towards the back, with a curved projecting beak: margin thin, sharp.

Pit of the hinge arched, and continued up the under side of the beak; muscular impression nearest to the left side; right edge thickened within into a projecting ledge, left edge almost reflected.

a. Stourhead. *b.* Dinton Park. *c.* Tinhead.

SPECIES 3.

Oval; lower valve equally convex, or scarcely at all lobate, the beak slightly curved, small; upper valve very concave.

Stourhead.

PECTEN.
SPECIES 1.

Pecten quadricostata. *Min. Conch.*

Fig. 8, Green Sand, 2d Plate.

Triangular, nearly even, front semicircular, margin notched; convex valve ribbed, larger ribs six, three smaller between each: posterior auricle large.

Near Warminster.

SPECIES 2.

Pecten quinquecostata. *Min. Conch.*

Subtriangular, rather oblique, front semicircular, toothed; convex valve ribbed, principal ribs six, four smaller ones between each; upper valve sulcated, flat-toothed; surface finely striated transversely.

Chute Farm.

SPECIES 3.

Pecten sexcostata.

Subtriangular, oblong, front semicircular, margin toothed; convex valve ribbed, principal ribs six, five lesser ones between each; surface deeply hollowed between the principal ribs.

Chute Farm.

SPECIES 4.

Fig. 3, Green Sand, 2d Plate

Orbicular, depressed, longitudinally undulated; nearly twenty principal ridges covered with short spinous tubercles, and four or five lesser tuberculated ridges alternating with each of the principal ones.

31

Length and breadth nearly equal, two or three inches.

Chute Farm.

SPECIES 5.

Fig. 9, Green Sand, 2d Plate.

Oblong, very depressed, front semicircular; covered with many acute crenated threads, and intermediate decussated striæ.

Valves almost equally convex; the threads about one-third more numerous on the longer valve than on the shorter.

Chute Farm.

SPECIES 6.

Suborbicular, much depressed, about fifteen acute smooth ribs; ears reticulated, triangular.

Longleat Park.

SPECIES 7.

Orbicular, very depressed, transversely striated, smooth; ears large, smooth, triangular.

    a. Longleat Park. *b.* Warminster.

TEREBRATULA.
NOT PLICATED.
SPECIES 1.

Terebratula biplicata. *Min. Conch.*

    Oblong, gibbous; beak prominent, sides rounded, front straightish, when full grown elevated with two distinct risings at the angles.

        Lines of growth strong, sometimes irregular.

        a. Chute Farm. *b.* Near Warminster. *c.* Rundaway Hill.

PLICATED,
SPECIES 2.

Wider than long, depressed, beak very acute, front elevated with one wave rounding into the sides; plaits numerous, entire.

    The lateral plaits are blended with those on the middle of the shell; width less than an inch; upper valve most convex.

    a. Chute Farm. *b.* Warminster.

SPECIES 3.

Upper valve gibbous; front straightish, much elevated with one large wave rounding into the sides; plaits numerous, entire; beak acute, very projecting.

32

The lateral plaits are blended with those on the middle of the shell: width less than half an inch; lower valve very depressed. This species differs from SPECIES 4 of the chalk in the greater convexity of the upper valve, and in the very slight incurvation of the beak.

    a. Chute Farm. *b.* Warminster.

SPECIES 4.

Terebratula obsoleta. *Min. Conch.*

    The plaits are sharper than in Mr. Sowerby's figure, and the elevation in the front is more angular.

    Near Warminster.

SPECIES 5.

Fig. 6, Green Sand, 2d Plate.

    Subtriangular, wider than long, plicato-striated; front elevated with one wave rounding into the sides; plicæ numerous, rounded; beak acute, perforation large, triangular ? lower valve advanced much beyond the upper.

    a. Chute Farm. *b.* Warmiuster.

SPECIES 6.

Terebratula pectinata. *Min. Conch.*

    Fig. 4, Green Sand, 2d Plate.

    Orbicular, gibbose, plicato-striated; a flattish space extending from the front to the beaks; beak of the lower valve prominent, slightly incurved; back of the upper valve straight, with an incurved beak.

    The plicæ are small, rounded, and often furcate, on which account they are not much larger at the front than at the beaks. Length not more than one inch.

    a. Chute Farm. *b.* Warminster.

SPECIES 7.

Terebratula lyra. *Min. Conch.*

    Fig. 5, Green Sand, 2d Plate.

    Oblong, convex, with diverging furcated plaits, beak of the lower valve greatly elongated, that of the upper valve short, incurved.

    The length of the upper valve is equal to twice its width. The beak of the lower valve is equal in length to the upper valve.

Chute Farm.

33
ECHINI.
ANOCYSTI
CIDARIS.
SPECIES 1.

Circular, depressed, rays biporous; twenty rows of articulated eminences, which are nearly equal on the base, but unequal above, the two rows in each areola diminishing faster than those in the areæ; edges of the mouth turned inwards.

    Chute Farm.

SPECIES 2.

Rather pentagonal, depressed, top convex; rays biporous, two rows of small eminences in each areola, forming the angles, two rows of miliæ in each area; mouth large, its edges turned inwards.

    Near Warminster.

SPECIES 3.

Circular, depressed, with thirty rows of miliæ, two rows in each areola, and four rows in each area; rays biporous.

    Chute Farm.

SPECIES 4.

Cidaris diadema.

    Fig. 11, Green Sand, 2d Plate.

    Depressed, upper side convex, base rounded; ten rows of alternate mammellæ, two rows in each area; areolæ narrow, subflexuous, widest on the margin, each side bordered by a row of small eminences; mouth large, with ten rather unequal sides, and a deep notch at every angle.

    a. Chute Farm. *b.* Near Warminster.

    A curious anal appendage may be observed on most of the specimens obtained from this Stratum; a kind of frill surrounds the vent, and a tubular body projecting from it.

SPECIES 5.

Rather high; ten rows of mammellæ, two rows in each area, five mammellæ in a row; areolæ narrow, flexuous; apertures large.

    Chute Farm.

F

34

SPECIES 6.

Subglobose, circular or pentagonal; rays biporous; depressed areæ swelling; surface rough with small points.

    VAR. with both the upper surface and base flattish.

    Chute Farm.

PLEUROCYSTI.
SPATANGUS.
RAYS PLACED INFURROWS.

SPECIES 1.

Cordate, margin rounded; dorsal furrow large, dorsal ridge high; height of the shell two thirds of the length.

    a. Charmouth, high variety. *b.* Melbury

SPECIES 2.

High, base flattish; rays short, indented; dorsal furrow wide, not deep, ridge rising very high; vent placed as high as the apex; length one third of an inch, height and breadth one fourth.

    Chute Farm.

RAYS NOT PLACED IN FURROWS.
SPECIES 3.

Fig. 14, Green Sand, 2d Plate.

    Base flat, top convex, or rather flattened; dorsal groove short; rays ten biporous lines diverging in pairs.

    a. Chute Farm. *b.* Near Warminster

    ECHINITES lapis cancri *Leske,*

    Fig. 13,Green Sand, 2d Plate.

    Obtusely ovate, gibbous, broader at one end than at the other; vent above the margin at the broad end, placed over a small depression or furrow; rays biporous; mouth five angled, small, near the narrow end; base swelling

    Chute Farm

CATOCYSTI.
CONULUS.

Fig. 12,Green Sand, 2d Plate.

    Convexo-conical, circular, base concave in the middle; rays ten, diverging in five pairs, the two rays near together separated by a flat rising; mouth ten-angular, vent oblong.

35

    a. Chute Farm. *b.* Near Warminster

BONES.
TEETH
SPECIES 1

One side flat, the other round, two-edged

    Chute Farm.

SPECIES 2

Conoidal, flat, keen edged

    Chute Farm.

F2

36
~~BRICK EARTH.~~
GOLT
TESTACEA.
UNIVALVIA.
MULTILOCULAR UNIVALVES.
BELEMNITES.

Fig. 4 and 5, Brick Earth Plate.

    Small, fusiform, swelling below the apex. Diameter less than half an inch, generally about a fourth. In some specimens there appear two very small grooves from the apex on opposite sides of the shell.

    a. North of Riegate. *b.* Near Godstone. *c.* Near Grimston. *d.* Steppingley Park. *e.* Prisley Farm. Leighton Beaudesert. Westoning.

AMMONITES.
A KEEL ROUND THE BACK.

SPECIES 1.

Much depressed, inner volutions not much concealed; radii unequal, dividing from small knobs on the inner part of the volution, prominent on the outer edge, obscure on the middle.

    M[W]esterham, out of a deep well.

A FURROW ROUND THE BACK.
SPECIES 2.

Fig. 1, Brick Earth Plate.

    Depressed, volutions increasing quickly, back wide, concave, with deeply furrowed edges; radii numerous, sharp, bifurcating from an oblong tubercle on the inner margin; edges of the back alternately indented; aperture oblong, sides almost parallel: inner volutions half exposed.

    a. Near Godstone. *b.* Steppingley Park. *c.* Prisley Farm.

37
HAMITES.

Fig. 2, Brick Earth Plate.

    Limbs straightish, a little depressed; outer part of the limb tubercled on both sides; each tubercle dividing into two small ribs crossing the inner part, two annular ribs between the tubercles. Greatest thickness about half an inch.

    Near Grimston.

BIVALVIA.
INEQUIVALVED BIVALVES.
PERNA.

Perna aviculoides? *Min. Conch.*

    Godstone.

OSTREA.

A lower valve; gibbous, small.

    Steppingley Field.

INOCERAMUS.

Fibrous shell.

    a. Prisley Farm. *b.* Near Grimston.

ECHINI.
PLEUROCYSTI.
SPATANGUS.

Fig. 3, Brick Earth Plate

    Cordate, depressed, dorsal furrow not deep; rays long, deeply hollowed; mouth depressed.

    Near Devizes.

VERTEBRÆ OF SOME FISH.

Very small, concave at both ends, slender in the middle; ends rather oval

    North of Riegate.

    No Stone no Terebratula

38
PORTLAND ROCK.
WOOD.

Woburn. Fonthill. Swindon.

ZOOPHITA.
MADREPORA.

Stars angular, concave, numerous; radiating lamellæ twenty or more, diverging in pairs or in small bundles.
 Tisbury.

TESTACEA.
UNIVALVIA
TROCHUS.

Conical, sides undulated; volutions about six, the upper part flattish.
 Swindon.

TURRITELLA.

Fig. 2, Portland Rock Plate.
 Turreted; volutions about twelve, the upper edge projecting into a crenulated rim, lower part rounded with a row of small protuberances almost concealed by the next volution: middle of the spire with three or four obscurely crenated striæ; base with crenated striæ: aperture rhomboidal, acute at the upper and lower edges.
  a. Portland. *b.* Swindon.

NATICA.

Fig.1, Portland Rock Plate
 Subglobose, smooth, volutions few.
 Swindon.

39
MULTILOCULAR UNIVALVES.
AMMONITES.
NO KEEL OR FURROW ON THE BACK.

Ammonites Nutfieldiensis *Min.Conch.*
 Involute, volutions four or more, nearly concealed; radii numerous, prominent, with shorter intermediate ones over the rounding back: aperture obcordate.
 Foothill. Swindon.

BIVALVIA.
EQUIVALVED. BIVALVES.
TRIGONIA.
SPECIES I.

Ovate, with many small roundish tubercles in quincuncial order, which terminate before a longitudinal ridge bounding the smooth interior side; posterior side rounded, anterior side narrow, straightish at the edge.
 The small tubercles are often united on the posterior side into connected oblique ridges
  a. Foothill. *b.* Swindon. *c.* Chicksgrove. *d.* Teffont. Garsington Hill.

SPECIES 2.

Much elongated transversely.
 In the cast the anterior slope is straight or concave, showing a large protuberance in the situation of the muscular impression. The hinge seems to have projected less into the shell in this than in the other species.
 Swindon.

CARDITA.

Quadrangular, gibbous, beaks placed at one of the angles, and hooked; transversely furrowed; anterior side flattened and acuminated.
 Crockerton.

ASTARTE.

Astarte cuneata. *Min. Conch.*
 Fig. 3, Portland Rock Plate
 Subcordate, acuminated, gibbous, with small transverse costæ, lunette cordate, margin entire within.
 The cast of the inside is triangular and acuminated at the anterior side.
 Swindon.

40
VENUS.
SPECIES 1.

Ovate, wider than long, sides almost equal, beaks rather hooked.
Pottern.

SPECIES 2.

Fig. 5, Portland Rock Plate.
 Subcordate, wider than long, gibbous; smooth.
 Chicksgrove Swindon.

UNIO.

A species resembling Unio uniformis *Min. Conch.* but seems wider in proportion, with smaller beaks.
 Swindon

SMALL BIVALVES.

Teffont, in thin cherty stone.
 Lady Down.

INEQUIVALVED BIVALVES.
OSTREA.

Irregular, flattish, shell thin.
 Swindon.

PECTEN.

Fig.6 Portland Rock Plate
 Circular, depressed, with transverse squamous lines of growth; valves almost equal; ears large, rectangular.
 Length more than three inches.
 Chicksgrove. Swindon

 Inoceramus – very thin shells, Perna (casts)
 Pholas Quainton in Museum Terebratula if any not noticed

41
OAKTREE CLAY.
TESTACEA.
UNIVALVIA
TROCHUS.

Fig. Oaktree Clay Plate. 3
 Conical, sides undulated; volutions convex, the upper part flattish, bounded by a spiral crenulated rim; reticulato-striated; base rather convex, without an umbilicus.
 VARIETY. Volutions subtuberculated. on the upper part.
 North Wilts Canal.

TURBO.

Fig. Oaktree Clay Plate. 2
 Oblong, subturreted; volutions of the spire six, covered with rows of small tubercles, of which two rows in the middle of the spire are larger than the others: aperture about half the length of the shell.
 Length about an inch.
 North Wilts Canal.

MELANIA.

Melania Heddingtonensis. *Min. Conch,*
 Volutions of the spire eight or more; surface of each volution concave near the middle, with an obtuse-angled rising near the upper part; above three times as long as the diameter; lines of growth deep.
 North Wilts Canal.

TUBULAR IRREGULAR UNIVALVES.
SERPULA.
SPECIES 1.

Cylindrical, straightish, with distant annular risings, smooth; diameter not more than half an inch; thickness of the shell one sixth of the diameter.
 North Wilts Canal. Bagley Wood Pit.

SPECIES 2

Elongated, rough, with five longitudinal undulations crossed by transverse wrinkles; diameter one third of an inch; thickness of the shell one fourth of the diameter; opening round.
      G

42
a. Brinkworth Common. *b.* Hinton Waldrish. *c.* Portland. North Wilts Canal. Bagley Wood Pit.

MULTILOCULAR UNIVALVES.
NAUTILUS.

Umbilicus open ?; septa broad, with one wave toward the aperture; back flattened; shell thick; siphuncle about a third of the length of the septum from the inner side.

Longest diameter from four to twelve inches, depth almost equal to the diameter.
 North Wilts Canal.

AMMONITES.
NO KEEL OR FURROW ON THE BACK.
SPECIES 1.

Depressed, acuminated at the outer edge, inner volutions half exposed; radii numerous, unequal prominent on the inner part, then furcate, or with one to three intermediate ones over the outer half of the volution, curving toward the aperture.
 Longest diameter less than an inch.
  a. Brinkworth Common. *b.* Portland.

SPECIES 2.

Gibbous, inner volutions half concealed, radii unequal, very small and numerous sharp across the back; aperture wider than long, back broad.
 Longest diameter less than an inch.
  a. Brinkworth Common. *b.* Portland. Dun's Well, Silton Farm.

SPECIES 3

Fig. 7 Oaktree Clay Plate.
 Depressed, volutions numerous, the inner ones two thirds exposed; radii numerous, large, furcating, smoothed over the back; outer volutions plain; aperture oval indented.
 North Wilts Canal. Well near Swindon, Wilts and Berks Canal.

SPECIES 4

Volutions concealing each other?, thickest near the center, nearly smooth
Well near Swindon Wilts and Berks Canal.

43
SPECIES 5.

Volutions armed with two rows of large tubercles, those on each side of the back most projecting; inner volutions little concealed; mouth squarish
Greatest diameter four inches.
 Well near Swindon, Wilts and Berks Canal.

A KEEL ON THE BACK
SPECIES 6.

Volutions much depressed, with a high thin keel serrated on the edge; radii: many, unequal, prominent about the middle, and on the edge of the back.
 The tubercles on the edge of the back are more in number than those on the middle of the volution.
 Well near Swindon, Wilts and Berks Canal.

BELEMNITES.

Rather four sided, elongated, tapering quickly to the apex.
Well near Swindon, Wilts and Berks Canal. North Wilts Canal.

BIVALVIA.
EQUIVALVED BIVALVES.
MODIOLA.

Transversely oblong, gibbous diagonally from the beaks; posterior side blunt, rounded in front; beaks small, hooked; back straightish, rounded into the anterior end; lines of growth sharp: shell very thin. Depressed in front of the gibbous part.
 North Wilts Canal.

TRIGONIA
SPECIES 1.

Trigonia costata. *Min. Conch. Park.*
 North Wilts Canal.

SPECIES 2.

Trigonia clavellata. *Min. Conch. Park.*
Triangular, rather wider than long, with ten or more oblique rows of tubercles; anterior side straight with three longitudinal knotted ridges.
North Wilts Canal.

      G 2

44
SPECIES 3.

Trigonia curvirostra.

Oblong, triangular, narrow towards the beak; anterior side depressed, bounded by a very sudden termination of the other more convex part of the shell; posterior side rounded from the beaks into an oblique straightish front; covered by small transverse furrows which are diminished in size on the anterior side; beaks much hooked from the anterior side.

Length about an inch.

North Wilts Canal.

CARDITA.
SPECIES 1

Subtriangular, gibbose; beaks prominent; anterior side narrow, straightish, bounded by a smooth rising extending from the beaks to one angle; closely and finely striated transversely, on the anterior side a few obscure longitudinal striæ, length not more than half an inch.

Well near Swindon, Wilts and Berks Canal. North Wilts Canal.

CARDIUM.
SPECIES 1.

Circular, gibbose; beaks prominent, contiguous; faintly striated transversely. Length about an inch.

North Wilts Canal.

SPECIES 2.

Wider than long, gibbose; beaks prominent incurved, placed near one side; the opposite side produced; many longitudinal ridges crossed by transverse furrows.

North Wilts Canal. Well near Swindon, Wilts and Berks Canal.

ASTARTE.

Astarte ovata.

Fig. Oaktree Clay Plate.

Transversely oblong, depressed, anterior side lengthened; transversely striated; lunette elliptical; margin crenulated within; shell thick; beak acute, solid: a small pit beneath the posterior slope of the hinge.

North Wilts Canal.

MACTRA.

Transversely oblong, posterior side straightish up to the beaks, anterior side produced, gaping; transversely furrowed. Length more than an inch, breadth almost twice the length.

The posterior side very narrow, almost at a right angle to the front with an obtuse angle in the middle.

45

Well near Swindon, Wilts and Berks Canal. North Wilts Canal.

TELLINA.

Transverse, ovate, beaks small; closely striated transversely; a slight inflexion on the more lengthened side; shell thin.

Length an inch and a half.

Well near Swindon, Wilts and Berks Canal.

INEQUIVALVED BIVALVES.
CHAMA.
SPECIES 1.

Oblong, lower valve deep, the left side somewhat lobate, beaks subinvolute; upper valve flat; margin entire within.

North Wilts Canal. Well near Swindon, Wilts and Berks Canal. Bagley Wood Pit.

SPECIES 2.

Chama striata.

Oblong, elongated, curved, longitudinally striated; striæ irregular.
Bagley Wood Pit. North Wilts Canal.

OSTREA.
SPECIES 1.

Ostrea deltoidea. *Min. Conch.*

Fig.6 Oaktree Clay Plate.

Equivalved, flat, thin, deltoidal, with a deep sinus on one side, and a produced straight beak.

Kennet and Avon Canal at Seend. North Wilts Canal. Well near Swindon, Wilts and Berks Canal. Bagley Wood Pit. Wilts and Berks Canal near Shrivenham Even Swindon. Near Wotton Basset. Kirby Moorside, Malton and Little Brickhill

SPECIES 2

Ovate, hooked, depressed; shell thin, with large transverse undulations; beak pointed.

Length an inch and a quarter, breadth three quarters.
Well near Swindon, Wilts and Berks Canal.

46

SPECIES 3.

Obliquely ovate surface even, smooth; lower valve deep, beak not projecting; upper valve flat: shell thin.

North Wilts Canal.

SPECIES 4.

Ostrea crista galli. Cockscomb oyster.
North Wilts Canal. Bagley Wood Pit.

SPECIES 5.

Depressed, uneven, with many roundish longitudinal ribs, crossed by imbricated lines of growth, forming distant rugous projections; inside of the shell plain.

North Wilts Canal.

AVICULA.

Avicula costata.
Brinkworth Common.

PECTEN.
SPECIES 1.

Nearly circular, depressed, closely striated longitudinally; beak rectangular, ears produced, straight, rough.

North Wilts Canal.

SPECIES 2.

Circular, gibbose, many rough longitudinal ridges with smaller ridges interposed.

North Wilts Canal.

SPECIES 3.

Depressed, with roundish imbricated ribs.
Brinkworth Common.

TEREBRATULA.
PLICATED.

Fig. 9 Oaktree Clay Plate.

Large, globose, the plaits on the middle of the shell blending with those on the sides; beak acute, much incurved. [on]ly one [rem]aining [wi]th septaria

North Wilts Canal Well near Swindon, Wilts and Berks Canal. Bagley Wood Pit.

47

CORALINE OOLITE
CORAL RAG AND PISOLITE.
ZOOPHITA.

MADREPORA.

SPECIES 1.

Fig. 3 Coral Rag and Pisolite Plate.

Dichotomous; branches rough, closely striated longitudinally; the upper ends rather concave, radiated, lamellæ rough.

a. Steeple Ashton. *b.* Longleat Park. *c.* Stratton. *d.* Ensham Bridge. Wotton Basset. Banner's Ash. Well near Swindon, Wilts and Berks Canal. Shippon. Bagley Wood Pit. Stanton near Highworth.

AGGREGATED.

SPECIES 2.

Upper side round or ovate, convex in the middle, covered with many hollow stars not divided by septa; radii numerous, unequal; lower side closely striated from the place of attachment.
Steeple Ashton.

SPECIES 3

Fig. 1 Coral Rag and Pisolite Plate.

Upper side covered with large pentagonal or hexagonal radiated cells with a central knob; radii numerous, unequal; lower side closely striated from the place of attachment.

The upper side frequently cordate or heart-shaped.

Stanton near Highworth. South of Bayford. Shippon. Bagley Wood Pit. Banner's Ash.

48

Well near Swindon, Wilts and Berks Canal. Steeple Ashton.

FASCICULATED
SPECIES 4.

Madrepora flexuosa?

Spreading, branches cylindrical, striated longitudinally, rough with transverse wrinkles, concave at the end; radii unequal in length.
Heddington Common. Wotton Basset.

TESTACEA.
UNIVALVIA.
TROCHUS.

SPECIES 1.

Depressed; volutions few, angular, upper part flattish with a row of sharp projecting tubercles.
Derry Hill.

SPECIES 2.

Trochus. *Oaktree Clay*.

Sandford Church Yard. Cast of the inside. South of Bayford. Cast of the inside, more depressed.

MELANIA.
SPECIES 1.

Melania striata. *Min.Conch.*

Fig. Coral Rag and Pisolite Plate.

Volutions of the spire six or more, with about sixteen rounding furrows, more distant in the concealed parts: about 2 ½ times as long as the greatest width.

a. Calne. *b.* Steeple Ashton. Silton Farm. Banner's Ash. Well near Swindon, Wilts and Berks Canal. South of Bayford.

SPECIES 2

Melania Heddingtonensis. *Min. Conch.*

a. Heddington Common.

49

b Steeple Ashton. Silton Farm. Well near Swindon, Wilts and Berks Canal. South of Bayford.

TURBO.

Turbo. *Oaktree Clay*.

Fig. Coral Rag and Pisolite Plate.

Oblong, subturreted; volutions of the spire six, covered with rows of small tubercles, of which two rows in the middle of the spire are larger than the others: aperture about half the length of the shell.

Length not more than an inch.

a. Longleat Park. *b.* Derry Hill. *c.* Steeple Ashton. Banner's Ash. Wotton Basset. Bagley Wood Pit.

TURRITELLA.

Very long, sides straight, volutions smooth, even.
Derry Hill.

AMPULLARIA.

Fig. Coral Rag and Pisolite Plate.

Oblong, spire acute, convex, smooth; volutions four or five, aperture oblong, narrow in the upper part.

a. Longleat Park. *b.* Marcham. Kennington. Silton Farm. South of Bayford. Hinton Waldrish.

HELIX.

Conoidal, short; volutions four, convex, smooth aperture half the length of the shell, umbilicus small.

Longleat Park.

H

50

TUBULAR IRREGULAR UNIVALVES.
SERPULA.

Elongated, with five obscure longitudinal undulations, crossed by transverse wrinkles: thickness of the shell a fourth of the diameter; opening round.

a. Longleat Park. *b.* Derry Hill; almost spiral. *c.* Steeple Ashton; almost spiral. Shippon, almost spiral. Kennington.

MULTILOCULAR UNIVALVES.
BELEMNITES.
Elongated, rather four-sided; diameter less than an inch.
  Wotton Basset. Shippon.

BIVALVIA
EQUIVALVED BIVALVES.
MODIOLA.
SPECIES 1.
Coated muscle.
  Long oval, convex, oblique, transversely striated.
  a. Wilts. *b.* Dry Sandford. Well near Swindon, Wilts and Berks Canal.
Shippon. Sunningwell. Bagley Wood Pit.

SPECIES 2.
A cast of the inside; long oval, depressed sides straightish, anterior end widest.
  Hilmarton. Banner's Ash.

51

TRIGONIA.
SPECIES 1.
Trigonia costata.
Silton Farm. South of Bayford.

SPECIES 2.
Trigonia curvirostra. *Oaktree Clay.*
  Longleat Park.

ASTARTE.
Astarte ovata. *Oaktree Clay.*
South of Bayford. Well near Swindon, Wilts and Berks Canal. Cast of the inside. Shippon. Kennington. Cast of the inside. Inside casts of a small bivalve; roundish, depressed. South of Bayford.

MYA. *Linn.*
Cast of a depressed wide shell.
  South of Bayford.

INEQUIVALVED BIVALVES.
PLAGIOSTOMA.
SPECIES 1.
Oblique, deltoidal, anterior side straight, posterior side circular, rounded into the front; ears short; anterior one placed in a wide furrow; many longitudinal sharp threads decussated near the edge by a few lines of growth.
  Length two inches and a quarter.
  Heddington Common.

SPECIES 2.
Plagiostoma gigantea ? *Min. Conch.*
  A small variety. Length not two inches.
  Westbrook. Calne. Banner's Ash. Well near Swindon, Wilts and Berks Canal.

H2

52

CHAMA.
Chama, Species 1. *Oaktree Clay*
  Westbrook. Banner's Ash. Sunningwell. Kennington. Sandford Churchyard. South of Bayford. Silton Farm.
  Specimens apparently of the same species:
  a. Longleat Park. *b.* Derry Hill.

OSTREA.
SPECIES 1.
Ostrea crista galli.
  Fig. 4 *Coral Rag and Pisolite Plate.*
  Convex, oblong, curved; with many very sharp unequal plaits proceeding from the beaks, and dividing along the middle of the shell; lines of growth distinct; beak of the lower valve subinvolute attached.
  a. Wilts. *b.* Shotover Hill. *c.* Westbrook. *d.* Longleat Park. South of Bayford. Wotton Basset.

SPECIES 2.
Circular; lower valve convex, depressed, slightly lobate on the left side; beak much curved; upper. valve flat or concave; transversely laminated.
  Length about five inches.
  Steeple Ashton.

PECTEN.
SPECIES 1.
Pecten fibrosus. *Min. Conch.*
  a. Longleat Park. *b.* Heddington Common. Kennington.
  Perna aviculuoides Silpho. Filey Bridge
  ?Trigonia in this Rock
  no Terebratula noticed

53

SPECIES 2
Oblong, depressed; with twenty or more smooth ribs, and minute transverse striæ
  Highworth. Sunningwell. Westbrook.

SPECIES 3.
Circular, flattish, transversely striated; with twenty or more longitudinal ribs crossed by high transverse ridges.
  Kennington. Calne.

ECHINI.
ANOCYSTI.
CIDARIS.
SPECIES 1.
Depressed, upper side convex; apparently without any rows of eminences; areolæ prominent.
  Near Abbotsbury.

SPECIES 2.
Pentangular, depressed, with thirty rows of small mammellæ which are almost equal on the sides; the row on each side of the areæ smaller than the others; rays obliquely triporous: mouth ten-sided, with a large notch at each angle.
  Hilmarton. Wotton Basset.

SPECIES 3.
Fig. 5 *Coral Rag and Pisolite Plate.*
  Subglobose, with ten rows of articulated mammellæ, each a little sunk and surrounded by a ring of small points, two rows in each area, separated by numerous small points; rays double, biporous, subflexuous, enclosing two rows of small points: many distinct points on each side of the area: apertures large.
  Hilmarton. Well near Swindon, Wilts and Berks Canal.

SPECIES 4.
Cidaris diadema. *Linn.*
  Hilmarton. Calne.

54

SPECIES 5.
Globose or conical, the top rounded, base flattish; ten rows of very prominent articulated mammellæ two rows in each area, separated by two rows of small distinct eminences; each side of the area bordered by a row of small distinct eminences; rays subflexuous, biporous; areolæ narrow, edged by two prominent rows of points enlarged on the margin, widening from the vent downwards to the margin; vent small.
  The mammellæ are not separated from each other by any eminences, but the smooth base of one mammella touches the base of another.

CLYPEUS.
Fig. 6 *Coral Rag and Pisolite Plate.*
  Oblong, subquadrangular; base flattish, concave in the middle; mouth small, five angled; upper side convex, with a large deep furrow on one side from the apex to the margin; rays ten biporous lines in five pairs, depressed on the base: apertures opposite, excentric from the furrowed end. Shell unequally covered with small granulæ, most numerous on the base.
  The furrow on the upper side is slight near the apex, then very deep, expanding toward the widest end, indenting the margin.
  a. Meggot's Mill, Coleshill. *b.* Longleat Park. *c.* Hinton Waldrish.

SPINES OF ECHINI.
Subcylindrical, elongated, smooth.
  Hilmarton.
  Clavicula cucumerina.
  Longleat Park. Derry Hill.
  Very much lengthened, muricated.
  Westbrook.
  Calcareous Grit Perna aviculuoides Filey ?oolite

55

CLUNCH CLAY AND SHALE.
TESTACEA.
UNIVALVIA.
ROSTELLARIA.
Volutions of the spire five or six, a row of small studs on each margin; beak short.
  Dudgrove Farm.

TUBULAR IRREGULAR UNIVALVES.
SERPULA.
Serpula, Species 2. *Oaktree Clay.*
  This specimen is adherent and twisting.
  Steeple Ashton.

MULTILOCULAR UNIVALVES
BELEMNITES.
SPECIES 1.
Fig. Clunch Clay Plate.
  Large, squarish, quickly tapering to the apex; diameter one inch at the large end, length four or five inches.
  a. Dudgrove Farm. *b.* North Wilts.

SPECIES 2.
Very long, slender, tapering gradually to a sharp point, furrow large in the upper part; length five inches, diameter half an inch.
  Dudgrove Farm.

AMMONITES.
NO KEEL OR FURROW ON THE BACK.
SPECIES 1.
Ammonites communis. *Min. Conch.* This shell varies extremely, in some specimens the aperture is oval, in others wide.
  In this stratum generally wide.
  Whitby.

56

SPECIES 2
Ammonites, Species 3. *Kelloways Stone.*
  Holt.

A KEEL ROUND THE BACK.
SPECIES 3.
Fig. Clunch Clay Plate.
  Inner volutions two thirds concealed; radii many, sharp, twice curved, tubercular twice on the inner margin, and again on the outer. Shell very much compressed.
  a. Thames and Severn Canal. *b.* Tytherton Lucas.

~~SPECIES 4.~~
See p.117-In alum shale-no business here
  Ammonites Walcotii. *Min. Conch.*
  Depressed volutions four, three fourths exposed, with a concentrate furrow; lunate undulations over half the sides; back with a keel between two furrows: aperture oblong, one third of the diameter.
  Each volution divided into two parts by an obtuse furrow; inner half nearly smooth.
  Whitby.

BIVALVIA.
EQUIVALVED BIVALVES.
TELLINA.
Wider than long, gibbous, smooth, one side produced into a short thick beak, the other rounded and blunt; beaks incurved.
Whitby.

INEQUIVALVED BIVALVES.
OSTREA.
Gryphaea dilatata *Min. Conch.*
  Circular, obscurely lobed; upper valve flat, lower valve hemispherical.
  Fig. 2&3 *Clunch Clay Plate.*
  VARIETY 1. Not very convex, large and broad, beak not much curved over the hinge; obscurely lobed: length from three to five inches
  a. Meggot's Mill, Coleshill. *b.* Derry Hill. *c.* Between Weymouth and Osmington *d.* Tytherton Lucas. Little Harwood

----

Dudgrove Farm; smaller, attached at the beak.

VARIETY 2. Lobate oyster; left side very much lobed, lower valve deep.

a. Steeple Ashton. b Bubdown.

AVICULA.

Avicula costata.

Dudgrove Farm.

TERBBRATULA.

Terebratula obsoleta? *Min. Conch.* Only one-? if that may not belong to top of Kelloways stone

Dudgrove Farm.

I

KELLOWAYS STONE.
TESTACEA.
UNIVALVIA.
ROSTELLARIA.

Fig. 1 Kelloways Stone Plate.

Volutions seven, or more, with two smooth angular carinæ, the upper one very prominent, the other smaller and concealed; many fine striæ Kelloways. Wilts and Berks Canal.

TURRITELLA.

Turreted, volutions five or six, angular, with many crenulated lines; aperture roundish.

a. Thames and Severn Canal. *b.* Dauntsey House, in stone. *c.* Kelloways.

MULTILOCULAR UNIVALVES.
NAUTILUS.

Subglobose, volutions rounded, diminishing fast, smooth; umbilicate; many fine striæ across the back; shell thin.

Kelloways.

BELEMNITES.

Very long, slender, tapering gradually to a sharp point, furrow large.

Wilts and Berks Canal.

AMMONITES.
NO KEEL OR FURROW ON THE BACK.
SPECIES 1.

Ammonites sublaevis *Min. Conch.*

Fig. 2 Kelloways Stone Plate.

Globular, (rather depressed when young), inner volutions exposed within the umbilicus, which is deep, undulated, and has an angular edge: septa numerous, with five principal undulations.

Aperture very wide, semicircular, truncated at the sides.

a. Kelloways. b. Ladydown Farm. Christian Malford.

SPECIES 2.

Fig. Kelloways Stone Plate.

Volutions six or more, half concealed back round; radii numerous, unequal, united on the inner part of the volution by pairs or more into compressed oblong tubercles sometimes with shorter intermediate radii over the back; aperture oblong widest in the inner part, inner angles rounded.

Diameter about two inches.

a. Kelloways. *b.* Dauntsey House. *c.* Wilts and Berks Canal. *d.* Kennet and Avon Canal.

SPECIES 3.

Volutions two thirds concealed, gibbous, with oblong sharp ridges on the inner part, from which proceed very numerous small radii; back wide, rounded; aperture obcordate, more than one third of the diameter in length, and as wide as long.

Diameter four inches.

Christian Malford.

SPECIES 4.

Ammonites Calloviensis. *Min. Conch.*

Fig. 3 Kelloways Stone Plate.

Involute, subumbilicate, rather depressed; volutions about five, three fourths concealed back flat; radii small, very numerous, alternately one long one prominent near the inner edge and from two to five short, obscure in the latter whorls of old shells; aperture roundish when young, deltoid with the angles truncated when old.

a. Kelloways. *b.* Wilts and Berks Canal.

VARIETY. Depressed, volutions more than half concealed, radii twice prominent on the inner part, with from two to five shorter ones over the back.

Tytherton Lucas.

SPECIES 5.

Thickish, subumbilicate; radii twice very prominent or tuberculated on the inner part of the volution, with from two to five shorter ones on the outer part; back flat, edged by many small tubercles.

Tytherton Lucas.

I2

SPECIES 6.

Gibbose, subumbilicate; volutions nearly concealed; radii close, alternately divided, tuberculated on the inner and outer margins; back flat.

Diameter one third of an inch.

Kelloways.

SPECIES 7.

Volutions four or five, exposed, with pointed tubercles on the inner part dividing into two or three sharp radii; a slight depression along the back. Tubercles more obscure in the outer volutions.

Tytherton Lucas.

BIVALVIA.
EQUIVALVED BIVALVES.
ARCA.

Much wider than long, ovate, depressed, with small transverse furrows; sides unequal; beaks small; shell thin.

Thames and Severn Canal.

CARDITA?
SPECIES 1.

Transverse, ovate, convex, subequilateral, with small transverse furrows, margin thick; breadth above an inch.

Kelloways.

SPECIES 2.

Subtriangular, gibbous, beaks prominent, anterior side narrow, straightish, bounded by a smooth rising extending from the beaks to one angle; closely and finely striated, both longitudinally and transversely, margin crenulated within.

Length about half an inch.

a. Thames and Severn Canal. *b.* Dauntsey House. *c.* Kelloways.

MYA. *Linn.* UNIO? *Lam.*

Twice as wide as long, with obscure transverse undulations; anterior side produced, acuminated, posterior side blunt, front margin not much arched. Beaks rather prominent.

Wilts and Berks Canal. Thames and Severn Canal.

INEQUIVALVED BIVALVES.
OSTREA.

Gryphaea dilatata. *Min.Conch.*

Fig. 5 Kelloways Stone Plate.

VARIETY. Lobate oyster. Left side very much lobed, lower valve deep.

a. Kelloways. *b.* Wilts and Berks Canal. *c.* Ladydown on the Biss River. *d.* Bruham Pit. Experiment for Coal.

AVICULA.

Avicula costata.

Kelloways.

TEREBRATULA.

Terebratula ornithocephala. *Min.Conch.*

Fig. 6 Kelloways Stone Plate.

Ovato-rhomboidal; depressed when young, elongated and gibbous when old; front straight, bounded by two obtuse lateral depressions, similar in each valve.

a. Thames and Severn Canal. *b.* Dauntsey House. *c.* Kelloways. *d.* Wilts and Berks Canal.

CORNBRASH.
ZOOPHITA.
PENTACRINUS.

Vertebræ thin, with very projecting angles.

a. Wick Farm. b. Pipehouse. c. Well at Seagry.

TESTACEA.
UNIVALVIA.
VOLUTA.

Subcylindrical, smooth, spire short; aperture widest at the base.

Near Norton. North side of Wincanton.

TURBO.

Volutions few, angular in the lower part.

Sheldon.

TURRITELLA.

Sides straight, volutions smooth, even, with a small ridge below the upper edge.

a. Melbury. *b.* Lullington.

ROSTELLARIA.

Rostellaria. *Kelloways Stone.*

Melbury.

AMPULLARIA.

Depressed, small, volutions few.

Lullington.

NATICA?

Fig. 1, Cornbrash Plate.

Volutions three or four, the outer one very large, spire short, with an obtuse furrow beneath the projecting upper edge of the volutions. Aperture semicircular, almost four fifths as long as the whole shell.

a. Road. *b.* Sleaford. Wick Farm.

TUBULAR IRREGULAR UNIVALVES.
SERPULA.
SPECIES I.

Cylindrical, straightish, enringed with small projections, diameter from one fourth to one third of an inch

a. Melbury. b. Closworth. c. Farley. d. Sheldon.

SPECIES 2.

Cylindrical, small, contorted, lines of growth distinct.

a. Trowle. b. Holt. c. Sheldon.

MULTILOCULAR UNIVALVES
AMMONITES.
NO KEEL OR FURROW ON THE BACK

Ammonites discus. *Min. Conch.*

Fig. 2, Cornbrash Plate.

Discoid, smooth, outer edge acuminated; aperture sagittate, half the diameter of the shell in length, and one sixth in breadth: volutions concealing each other, septa numerous, largely undulated.

a. Closworth b. Road. Southwest of Wincanton.

BIVALVIA.
EQUIVALVED BIVALVES.
MODIOLA.

Fig. 3, Cornbrash Plate.

Transversely oblong, most convex diagonally from the beaks; posterior side rather blunt, rounded in front; back straightish, rounded into the anterior end; beaks small; lines of growth sharp; shell very thin.

Depressed in front of the gibbous part.

a. Closworth. *b.* Wick Farm. *c.* Holt.

UNIO.
SPECIES 1.
Depressed, triangular, broader than long, anterior and posterior sides acuminated, front margin straightish, length from half to three fourths of an inch.

    a. Norton. *b.* Near Tellisford.

SPECIES 2.
Twice as wide as long, much depressed, beak a little nearest one side, the other produced, front margin straight.

    Length three fourths of an inch.

    This much resembles Unio acutus. *Min. Conch.* Melbury.

SPECIES 3.
Fig. 7, Cornbrash Plate.

    Twice as wide as long, depressed, beaks nearest to one end, the other produced, front not much arched; transversely furrowed.

    a. North Cheriton. *b.* Road. *c.* Draycot. *d.* Maisey Hampton. *e.* Sleaford. *f.* Southwest of Tellisford. *g.* Sattyford.

Scarboro fine and long Gervillia

65

SPECIES 4.
Twice as wide as long, ovate, anterior side subacuminate, posterior side rather blunt; beaks not prominent; anterior slope arched, front straightish; transversely furrowed.

    Down Ampney.

TRIGONIA.
SPECIES 1.
Trigonia clavellata. *Min. Conch. Park.*

    a. Melbury. *b.* Woodford.

SPECIES 2.
Trigonia costata. *Min. Conch. Park.*

    Fig. 4, Cornbrash Plate.

    VARIETY with very sharp ribs.

    North side of Wincanton. Wick Farm.

CARDIUM.
Fig. 6, Cornbrash Plate.

    Subglobose, ovate, front and posterior sides rounded, anterior slope straight; surface undulated with about ten large ridges crossed by transverse furrows; beaks at one end, very protuberant, incurved.

    Length from two to four inches.

    a. Road. *b.* Elmcross. *c.* Wick Farm. A smaller VARIETY; the posterior side bounded by a very prominent ridge forming an angle in the contour: front straightish. *d.* Sleaford. *e.* Woodford. *f.* Near Peterborough.

MYA?
Twice as wide as long, beaks at one end which is truncated and gibbous, the other produced, acuminated; front not much arched, anterior slope straight; transversely furrowed.

    a. Redlynch. *b.* Near Tellisford.

VENUS?
SPECIES 1.
Fig. 5, Cornbrash Plate.

    Subcordate, gibbose, wider than long, anterior side subacuminated, posterior side blunt; beaks prominent, hooked, subincurved; transversely striated.

Thornbury Bucks

K

66

    a. Trowle. *b.* Sheldon. Southwest of Wincanton.

    VAR. Subcircular or deltoidal, gibbose, posterior side straightish, extended to a point, beaks very much hooked above the posterior side.

    a. Trowle. *c.* Norton.

SPECIES 2.
Circular, depressed, with transverse furrows.

    North of Latton.

SPECIES 3.
Small, depressed, beaks not curved, one side produced.

    Sheldon.

SPECIES 4.
Small, circular, convex, subequilateral, with transverse sharp costæ.

    Wick Farm.

INEQUIVALVED BIVALVES.
LIMA.
SPECIES 1.
Trigonal or semicircular, oblique, with short ears; one side straightish and lengthened, the other rounded; covered with many longitudinal sharp plaits.

    a. Melbury. *b.* Closworth. *c.* Norton. *d.* Wick Farm.

SPECIES 2.
Lima gibbosa. *Min. Conch.*

    North side of Wincanton.

OSTREA.
SPECIES 1.
Ostrea Marshii. *Min. Conch.*

    Oblique, both valves deeply plaited in seven or eight angular diverging undulations; edge thick, flatted.

67

a. Sleaford. *b.* Woodford.

SPECIES 2.
Oblong, lower valve convex; upper valve concave; surface irregularly undulated or imbricated.

    a. Melbury. *b.* Closworth. *c.* Sheldon. *d.* Draycot. *e.* Woodford. *f.* Norton.

SPECIES 3.
Oblong, upper valve concave, lower valve convex; with longitudinal elevated unequal threads.

    Woodford.

AVICULA
SPECIES 1.
Avicula echinata.

    Fig. 8. Cornbrash Plate.

    Subcircular, convex, beak rather prominent, with a short wing or ear from one side; surface covered with near thirty small threads roughened by projecting lines of growth.

    The length seldom exceeds two thirds of an inch.

    a. Closworth. *b.* North Cheriton. *c.* Lullington. *d.* Trowle. *e.* Sheldon. *f.* Draycot. *g.* Norton. *h.* Stony Stratford. *i.* Southwest of Tellisford. North side of Wincanton. Southwest of Wincanton.

    The under valve only is here described for the upper valve has not been observed among any of these specimens.

SPECIES 2.
Avicula costata.

    Stony Stratford.

K2

68

PECTEN.
Pecten fibrosus? *Min. Conch.*

    Depressed, circular, with a rectangular beak; valves unlike, one valve with about ten broadish diverging grooves and numerous sharp concentric striæ, the other valve with about ten diverging ribs and many larger concentric scales or tiles; ears equal, margin undulated, internally.

    The ribs in one valve are alternately larger and smaller answering to the grooves in the other.

    Length about an inch.

    a. Melbury. *b.* Sheldon. *c.* Woodford. North side of Wincanton. Southwest of Wincanton.

TEREBRATULA.
Numerous in this rock

NOT PLICATED.
SPECIES I.
Terebratula intermedia. *Min. Conch.*

    Obscurely five-sided, rather depressed, smooth, larger valve most convex, front margin undulated; three depressions in the smaller valve and two in the larger.

---

    a. Melbury. *b.* Bruham. *c.* Lullington. *d.* Road. *e.* Trowle. *f.* Maisey Hampton. *g.* Holt. A large specimen, two inches in length.

SPECIES 2
Terebratula digona. *Min. Conch.*

    Fig. 9, Cornbrash Plate.

    Triangular, oblong, gibbous; beak prominent; sides rounded; front either convex or concave, when old bounded by two prominent angles alike in each valve.

    This species is very variable in form, but specimens from this stratum are generally of the gibbous and shorter variety with the front margin slightly convex between the angles.

    a. Closworth. *b.* Redlynch. *c.* Trowle.

69

d. Wick Farm. *e.* Sheldon. *f.* Latton. *g.* Woodford.

PLICATED.

Terebratula obsoleta ? *Min. Conch.*

    Nearly round, gibbous, plaited; middle of the front a little elevated by seven plaits; sides having from seven to eleven plaits; beak projecting.

    a. Closworth. *b.* Draycot. *c.* Wick Farm. Southwest of Wincanton. North side of Wincanton.

ECHINI.
ANOCYSTI.
CIDARIS.
Cidaris, Species 2. *Clay over the upper oolite.*

    a Melbury, with smaller mammellæ.

    b Sheldon.

    c Norton.

    d Southwest of Tellisford. VARIETY with smaller mammellæ

    e Wick Farm.

CLYPEUS.
Clypeus. *Coral Rag and Pisolite*

    a. Bruham. *b.* Wick Farm. *c.* Wraxhall. *d.* Sleaford. *e.* Trowle. *f.* Southwest of Tellisford. Southwest of Wincanton.

70

CATOCYSTI.
CONULUS.
Conulus. *Fuller's Earth Rock.*

    Nearly circular, convexo-conical, base concave; covered by small prominences particularly on the base of the shell; rays ten biporous lines diverging in five pairs, pores very close on the upper part, more distant on the base.

    Woolverton. Southwest of Wincanton.

71

FOREST MARBLE.
ZOOPHITA.
MADREPORA.
AGGREGATED
SPECIES 1.
Circular, upper part convex, with large unequal radiated cells; lower part flat, closely striated from the center.

    A transverse semicircular ostrea adhering to the lower part.

    Laverton.

SPECIES 2.
Upper side flat with large close cells; lower side convex, closely striated.

    Stunsfield.

TESTACEA.
UNIVALVIA
PATELLA.
Patella – Stunsfield, *Lhwyd*

Patella rugosa. *Min. Conch.*

    Fig. 1, Forest Marble Plate.

    Depressed, obovate, radiated; apex eccentric, depressed, slightly recurved; back concave above, with reflected undulations.

    a. Minching Hampton Common. *b.* Hinton.

ANCILLA
SPECIES 1.

Fig. 2, Forest Marble Plate.

Subcylindrical, smooth, volutions square and subcrenulated at the upper edge; spire short, turreted; aperture two thirds of the length, widest at the base.

Farley.

72

SPECIES 2.

Fusiform, spire short, acute, base pointed, volutions smooth, slightly angular at the upper edge; aperture acute at the ends, widest in the middle, rather more than two thirds of the length.

Wincanton. see p. 150 Phillips spec. 2, a Trigonia Bransby [ ] at White Nab

I believe Gervillia acuta so common in Bransby roadstone and in large slabs of stone at Lincoln belongs to the Stunsfield Slate. Is at Collyweston fide Woodward

TURRITELLA.
SPECIES 1.

Slender, volutions many, angular, concave beneath the upper edge. Marston, near Frome.

ROSTELLARIA.

Fig.3, Forest Marble Plate.

Elongated, spire with longitudinal ridges acute on the upper edge, and transverse striæ

Length not more than three fourths of an inch.

Poulton.

TUBULAR IRREGULAR UNIVALVES.
SERPULA.

Cylindrical, small, contorted.

Farley.

BIVALVIA.
EQUIVALVED BIVALVES.
TRIGONIA.
SPECIES 1.

Trigonia costata. *Park. Min. Conch.* The ribs very sharp, length one inch.

Wincanton.

SPECIES 2.

Triangular, wider than long, depressed, anterior side straight, posterior side rounded; with ten or more rather oblique rows of small tubercles, twenty or more tubercles in a row; two or three tuberculated ridges on the posterior side.

Length one inch.

Stunsfield.

73

VENUS. *Linn.*

Cast of the inside:

Transversely ovate, subequilateral; length one inch.

Road Lane.

MYA.

Transverse, gibbous, breadth three times the length; anterior end elongated, pointed, gaping for half the breadth; beaks small, one sixth of the breadth from the posterior end; transversely striated; thickness equal to the length, shell thin.

Stunsfield.

INEQUIVALVED BIVALVES.
OSTREA.
SPECIES1.

Ostrea crista galli.

Stunsfield.

SPECIES 2.

Lower valve convex, oblique, widest and deepest near the front, flattened and attached. toward the back.

Orchardleigh.

SPECIES 3.

Fig. 4, Forest Marble Plate.

Oval, flattish, depressed; upper valve flat, surface longitudinally wrinkled. Pit oblong; shell hollow beneath the pit. The pit of the upper valve is formed by the projection of the beak. Length one inch.

a. Wincanton. *b.* Road, Coal Experiment.

PECTEN.
SPECIES 1.

Fig. 5, Forest Marble Plate.

Large, convex, eared, ribbed longitudinally, with forty or fifty wide smooth ribs; striated transversely, striæ obscure on the ribs.

Length, two inches and a quarter.

The ribs are obscure toward the beaks.

a. Siddington. *b.* Foss Cross.

L

74

SPECIES 2.

Large, oblong, depressed, sides rather unequal, ribbed longitudinally with forty or fifty large ribs, often with an intermediate smaller one.

Length, three inches and three quarters.

Laverton.

SPECIES 3.

Pecten fibrosus ? *Min. Conch.*

The diverging furrows are only near the front and are striated, the intermediate spaces plain.

Stunsfield.

SPECIES 4.

Fig. 6, Forest Marble Plate.

Circular, depressed, striated longitudinally; striæ numerous, fine, dividing; intersecting near the beaks? ears large, rough.

Farley.

SPECIES 5.

Circular, depressed; transversely imbricated, faintly striated longitudinally; ears equal, rough; length two inches.

Farley.

SPECIMENS OF THE STONE
Contain

ROSTELLARIA.
HELIX.

Smooth conoidal, obtuse.

Farley.

VENUS.

An oval transverse striated shell.

Farley.

OSTREA.

Rough, irregular.

Farley.

Wincanton.

SPINES OF ECHINI.

Slender, subcylindrical, smooth.

Farley.

no Terebratula noticed

75

BONES.

A long slender bone. Length, four inches and a half.

Stunsfield.

TEETH.
BUFONITÆ.
SPECIES 1.

Fig. 7, Forest Marble Plate.

Oval.

a. Stunsfield. *b.* Pickwick.

SPECIES 2.

Fig. 8, Forest Marble Plate.

Circular: diameter a quarter of an inch.

a. Stunsfield. *b.* Pickwick. *c.* Didmarton.

OBLONG, POINTED.
SPECIES 3.

Fig. 11, Forest Marble Plate.

Curved, tapering, round, with two sharp edges. Diameter from three sixteenths to one third of an inch, length five times the diameter.

a. Stunsfield. *b.* Pickwick.

SPECIES 4.

Curved or oblique, flattened. Length one inch, diameter three sixteenths of an inch.

Stunsfield.

SPECIES 5.

Curved, a little flattened near the point, cylindrical at the base. Length three fourths of an inch, diameter one twelfth.

Stunsfield.

SPECIES 6.

Flattish, triangular, with two sharp edges and two small lateral teeth, one on each side. Length, half an inch.

L2

76

a. Stunsfield. *b.* Pickwick.

PALATES OF FISH.
SPECIES 1.

Fig. 9, Forest Marble Plate.

Foursided, angles acute and obtuse, depressed; sides parallel, one of them defined by an edge; surface uneven, covered with very small hollows.

Pickwick.

SPECIES 2.

Elongated, with parallel flattened sides, one of them defined by an edge; surface uneven, covered with small hollows.

Pickwick.

SPECIES 3.

Fig. 10, Forest Marble Plate.

Deltoidal or cap formed, much elevated in the middle; smooth.

Pickwick.

77

CLAY over the UPPER OOLITE.
ZOOPHIA.

TUBIPORA.

Roundish, lengthened, composed of very small angular closely aggregated tubes.

Broadfield Farm.

Farley.

MADREPORA.
SPECIES 1.

Madrepora porpites. *Linn.*

Broadfield Farm.

SPECIES 2.

Circular, convex and uneven above, with many equal concave stars.

Hinton.

MILLEPORA.

Fig. 5, Clay over the Upper Oolite Plate.

Ramose, branches round, composed internally of layers or coats of tubes opening into reticulating angular cells on the surface; branches undulated, sometimes spirally.

Broadfield Farm. Farley. Hinton. Pickwick. Westwood.

ENCRINUS.

Pear Encrinus.

Fig. 1, 2, and 3, Clay over the Upper Oolite Plate.

Bradford. Heads, and vertebræ. Farley. vertebræ. Hinton. vertebræ. Winsley. vertebræ. Pickwick. vertebræ.

W of Wincanton omitted [Wincanton not shown as a locality]

78

PENTACRINUS.

Vertebræ, with blunt projecting angles.

Towcester. ?

TESTACEA.
UNIVALVIA.
TROCHUS.
SPECIES 1.

Conical, sides undulated; volutions four or five, angular, the upper part flat; the lower edge keeled; striated spirally, on the sides a few oblique threads across the spire.

Bradford Lock.

SPECIES 2.

Short, conical, striated; volutions four or five, lower edge thin, strongly crenated; lines of growth distinct; umbilicate.

Bradford Lock. Broadfield Farm.

TURRITELLA.

Long, slender, a spiral groove in the lower par of the volutions

Farley. the same as at [ ]mill Lincoln

TUBULAR IRREGULAR UNIVALVES.
SERPULA.
SPECIES 1.

Elongated, conical, twisting at the small end, quadrate with four projecting crenated angles or ridges; opening round.

a. Westwood. *b.* Farley. *c.* Broadfield Farm.

SPECIES 2.

Large, cylindrical, straightish, smooth.

Farley.

79

MULTILOCULAR UNIVALVES.
BELEMNITES.

Small, slender.

Stoford.

BIVALVIA.
EQUIVALVED BIVALVES.
MODIOLA.
SPECIES 1.

Mytilus tunicatus or coated muscle. Fistulana. *Lam.*

Combhay.

SPECIES 2.

Small, elongated, widest in front; one side straightish and gibbous, the other rounded; longitudinally striated, striæ unequal in length.

Farley.

SPECIES 3.

Much elongated, curved, ends acuminated; most convex near the beaks; on the outer side of the arch near the beak a fold or constriction; lines of growth sharp.

Farley.

Modiola, *Cornbrash.*

Westwood.

TRIGONIA.

Trigonia costata. *Min. Conch.*

VAR. The anterior side wider than the posterior; length two inches and a quarter, breadth one inch and a half.

Hinton.

VENUS?
SPECIES 1.

Inside casts of a small species, flattish sides almost equal.

Combhay.

80

SPECIES 2.

Ovate, wider than long, gibbous; depth equal to the length; beaks large, hooked; transversely striated.

Poulton Quarry, Bradford.

INEQUIVALVED BIVALVES.
PLAGIOSTOMA.
SPECIES 1.

Fig. 7, Clay over the Upper Oolite Plate.

Ovate, depressed, front semicircular, back straight; closely striated longitudinally and finely decussated; ears small, one of them placed in a wide deep furrow; beaks flattened.

The longitudinal striææ re rather unequally distant on the margin and are finely decussated.

Bradford.

SPECIES 2.

Oblong, one side straight, the other semicircular; deeply striated longitudinally, striæ forty or more, decussated; ears small. There appears to be a projecting flat surface beneath the beaks.

Farley.

VARIETY.

With more numerous striæ

Combhay.

CHAMA.
SPECIES 1.

Chama crassa.

Fig. 6, Clay over the Upper Oolite Plate.

Very long, narrow, deep around one side, smooth; beak subinvolute; upper valve flat, tooth of the hinge small, blunt; margin entire within.

Length almost three times as great as the breadth.

Stoford.

SPECIES 2.

Oblong, gibbous, lobate in front; beak subinvolute; upper valve flat; margin entire within.

Length one inch and three eighths, breadth four fifths of an inch.

a. Stoford *b.* Combhay.

? any clay over Gt. oolite at Combhay

81

SPECIES 3.

Gibbous, beaks greatly curved, pit of the hinge large and deep; margin entire within.

Breadth four fifths of the length.

Pickwick.

OSTREA.
SPECIES 1.

Ostrea crista galli. Cock's comb oyster.

a. Farley. *b.* Combhay. *c.* Hinton.

SPECIES 2.

Circular, depressed, longitudinally plaited; plaits unequal, often dividing; lines of growth distinct; beak central.

Farley.

SPECIES 3.

Ostrea acuminata. *Min. Conch.*

Depressed, very long, curved, with large subimbricated transverse waves beneath; beaks and front acuminated; upper valve nearly even. Two or three times as long as wide.

Bradford.

PECTEN.
SPECIES 1.

Pecten fibrosus? *Min. Conch. Cornbrash.*

Farley.

SPECIES 2.

Circular, almost flat, smooth, ears small.

Farley.

AVICULA.

Avicula costata.

Fig. 8, Clay over the upper oolite Plate.

Oblique, subdepressed, left side extended, acuminated; wings unequal, the right wing short; valves unequal, lower valve convex, with about eight smooth ribs, and undulated internally, upper valve flat, with diverging striæ

M

82

is this the one so common to top of the rock Scarbro shore

a. Bradford, *b.* Hinton. *c.* Winsley.

TEREBRATULA.
NOT PLICATED.
SPECIES 1.

Terebratula digona. *Min. Conch.*

Fig. 9, Clay over the upper oolite Plate.

Triangular, oblong, gibbous; beak prominent; sides rounded; front either convex or concave, when old bounded by two prominent angles alike in each valve.

This species is very variable in form, but specimens from this stratum are generally of the lengthened variety with straightish flattened sides.

a. Farley. *b.* Stoford. *c.* Bradford. *d.* Winsley. *e.* Pickwick.

SPECIES 2.

Obscurely five sided, rather depressed, smooth; larger valve most convex; front margin undulated, with three depressions in the smaller valve and four in the larger.

Length more than an inch.

a. Farley. *b.* Stoford. *c.* Combhay. Winsley.

PLICATED.

SPECIES 3.

Terebratula obsoleta ? *Min. Conch.*

Nearly round, gibbous, plaited; middle of the front a little elevated with from six to eight plaits; sides having from nine to twelve plaits; beak projecting.

Depth about two thirds of the length.

Length from half an inch to an inch and a quarter.

a. Farley. *b.* Westwood. *c.* Winsley. *d.* Pickwick

Terebratula numerous

83

SPECIES 4.

Oval, convex; with many diverging sharp plaits furcating from near the beaks; front margin not elevated, beak prominent.

Farley.

SPECIES 5.

Terebratula reticulata. ?if all these 5 species do not belong to top of great oolite

Fig. 10, Clay over the upper oolite Plate.

Obtusely five sided, gibbous; with minutely echinated or reticulated striæ; surface uneven; larger valve with two very prominent folds continued from the front to the beak, and three large depressions, forming large angular notches on the front; upper valve with corresponding undulations.

a. Farley. Bradford. Stoford. *b.* Hinton. *c.* Winsley. *d.* Pickwick.

ECHINI.
ANOCYSTI.
CIDARIS.
SPECIES 1.

Circular, depressed, top convex; rays biporous; two rows of small eminences in each areola, two rows of miliæ in each area; mouth large, its edges turned inwards.

Broadfield Farm.

SPECIES 2.

Circular, rather depressed, with ten rows of contiguous mammellæ, (near the vent the first mammellæ in the rows are encircled), two rows in each area, separated by curvilinear rows of small eminences partly surrounding the mammellæ; areolæ with minute points encircling two rows of eminences; mouth large, decagonal, with a deep notch at every angle.

a. Pickwick. *b.* Farley.

CLYPEUS.

Clypeus. *Coral Rag and Pisolite.*

Broadfield Farm.

M2

84

UPPER OOLITE.
ZOOPHITA.
MADREPORA.
SIMPLE OR COMPOSED OF ONE SINGLE STAR.

SPECIES 1.
Madrepora turbinata. *Linn.*

Conical, longitudinally striated; upper part concave, radiated; radii numerous, unequal in length.
Farley.

AGGREGATED.
SPECIES 2.
Conical, covered by slightly concave, closely radiated stars.
Stoke.

SPECIES 3.
Large, depressed, concave and patulous above; stars concave, small, numerous; base closely striated from the pedicle.
Castle Combe.

SPECIES 4.
Large, convex above, with many equal concave stars.
a. Castle Combe. *b.* Combe Down.

SPECIES 5.
Large, convex above, covered with many small concave stars; surface undulated.
Vinyard Down.

FASCICULATED.
SPECIES 6.
Madrepora flexuosa. *Linn.*

Spreading; branches round, longitudinally striated, rough with transverse wrinkles concave at the upper end, with radii unequal in length.
Castle Combe.
Wellingbrough

85
SPECIES 7?
Spreading at the sides, composed of small round striated branches.
This may perhaps be a Tubipora.
a. Broadfield Farm. *b.* Combe Down.

SPECIES 8.
Part of a large cylindrical ramose Coral.
Castle Combe.

TESTACEA.
BIVALVIA.
INEQUIVALVED BIVALVES.
PECTEN.
SPECIES 1.
Subequilateral, convex, beak central; many close longitudinal ribs.
Length more than two inches.
Castle Combe.

SPECIES 2.
Pecten, Species 1. *Forest Marble*

Large, convex, eared, ribbed longitudinally with forty or fifty wide smooth ribs; striated transversely, striæ obscure on the ribs.
Length two inches or more.
Cotswold Hills.

PLAGIOSTOMA.
Plagiostoma, Species 2. *Clay over the upper oolite.*
VARIETY. More depressed.
Length one inch and a half.
Bradford?

OSTREA.
Ostrea crista galli, Cock's comb oyster.
Petty France.
Gervillia equivalved Scarbro, White Nab, Perna aviculliodes long slender Cloughton cliff
Pinna thick fibrous shell – do

86
TEREBRATULA.
NOT PLICATED
SPECIES 1.
Terebratula, Species I. *Clay over the upper oolite.*

Obscurely five sided, rather depressed, smooth; larger valve most convex; front margin undulated, with three depressions in the smaller valve and four in the larger.
Petty France.

PLICATED.
SPECIES 2.
Terebratula obsoleta? *Min. Conch.* See p. 82

Nearly round, gibbous, plaited; middle of the front a little elevated, with from six to eight plaits; sides having from nine to twelve plaits; beak projecting.
Petty France.

ECHINI.
ANOCYSTI.
CLYPEUS.
Clypeus. *Coral Rag and Pisolite.*
Hinton. Hogwood Corner.

? any Trigonia in this Rock – I do not recollect them near Bath – therefore rare. Scarboro small ones occur at White Nab – Trigo: of F. marble not noticed in this Work

---

87
FULLER'S EARTH ROCK.
TESTACEA.
UNIVALVIA.
TROCHUS.
Cast of the inside of a Trochus with roundish volutions.
Charlton Horethorn.

TUBULAR IRREGULAR UNIVALVES.
SERPULA.
SPECIES 1.
Elongated, conical, twisting at the small end; quadrate with four projecting crenated angles or ridges; aperture round.
a. Orchardleigh. *b.* Charlton Horethorn.

SPECIES 2.
Serpula crassa. *Min. Conch.*

Acutely conical, round within, three-sided externally, about four times as long as the diameter of the end at the aperture.
Charlton Horethorn.

MULTILOCULAR UNIVALVES.
NAUTILUS.
Fig. 1, Fuller's Earth Rock Plate.

Flatted globose, umbilicate; shell with transverse ridges curving from the aperture; aperture wider than long, siphunculus central.

It seems as if the transverse ridges are formed by the endings of thick plates, and at first sight they resemble septa, but curve from the aperture.
Lansdown.

88
BELEMNITES.
Slender, with a deep groove from the apex.
Charlton Horethorn.

AMMONITES.
SPECIES 1.
Ammonites modiolaris.
Fig. 2, Fuller's Earth Rock Plate.

Subglobose, inner volutions convex, exposed within a large conical hollow or umbilicus; back wide; aperture semilunate, rounded at the extremities, three times as wide as long.

The inner volutions are convex and sharply undulated within the umbilicus, with many large furrows across the back curving toward the aperture; the outer volutions are irregularly swelled on the inner edge, and the undulations across the back are obscure. The umbilicus is one third of the greatest diameter.

This species may be distinguished from Ammonites sublaevis by the large size of the umbilicus, and the obtuseness of the angle which bounds it.
Dundry. Rowley Bottom.

SPECIES 2.
Subglobose, convex, deeply umbilicate; umbilicus narrow, undulated, with a sharpish margin; transverse radiating undulations across the back

uniting on the inner part: aperture semilunate or deltoidal, truncated at the sides, the width two and a half times as great as the length.
Hardington ? Broadfield Farm.

BIVALVIA.
EQUIVALVED BIVALVES.
MODIOLA.
SPECIES 1.
Coated muscle.
Near Bath.

SPECIES 2.
Elongated, slender, sides subparallel, one side thinned and projecting; flattish, lines of growth distinct.
Ancliff.

89
SPECIES 3.
Long, with subparallel sides; gibbous diagonally from the beaks.
Near Bath. A large cast of the inside.

SPECIES 4.
Modiola anatina.
Fig. 3. Fuller's Earth Rock Plate.

Oblong, very gibbous, smooth; beaks prominent, hooked, subinvolute; one side arched into the front; the other oval, flat or concave with a very thick blunt projection near the beaks; shell with fine striæ or lines of growth.

Length twice the width, thickness two thirds of the length.
In a side view the shell is regularly oval with a notch between the beaks.
Ancliff.

UNIO.
SPECIES 1.
Transverse, elongated, depressed, transversely furrowed, beaks pointed, nearest to one end; front margin almost straight: length not half the breadth; thickness half the length.
a. Grip Wood. Cast of the inside. *b.* Hardington. Cast of the inside.

SPECIES 2.
More than twice and a half as wide as long, transversely striated, front straight, sides acute, posterior side swelled near the edge; beaks nearest to one end.
a. Turnpike near Bratton. *b.* Grip Wood.

SPECIES 3.
Triangular, wider than long, smooth, sides acute; anterior side projecting; beaks hooked above the posterior flat side; front margin concave near the anterior angle.
Grip Wood?

ASTARTE.
Cast of the inside of Astarte ovata.
Grip Wood.

TRIGONIA.
SPECIES 1
Trigonia clavellata. Small
Orchardleigh.

N

90
SPECIES 2.
Cast of a large species; cuneiform, very thick, with two muscular impressions.
Breadth three inches and a quarter.
Devonshire Buildings, Bath.

SPECIES 3.
Cast of the inside; transversely elongated, cuneiform, very gibbous: one end pointed, two muscular impressions.
Grip Wood.

SPECIES 4.
Cast of the inside; transversely elongated, pointed; beaks close to the short rounded side; breadth twice the length.

CARDITA.
SPECIES 1.
Fig. 4, Fuller's Earth Rock Plate.
Large, rhomboidal, very gibbous, beaks at one of the angles, hooked; surface covered with obscure curvilinear transverse furrows and a few longitudinal ones.
  a. Grip Wood. *b.* Hardington.

SPECIES 2.
Deltoidal, very gibbous, beaks subinvolute, curved over the posterior flat side; transversely striated; thickness equal to the length.
  Ancliff.

SPECIES 3.
Cast of the inside of a small species; circular, gibbous, margin crenulated within.
  Near Bath.

CARDIUM.
Cardium. *Cornbrash.*
  Fig. 5, Fuller's Earth Rock Plate.
Subglobose, ovate, anterior slope straight; surface undulated with about ten large ridges, crossed by transverse furrows; beaks at one end, very protuberant, incurved.
  Length two or three inches.
  Specimens from this stratum are generally wider and less globose than in the Cornbrash; generally a large prominent ridge bounding the posterior side. The longitudinal ridges are widened and flattened in the anterior part.

91

a. Charlton Horethorn. *b.* Near Gagenwell. *c.* Near Redlynch.

MACTRA. *Linn.*
SPECIES 1.
Transversely subovate, or four sided, gibbous, subequilateral; beaks prominent, front straight, sides truncated, gaping, transversely furrowed.
  Grip Wood.

SPECIES 2.
Transversely elongated, arched, depressed; covered with longitudinal furrows; posterior side rounded; anterior side flattened, a little gaping, not expanded. Breadth twice the length and three times the depth.
  The longitudinal furrows are decussated by distant broad transverse undulations.
  Cotswold Hills.

SPECIES 3
Mactra gibbosa. *Min. Conch.*
  Gibbose, anterior side much wider than the posterior, recurved, truncated, gaping: length and depth about equal, breadth equal to twice the length: posterior side rounding.
  Mitford, a very large specimen, six inches wide.

VENUS?
SPECIES 1.
Venus, Species 1. *Cornbrash.*
  VARIETY. Wider.
  Near Gagenwell.

SPECIES 2
Circular, flattish; beak prominent.
  Charlton Horethorn. Cast of the inside.

SPECIES 3.
Oval, wider than long, thickish, transversely sulcated.
  Bath. Cast of the inside.

TELLINA.
Fig. 6, Fuller's Earth Rock Plate.
  Transverse, elongated, one side extended into a long beak, the other flattish and circular at the extremity; transversely furrowed.
  N2

92

The back is arched from the posterior or circular end, the elongated side straight and hollowed under the beaks: a wide depression from the beaks near the posterior end; width three or four times the length.
  a. Ancliff. *b.* Hardington.

MYA?
SPECIES 1.
Transverse, ovate, beaks close to the posterior side; anterior side acute; transversely furrowed.
  a. Dundry. Sherborn.

SPECIES 2
Mya intersectans.
  Depressed, wide, anterior side expanded; covered by intersecting furrows, longitudinal on the anterior part, oblique on the posterior part, meeting in an oblique line: beaks prominent, nearest to the posterior end.

INEQUIVALVED BIVALVES.
OSTREA.
SPECIES 1.
Ostrea Marshii. *Min. Conch.*
  Fig. 8, Fuller's Earth Rock Plate.
  Oblique, both valves deeply plaited in seven or eight angular diverging undulations; edge thick, flatted.
  a. Monkton Combe. *b.* Cotswold Hills. This has fine longitudinal striæ.

SPECIES 2.
Ostrea rugosa.
  Valves equal, oblong, depressed, one side eared; very rough, with eight or more broad longitudinal ridges elevated into projecting spinous tubercles: hinge square, flat, pit hollowed, with straight parallel edges, the posterior end curving to the beak.
  The shell is uncommonly thick; the hinge very massive, and projecting far into the shell; one of the flat lateral parts forms a rectangular ear.
  a. Monkton Combe. *b.* Between Nunny and Frome.

93

SPECIES 3.
Circular, smooth.
  Orchardleigh, upper valve, small.

TEREBRATULA.
NOT PLICATED.
SPECIES 1.
Terebratula ornithocephala. *Min. Conch.*
  Ovato-rhomboidal; depressed when young, elongated and gibbous when old; front straight, bounded by two obtuse lateral depressions, similar in each valve.
  a. Turnpike near Bratton. *b.* Near Bath.
  VARIETY.
Very long, gibbous, nearly as thick as wide; valves subcarinated along the middle; front narrow, beaks much elongated and curved.
  a. Near Bath. *b.* Writhlington. *c.* Turnpike near Bratton.

SPECIES 2.
Terebratula intermedia. *Min. Conch.*
  Some of the specimens resemble Terebratula biplicata.
  Near Bath.

PLICATED.
SPECIES 3.
Terebratula media. *Min. Conch.*
  Fig. 9, Fuller's Earth Rock Plate. fig 7 numerous
  Very obtusely deltoid, gibbous, plaited; front rounded, with a rising in the middle, composed of six sharp plaits approaching those in the sides; beak a little incurved.
  a. Near Bath. *b.* Charlton Horethorn. *c.* Orchardleigh.

94

ECHINI.
CATOCYSTI.
CONULUS.
Nearly circular, convexo-conical, covered by small prominences, particularly on the base of the shell; rays ten biporous lines diverging in five pairs; pores very close on the upper part, more distant on the base, which is concave.
  Canal at Bradford.

95

UNDER OOLITE.
ZOOPHITA.
MADREPORA.
SIMPLE, COMPOSED OF ONE STAR.
SPECIES 1.
Madrepora porpites. *Linn*
  a. Bath. *b.* Churchill.

SPECIES 2.
Circular, discoidal; upper side flat, with many radii unequal in length, lower side with two or three circular furrows, closely striated from the center.
  Bath.

AGGREGATED.
SPECIES 3.
Stars oblong, very unequal, irregular, radii unequal in length, diverging in pencils or small bundles.
  a. Dundry. *b.* Bath Hampton.

SPECIES 4.
Stars pentagonal or hexagonal, deeply hollowed, radiate, septa distinct, stars small, regular.
  Dundry. Tucking Mill. Crickley Hill.

SPECIES 5.
Columnar, reticulated.
  Bath Hampton.

A CORAL.
Composed of cylindrical ramose striated branches.
  Bath.

96

PENTACRINUS.
Small, angles acute, very projecting.
  Mitford. Mass.

TESTACEA.
UNIVALVIA.
CONUS.
Conical, spire short, pointed, one sixth of the length; aperture narrow. Length an inch and a half.
  Near Bath. A cast of the inside.

MELANIA.
SPECIES 1.
Small elongated, aperture roundish, oblong; spire set with oblong tubercles.
  Tucking Mill. A cast of the inside.

SPECIES 2.
Casts of a Melania, four or five times as long as the diameter.
  a. Coal Canal. *b.* Tucking Mill. *c.* Near Bath.

SPECIES 3.
Melania striata. *Min. Conch.*
  Caisson.

TROCHUS.
SPECIES 1.
Conical, high; volutions seven or eight, the lower part swelling into a prominent crenated rim, the upper edge of one volution touching the rim of the next; shell reticulato-striated; a few longitudinal wrinkles on the upper part of the volution; base flat, no umbilicus.
  Near Bath.

SPECIES 2.
Conical, high; volutions five or six, even, with a crenulated rim on the lower edge.
  a. Coal Canal. Cast of the inside. *b.* Mitford Inn. Cast of the inside.

97

SPECIES 3.
Conical, volutions angular, increasing quickly, flat in the upper part; base flattish, columella perforate.
  Coal Canal. Cast of the inside.

SPECIES 4.

Conical, sides even, volutions five or six, base convex; columella perforate.

    Coal Canal. Cast of the inside.

SPECIES 5.

Short conical, volutions four, the upper ones roundish, the lower ones angular, with a projecting upper edge.

    a. Coal Canal. Cast of the inside. *b.* Tucking Mill. Cast of the inside.

SPECIES 6.

Conical, volutions few, roundish.

    a. Coal Canal. Cast of the inside. *b.* Tucking Mill. Cast of the inside. *c.* Between Cross Hands and Petty France. Cast of the inside.

SPECIES 7.

Depressed, very short, volutions three or four, opening roundish or ovate, wider than long.

    a. Coal Canal. Cast of the inside. *b.* Tucking Mill. Cast of the inside.

SPECIES 8.

Short conical, depressed, volutions three, angular toward the lower part, base discoidal convex.

    a. Coal Canal. *b.* Near Bath.

SPECIES 9.

Depressed, volutions four or five, with two small rims on the lower part, the upper one nearly smooth, the lower one crenated; shell reticulato-striated; base convex, without an umbilicus; opening roundish.

    Sherborn. Bath.

O

98

PLANORBIS.

Flat above; volutions few, angular, roundish on the inside, widest above.

    a. Tucking Mill. Cast of the inside. *b.* Near Bath. Cast of the inside.

TURRITELLA.
SPECIES 1.

Elongated, volutions numerous, with a deep spiral groove.

    a. Smallcombe Bottom. Cast of the inside. *b.* Coal Canal. Cast of the inside. *c.* Tucking Mill. Cast of the inside.

SPECIES 2

Very much elongated, slender; one distinct spiral projection in the upper part and many spiral striæ: aperture oblong, narrow. In one cast there appear three projections.

    Near Bath.

SPECIES 3.

Turreted with many small costæ, acute on the upper edge.

    a. Churchill. VARIETY With spiral striæ. *b.* Near Bath.

AMPULLARIA.
SPECIES 1.

Very small, subglobose, spire very short, aperture semicircular.

    Crickley Hill. Cast of the inside.

SPECIES 2.

Volutions three or four, the outer one large, spire short, with an obtuse furrow beneath the upper edge of the volutions: aperture semicircular. Length about an inch and a half.

    a. Coal Canal. Cast of the inside. *b.* Bath. Cast of the inside.

SPECIES 3.

Ovate, spire acute, volutions three or more, convex, smooth. Aperture half the length of the shell. Length not more than one inch.

    a. Tucking Mill. Cast of the inside. *b.* Coal Canal. Cast of the inside. *c.* Near Bath. Cast of the inside.

99

TURBO.

Volutions about six, with several muricated lines; one at the upper edge, another projecting about the middle of the volution, and five or more beneath it; many longitudinal striæ crossing from one row to another: mouth rather oblong, base of the columella acute.

    Length from half to one inch. .

    The tubercles are sharp and very regular, the cross striæ are about three to each tubercle,

    a. Tucking Mill. *b.* Near Bath. Sherborn.

TUBULAR IRREGULAR UNIVALVES.
SERPULA.

SPECIES 1.

Cylindrical, twisting; diameter one fourth of an inch.

    Near Bath.

SPECIES 2.

Elongated, conical, twisting at the small end, quadrate with four projecting crenated angles or ridges; aperture round.

    Churchill.

MULTILOCULAR UNIVALVES.
NAUTILUS.
SPECIES 1.

Volutions partly visible in the cast, back round; aperture ovato-lunate, its breadth twice its length; septa many, siphuncle nearest to the outside.

    Depth three fourths of the longest diameter, which in one specimen is six inches and a half.

    Sherborn.

SPECIES 2.

Convex, back flatted, inner volutions concealed in the cast; siphuncle central; mouth lunate, narrow at the extremities; length two thirds of the breadth.

    Longest diameter four inches and a half.

    Sherborn.

SPECIES 3.

Subglobose, umbilicate, back very wide, volutions few; siphuncle central; aperture twice as broad as long.

O 2

100

Shell longitudinally striated; lines of growth distinct.

    a. Sherborn. *b.* Between Sherborn and Yeovil. *c.* Charlton Horethorn.

BELEMNITES.
SPECIES 1.

Slender, with a deep groove from the apex.

    Tucking Mill. Sherborn.

SPECIES 2.

Long, slender, without any groove.

    a. Yeovil. *b.* Wotton Underedge.

AMMONITES.
NO KEEL OR FURROW ON THE BACK.
SPECIES 1.

Ammonites modiolaris.

    Subglobose, inner volutions convex, exposed within a large conical hollow or umbilicus; back wide; aperture semilunate, rounded at the extremities, three times as wide as long.

    Lansdown.

SPECIES 2,

Ammonites calix.

    Discoidal, concave or cup formed, radiated; back wide, slightly convex; radii prominent, rather distant, terminating in tubercles, and forming a deeply indented margin to the cup; tubercles dividing over the back into three transverse ribs: aperture much wider than long.

    The longest diameter in one specimen is five inches.

    The transverse ribs are in number about three to each tubercle, on the outer volutions four, or more. The aperture is a portion of a circular ring bounded by two radiating lines.

    Sherborn.

SPECIES 3.

Subglobose when young, more depressed when old, umbilicate; margin of the umbilicus rounded; very numerous small radii across the back, united on the inner part of the volution, undulating the umbilicus; aperture three times as wide as long, semicircular, the sides rounded into the umbilicus.

    Sherborn.

101

SPECIES 4.

Depressed, convex, volutions seven, roundish on the back, the inner ones half concealed; radii numerous, large on the inner part, smoothed along the middle, very obscurely dividing into four or five, which are obsolete on the middle of the back; aperture oval, one third of the diameter long, inner edges obtuse.

    Longest diameter seven inches.

    Sherborn.

SPECIES 5.

Volutions five or six, inner ones exposed; concave in the middle; radii numerous, sharp, bifurcating over the wide back; aperture about two-fifths of the diameter in length and as wide as long.

    Sherborn. Dundry.

SPECIES 6.

    Ammonites communis. *Min.Conch.*

    Sherborn.

A KEEL ON THE BACK.
SPECIES 7,

Ammonites radiatus.

    Discoidal, very flat, concave in the middle, outer edge acuminated, with a swelling undulated keel; volutions very quickly increasing, leaving a central hollow; surface undulated with broad radiating undulations and many concentrate spreading furrows.

    The shell is very thin, with radiating and concentrate striae. Aperture sagittate, inner angles circular. Septa near together, very much undulated.

    Longest diameter almost eight inches.

    Between Sherborn and Yeovil.

SPECIES 8.

Small, discoidal, concave in the middle; volutions four, half concealed; radii obsolete; aperture oval; keel small, sharp.

    Near Bath.

SPECIES 9.

Ammonites concavus. *Min. Conch.*

    Involute, depressed, keeled, umbilicate; umbilicus a large hemispherical depression; volutions four, depressed near the center; radii numerous, curved, unequal in length, obsolete near the center; keel sharp, entire; aperture acutely triangular, external angle rounded, internal angles obliquely truncate.

102

VARIETY With obtuse radii, and each side of the back bevelled.

    Between Sherborn and Yeovil. Sherborn. Dunkerton.

A KEEL BETWEEN TWO FURROWS ON THE BACK
SPECIES 10.

Volutions four or five, almost half concealed; back wide, with a high keel and a slight furrow on each side; radii obtuse, unequal in length, some of them furcate, curved a little on the edges of the back; aperture oblong, its length two fifths of the diameter.

    Near Bath.

A FURROW ON THE BACK.
SPECIES 11.

Volutions five or six, gibbous, inner ones a third concealed, back rounded; radii many, sharp, bifurcate with a few distant alternating entire ones, acute on the edges of a flat or concave space along the back: aperture obcordate.

    Near Bath.

BIVALVIA.
EQUIVALVED BIVALVES.
MODIOLA.
SPECIES 1.

Coated Muscle. Fistulana *Lam.*

    a. Bath. *b.* Mitford. Incrusted with coral. Tucking Mill.

SPECIES 2.

Very much elongated, with parallel sides, narrowing at the extremities, gibbous diagonally from the beaks; back margin with oblique short furrows; lines of growth distinct: width four or five times the length.

    Churchill.

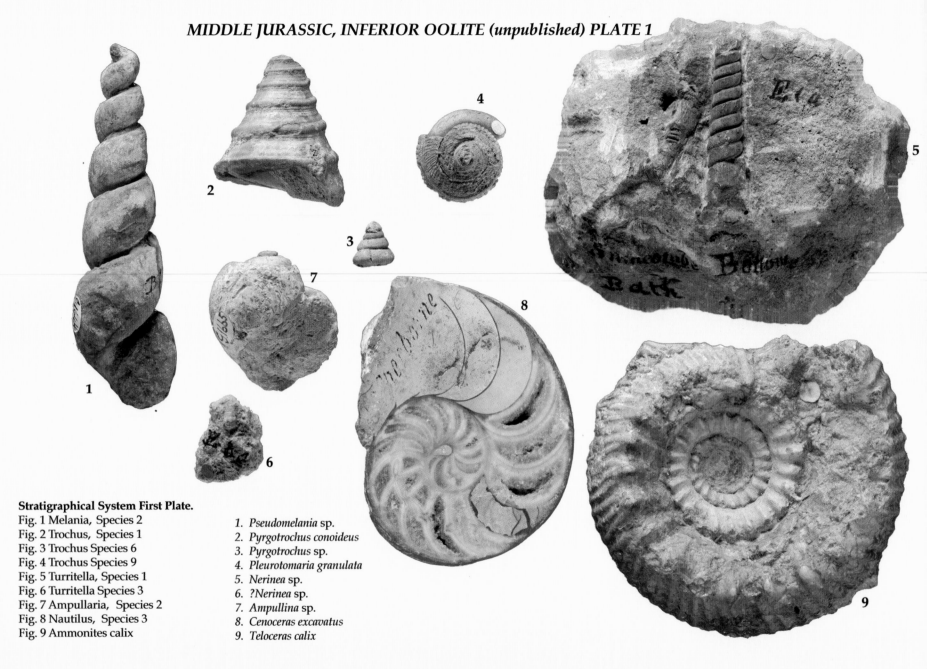

MIDDLE JURASSIC, INFERIOR OOLITE (unpublished) PLATE 1

Stratigraphical System First Plate.
Fig. 1 Melania, Species 2
Fig. 2 Trochus, Species 1
Fig. 3 Trochus Species 6
Fig. 4 Trochus Species 9
Fig. 5 Turritella, Species 1
Fig. 6 Turritella Species 3
Fig. 7 Ampullaria, Species 2
Fig. 8 Nautilus, Species 3
Fig. 9 Ammonites calix

1. *Pseudomelania* sp.
2. *Pyrgotrochus conoideus*
3. *Pyrgotrochus* sp.
4. *Pleurotomaria granulata*
5. *Nerinea* sp.
6. *?Nerinea* sp.
7. *Ampullina* sp.
8. *Cenoceras excavatus*
9. *Teloceras calix*

0 cm 1 2 3 4 5 6 7 8 9 10

PLATE 19

MIDDLE JURASSIC, INFERIOR OOLITE (*unpublished*) PLATE 2

Stratigraphical System Second Plate.
Fig. 1 Madrepora, Species 4
Fig. 2 Trigonia costata
Fig. 3 Trigonia costata
Fig. 4 Astarte ovata
Fig. 5 Pecten equivalvis
Fig. 6 Inoceramus
Fig. 7 Terebratula spinosa
Fig. 8 Clypeus sinuatus

1. Coral colony indet., not found
2. *Trigonia costata*
3. *Trigonia costata*
4. *Astarte elegans*
5. *Variamussium* cf. *pumilum*
6. Fragment of large *Trichites ploti*
7. *Acanthothyris spinosa* *
8. *Clypeus ploti*

0 cm 1 2 3 4 5 6 7 8 9 10

Fossils in silhouette have not been found
* *similar fossil substituted from Smith's collection*

PLATE 20

LOWER JURASSIC, BRIDPORT SAND (*unpublished*) PLATE

1

2

3

Stratigraphical System

1. Belemnites   1. *Belemnopsis* sp.
2. Ammonites Sp. 4.   2. *Pleydellia burtonensis*
3. Modiola   3. *Inoperna sowerbyana*

0 cm   1   2   3   4   5

PLATE 21

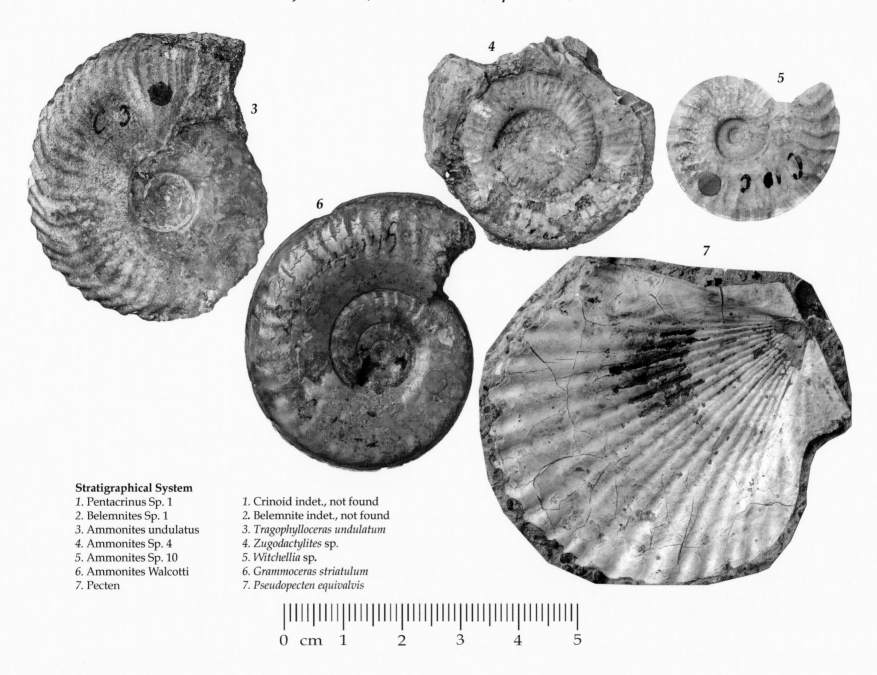

Stratigraphical System
1. Pentacrinus Sp. 1
2. Belemnites Sp. 1
3. Ammonites undulatus
4. Ammonites Sp. 4
5. Ammonites Sp. 10
6. Ammonites Walcotti
7. Pecten

1. Crinoid indet., not found
2. Belemnite indet., not found
3. *Tragophylloceras undulatum*
4. *Zugodactylites* sp.
5. *Witchellia* sp.
6. *Grammoceras striatulum*
7. *Pseudopecten equivalvis*

0 cm 1 2 3 4 5

PLATE 22

William Smith's Stratigraphic Table of Echini was one of four tables that Smith intended to include in Stratigraphical System of Organized Fossils. The other three being Ammonites, Terebratula and Zoophites. In the event only the Table of Echini was published.

In 1860 John Phillips published a Table of the Distribution of Ammonites (see overleaf) which he said was dictated to him by Smith in 1815. No examples of the other two tables have ever been found.

The two tables included in this publication have been redrawn and coloured using similar colours to that used on Smith's 1815 map. At least two versions of the Echini Table are extant. The tables are important in that they show that Smith was aware of the stratigraphic ranges of certain fossils and hence their usefulness in defining particular strata.

The version of the Table of Echini shown here includes corrections and additions (in blue script) which Smith made at some time after publication. Hugh Torrens discovered this later revision, in Smith's own hand, on an annotated copy of A Stratigraphical System of Organized Fossils (W. Smith Volume with DeGolyer Bookplate 551.7 Sm68s at the University of Oklahoma).

ANOCYSTI.

CIDARIS (columns 1–14) — **CLYPEUS** (columns 1–2)

DESCRIPTION AND NAMES

1. Subglobose, circular or pentagonal; rays biporous, depressed; areae swelling; surface rough with small ponts. Cidaris granulara. *Leske.*

2. Depressed, upper side convex; apparently without any rows of eminences: areole prominent.

3. Circular, depressed: shell thin, rather smooth? Cidaris coronalis? *Klein.*

4. Circular, depressed; ten rows of articulated eminences, two rows in each area.

5. Circular, depressed; rays biporous; twenty rows of articulated eminences, which are nearly equal on the base, but unequal above, the two rows in each areola diminishing faster than those in the areae; edges of the mouth turned inwards.

6. Circular, depressed, with thirty rows of miliae, two rows in each areola, and four rows in each area; rays biporous.

7. Rather pentagonal, depressed, top convex; rays biporous, two rows of small eminences in each areola, forming the angles, two rows of miliae in each area; mouth large, its edges turned inwards.

8. Pentangular; depressed, with prominent small mammellae; two contiguous rows in each areola, forming the angles; four converging in each area. two middle rows short and only on the side; rough with small points encircling the mammellae; rays oblique triporous.

9. Pentangular, depressed with thirty rows of sharp mammellae, which are almost equal on the sides; the row on each side of the areae smaller than the others; rays obliquely triporous; mouth ten sided, with a large notch at each angle.

10. Circular, rather depressed, with ten rows of contiguous mammellae, (near the vent the first mammellae in the rows are encircled), two rows in each area, separated by curvilinear rows of small eminences partially surrounding the mammellae; areole with minute points encircling two rows of eminences; mouth large, decagonal, with a deep notch at every areole; mammellae punctated, articulated.

11. Globose or conical; base flattish; ten rows of prominent mammellae, two rows in each area, separated by two rows of small eminences, each side of the area bordered by a row of small distinct eminences; rays subflexous, biporous, areola narrow edged by two rows of eminences enlarged on the margin, widening from the vent downwards to the margin; vent small; mammellae not encircled by a ring of points, the small globose top of each punctated, and surrounded by an articulated margin

12. Rather high; ten rows of mammellae, two rows in each area, five mammellae in a row: areole narrow, flexeous; apertures large, mammellae punctated at top, articulated.

13. Subglobose, with ten rows of large mammellae, each a little sunk and surrounded by a ring of small points; two rows in each area, separated by numerous small points; rays double, biporous, subflexeous enclosing two rows of small points; many distinct points on each side of the area; apertures large. Thesmall globose top of each mammellae is punctated, and surrounded by an articulated margin.

14. Subglobose, with ten rows of distant mammellae surrounded by seven eminences; two rows in each area; areole narrow, with two rows of small eminences; mouth not very large. Mammellae punctated at top, articulated

CLYPEUS

1. Clypeus sinuatus *Leske.* Circular, depressed, convex above, base rather concave, with five diverging furrows; rays ten, in five pairs, approaching each other on the circumference, transversely striated, with a line of pores on their margin: one of the area divided by a sharp furrow from the vertex; mouth small, pentagonal; shell covered by small eminences in circular depressions

2. Oblong subquandrangular; base concave in the middle; mouth small, five angled; upper side convex; with a long deep furrow on one side from the apex to the margin; rays ten biporous lines in five pairs covered with small granulae, most numerous on the base.

Strata containing Echini	No. of the Stratum	1	2	3	4	5	6	7	8	9	10	11	12	13	14	C1	C2
Chalk	5			*	*	*											
Green Sand	6	*				*	*	*					*		*		
Coral Rag and Pisolite	12		*								*	*	*		*		*
Cornbrash	16										*						*
Clay over the upper Oolite	19							*			*						*
Upper Oolite	20																*
Fuller's Earth and Rock	21																
Under Oolite	22							*	*							*	*

Yorkshire Lias

names wanting

Circular 1-10

Globose

TABLE 2 (AND FACING PAGE)

TABLE OF ECHINI.

PLEUROCYSTI							CATOCYSTI												
SPATANGUS							CONULUS					GALEA							
RAYS IN FURROWS					RAYS NOT IN FURROWS														
Oblong, cordate, rather high, margin rounded; dorsal furrow narrow, ray contained in it not distinct; dorsal ridge rising higher than the apex: covered in granula, particularly on the middle of the base.	Cordate, depressed, dorsal furrow narrow large, covered with granula, particularly on middle of the base	Cordate, margin rounded, dorsal furrow large, ridge high; height of the shell two thirds of the length.	High, base flattish; rays short; dorsal furrow wide, not deep, ridge rising very high; vent as high as the apex; length one third of an inch, height and breadth one fourth.	Long-cordate, the top rounded, with a short groove to the mouth; rays obsolete	Cordate, or roundish, base flat, top convex or rather flattened, dorsal furrow short; rays ten biporous lines diverging in pairs: vent oblong. Much resembles (if not the same) Spatangus subglobosus, Leske.	Echinites lapis cancri Leske. — Obtusely ovate, gibbose, vertex not central, with four pores; rays subpetaloidal, biporous, distinct almost half the height from the vertex, then suddenly lost, appearing again on the base in a quinque-petaloidal star round the mouth; vent at the widest end over a small furrow, round, mouth opposite the vertex, small pentagonal: base flattish.	Echin. alhogalerus. Leske. — Nearly circular, conical, vertex perforated by five holes: rays ten, biporous, in five pairs; mouth small, round, vent oblong; shell covered in small eminences; base flate.	Echin. vulgaris. Leske — Nearly circular, convex or subconical, rays ten, biporous, in five pairs; mouth small; base flattish, rather undulated.	Pentagonal, depressed, rays of pores ten, biporous, flexuous, depressed, the areæ swelling into rounded angles; mouth and vent rather large.	Convexo-conical, circular, base concave in the middle: rays ten,closely biporous, diverging in five pairs, the two rays near together separated by a flat rising, mouth ten sided, vent oval.	Convex, depressed, nearly circular, covered with small prominences particularly on the base of the shell, rays ten biporous lines diverging in ten pairs; the pores very close on the upper part, more distant on the base, which is concave in the middle; aperture large, vent oval	Echin. ovatus. Leske. — Ovate, shell distinctly assulated; rays ten, biporous, in five pairs, the pores opposite closest and most apparent near the vertex; base flat, rising in the middle, with many scattered granula and intermediate minute puncta; vent at the narrow end, roundish; mouth transverse, with several granula near it.	Echin. pustulosus. Leske — Ovate, narrowing at one end; rays pustulose, continuing from the vertex to the mouth, each pustula concealing top pores.	Subelliptical, round topped, not very pointed at the end; rays biporous on the top, pustulose on the base; pustule smaller than in Species 2.	Oval, very pointed at one end, rounded at the nother; ray biporous one third of the height downwards from the apex, distinct on the base; ridge sharp; apex excentric towards the broad end	Oval, pointed at one end, high, rays biporous two thirds of the height downwards from the apex; areæ flattened.	High with flattish sides, top rounded or flattened, rays biporous downwards to the margin; height almost equal to the length.	Three fourths elliptical, the base, forming the section, rounded, contracted	Broad ovate, one end pointed; margin of the base undulated beneath with fourteen projections, the areolae form five, the ridge one, and there are other areæ; a large depression on the upper part of the shell behind the apex.
1	2	3	4	5	6		1	2	3	4	5	1	2	3	4	5	6	7	8
*	*	*		*	*		*	*	*			*	*	*	*	*	*	*	*
		*	*		*	*				*									
											*								
											*								

The above Colours represent on my Maps and Sections courses and extent of the Strata containing Echini.

Ovate | Chordate | Circular | Pentagonal | Circular | all these oval or ovate

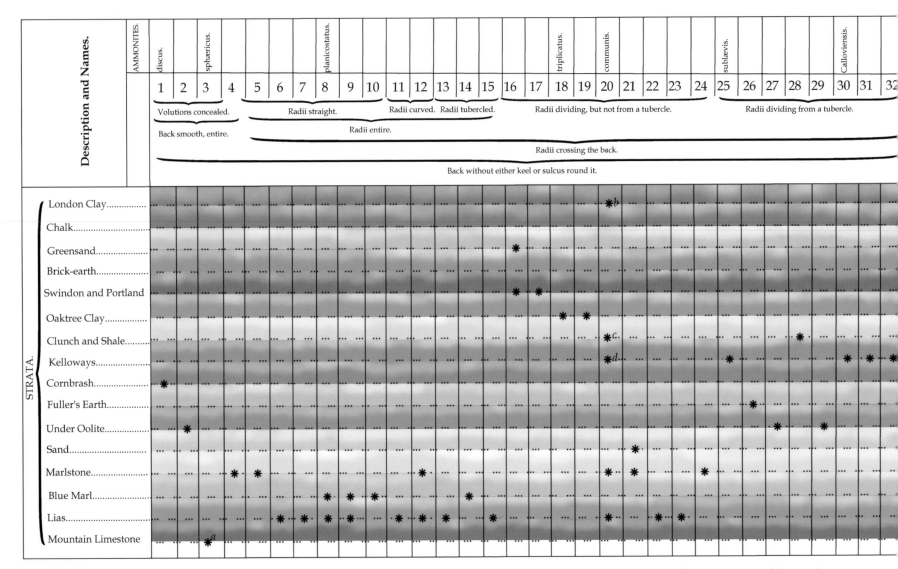

NOTE. (1) The Table was drawn up previously to the publication, in 1817, of the 'Stratigraphical Sustem of Organized Fossils', which contains a few more names of Ammonites - some proposed by Smith, as A. calix, which is now called A. Blagdeni. a, is Goniatites sphæricus.   b, was marked as a doubtful occurrence; it was probably a drifted specimen.   c, was erroneously marked in this deposit ; it was from the Upper Lias of Whitby.   d, a related species   e, erroneously marked in this deposit ; it was from the Upper Lias of Whitby.

(2) In the original, each species is described, except those to which names could not be affixed from Sowerby's ' Mineral Conchology', then in progress.

TABLE 3 (AND FACING PAGE)

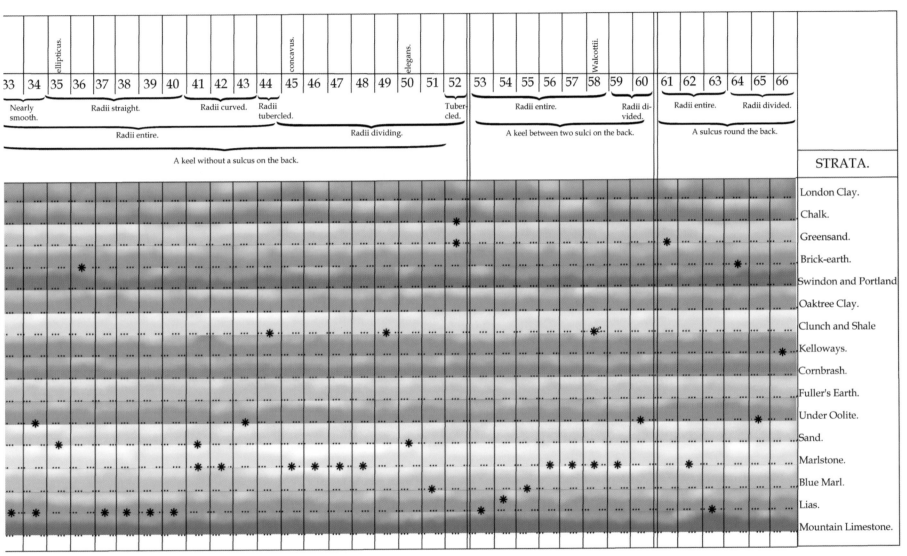

| | | | | | | | | | | | | | | | | | | | | | | | | | | | | | | | | | | STRATA. |
|33|34|35|36|37|38|39|40|41|42|43|44|45|46|47|48|49|50|51|52|53|54|55|56|57|58|59|60|61|62|63|64|65|66| |

Column annotations (above): ellipticus. (35), concavus. (45), elegans. (50), Walcottii. (58)

Groupings:
- Nearly smooth. (33–34)
- Radii straight. (35–40)
- Radii curved. (41–43)
- Radii tubercled. (44)
- Tubercled. (52)
- Radii entire. (33–44 / 53–58)
- Radii dividing. (45–52)
- Radii divided. (59–60 / 64–66)
- A keel without a sulcus on the back. (33–52)
- A keel between two sulci on the back. (53–60)
- A sulcus round the back. (61–66)

STRATA:
London Clay.
Chalk.
Greensand.
Brick-earth.
Swindon and Portland
Oaktree Clay.
Clunch and Shale
Kelloways.
Cornbrash.
Fuller's Earth.
Under Oolite.
Sand.
Marlstone.
Blue Marl.
Lias.
Mountain Limestone.

[Redrawn from *Quart. Journ. Geol. Soc.* vol. xvi., *to face page* xli.]

SPECIES 3.

Very large, twice as broad as long.

Oldford near Frome. Cast of the inside

SPECIES 4.

Modiola. *Cornbrash.* Churchill. Northwest of Northampton.

SPECIES 5.

Triangular, depressed, gibbous diagonally from the beaks; posterior side small, anterior side expanded, straight, diagonal; back and front straight; beaks small, close to the posterior end; greatest width almost three inches; greatest length, at the anterior end, above half the width.

Dundry.

UNIO.
SPECIES 1.

Subtriangular, broader than long, depressed, transversely striated; front margin straightish; an inflection on one side.

Between Sherborn and Yeovil.

SPECIES 2.

Wider than long, depressed, posterior side elliptical, arched round to the beaks, anterior side shorter, hollowed under the beaks.

Churchill.

SPECIES 3.

Unio Species 3. *Fuller's Earth Rock.*

Northwest of Northampton.

ARCA.

Wider than long, very gibbous, straightish at the edges, with sharp transverse lines of growth, and a few longitudinal striæ on the sides; beaks distant; shell thick.

Sherborn. Dundry. A very large cast of the inside.

TRIGONIA.
SPECIES 1.

Trigonia costata. Park. *Min. Conch.*

Triangular, with transverse smooth ribs; anterior side marked with many small and three large prominent longitudinal crenulated ridges.

Posterior angle very obtuse; anterior side large; the transverse ribs terminate before the first longitudinal ridge bounding the anterior side.

104

a. Cotswold Hills. Cast of the inside. b. Between Cross Hands and Petty France. Cast of the inside. c. Cross Hands. Cast of the inside. d. Mitford. Cast of the inside. e. Coal Canal. Cast of the inside. f. Tucking Mill. Little Sodbury.

SPECIES 2.

Cast of the inside; depressed, wider than long.

a. Crickley Hill. b. Nailsworth.

INSIDE CASTS OF BIVALVES,
WITH TWO MUSCULAR IMPRESSIONS IN EACH VALVE.
SPECIES 1.

Rhomboidal, gibbous in the middle, flattish at the sides; muscular impressions large, convex in the cast, furrowed; beaks of the cast distant. Length two inches or more.

a. Bath. b. Mells

SPECIES 2.

Circular, depressed, with projecting beaks; margin thin; muscular impressions convex in the cast, furrowed; beaks of the cast distant.

Bath.

CARDIUM.

Cardium. *Cornbrash.*

a. Writhligton. b. Between Sherborn and Yeovil c. Chipping Norton. d. Churchill. e. Dundry. Northwest of Northampton.

MACTRA
SPECIES 1.

Mactra, Species 2. *Fuller's Earth Rock.*

Transversely elongated, arched, depressed, covered with longitudinal furrows; posterior side rounded, anterior side flattened; a little gaping, not expanded; breadth twice the length, and three times the depth.

105

The longitudinal furrows are decussated by distant broad transverse undulations.

a. Crewkerne. b. Churchill.

SPECIES 2.

Mactra gibbosa. *Min. Conch.*

Gibbose, anterior side much wider than the posterior, recurved, truncated, gaping: Length and depth about equal, breadth equal to twice the length; posterior side rounding.

a. Tucking Mill. A very large specimen, six inches wide. b. Mitford.

SPECIES 3.

Large, squarish, subequilateral, gibbous, with contiguous prominent beaks; nearly straight at the edges, transversely undulated. Length three fourths of the breadth, depth two thirds of the breadth, which is about three inches.

Gloucestershire.

ASTARTE.

Astarte ovata. *Oaktree Clay.*

Transversely oblong, depressed, anterior side lengthened, transversely striated; lunette elliptical; margin crenulated within; shell thick; beak acute, solid: a small pit beneath the posterior slope of the hinge.

a. Between Sherborn and Yeovil. b. Coal Canal. Cast of the inside. c. Tucking Mill. Cast of the inside. d. Bath. Cast of the inside. e. Fulbrook. Cast of the inside. f. Between Cross Hands and Petty France. Cast of the inside. Mitford Inn. Cast of the inside. Northwest of Northampton. A very small Cast of the inside.

MYA.

Mya, Species 1. *Fuller's Earth Rock.*

Transverse, ovate, beaks close to the posterior side; anterior side acute; transversely furrowed.

Dundry.

INEQUIVALVED BIVALVES.
PLAGIOSTOMA.

A small variety of Plagiostoma gigantea. *Min. Conch.* with very distinct longitudinal striæ.

Tucking Mill.

P

106

LIMA.
SPECIES 1.

Lima gibbosa. *Min. Conch.*

Elongated, gibbose, smooth, longitudinally plicated in the middle; ears undefined; nearly twice as long as wide. About eighteen small sharp plaits in the middle.

Churchill.

SPECIES 2.

Trigonal, oblique, with short ears; one side straightish and lengthened, the other rounded, covered with many longitudinal sharp plaits.

Churchill.

CRENATULA.

Flat, or much depressed, oblong, sides subparallel, widest near the beaks, which are at one end of the hinge line.

Dundry

OSTREA.
SPECIES 1.

Ostrea rugosa. Species 2. *Fuller's Earth Rock.*

a. Tucking Mill. b. Between Sherborn and Yeovil. This is smaller, more regular and thinner.

SPECIES 2.

Oblong, straight, sides subparallel; depressed; lower valve with transverse imbricated waves; upper valve flat, transversely furrowed.

Chipping Norton. Northwest of Northampton.

SPECIES 3.

Ostrea acuminata. *Min. Conch.*

Churchill.

SPECIES 4.

Small, oblong, lobate.

Betwen Cross Hands and Petty France. Much distorted.

107

AVICULA.
SPECIES 1.

Avicula costata. VARIETY, with many ribs.

a. Between Cross Hands and Petty France. b. Tucking Mill.

SPECIES 2.

Similar to avicula costata, but the ribs are tuberculated.

Between Sherborn and Yeovil.

PECTEN.
SPECIES 1.

Pecten equivalvis. *Min. Conch.*

Lenticular, with rounded diverging ribs and many acute concentric striæ; valves equally convex, the lower one smoothest; ears equal.

a. Ilmington. b. Dursley. Dowdswell Hill. Sherborn.

SPECIES 2

Small, flattish, smooth.

Churchill.

SPECIES 3.

Pecten fibrosus. *Min. Conch.*

Churchill.

INOCERAMUS.

Fibrous Shell.

Between Cross Hands and Petty France. Monkton Combe. Tucking Mill. Bath.

P2

108

TEREBRATULA.
NOT PLICATED.

numerous

SPECIES 1.

Terebratula intermedia? *Min. Conch.*

a Batheaston. b. Near Lansdown. c. Tucking Mill. d. Between Sherborn and Yeovil. e. Churchill.

f Chipping Norton. g. Fulbrook.

SPECIES 2.

Terebratula ornithocephala. *Min. Conch.*

VARIETY. The edges flattened.

Tucking Mill. Sherborn.

PLICATED.
SPECIES 3.

Terebratula obsoleta ? Species 3. *Clay over the upper Oolite.*

a. Between Cross Hands and Petty France. b. Tucking Mill. c. Churchill. d. Chipping Norton. e. Fulbrook.

SPECIES 4.

Terebratula spinosa.

Circular, convex, with many roundish plaits set with long slender spines in quincuncial order; middle of the front elevated in a large wave rounding into the sides; beak small, incurved; upper valve most convex.

a. Bath. b. Tucking Mill. Chipping Norton. Limpley Stoke

109

ECHINI.
ANOCYSTI.
CIDARIS.
SPECIES 1.

Cidaris, Species 1. *Clay over the upper oolite.*

Tucking Mill.

SPECIES 2.

Pentangular, depressed, with projecting rather distant small mammellæ; two contiguous rows in each areola, and four converging rows in each area; the two middle rows short and only on the side or widest part of the area; rough with small points encircling the mammellæ; rays obliquely triporous.

The areolæ form the angles of the pentagon. The two longer rows of mammellæ in each area are parallel to the rays and converge to the aperture, and the space between them on the side is occupied by two shorter converging rows.

Tucking Mill.

SPECIES 3.

Cidaris, Species 3. *Coral Rag and Pisolite.*
Tucking Mill.

CLYPEUS.
SPECIES 1.

Clypeus sinuatus. *Leske.*
Circular, depressed, convex above, base rather concave, with five diverging furrows; rays ten, in five pairs, approaching each other on the circumference, transversely striated with a line of pores on their margin; one of the areæ divided by a deep sharp furrow from the vertex; mouth small, pentagonal; shell covered by small eminences in circular depressions.
a. Monkton Combe. *b.* Stunsfield. *c.* Chipping Norton. *d.* Churchill. *e.* Fulbrook. *f.* Near Naunton. *g.* Stow on the Wold. Northwest of Northampton.

110

SPECIES 2.

Clypeus. *Coral Rag and Pisolite.*
Churchill.

CATOCYSTI.
CONULUS.

Conulus. *Fuller's Earth Rock.*
Tucking Mill.

Reference to the figures in the Plates of this Stratum, which will be given in "Strata identified by Organized Fossils," not having been regularly inserted, it is necessary to observe that the following species will be figured.

First Plate

Melania,	Species 2 . . .	Fig.1
Trochus,	Species 1	2
	Species 6	3
	Species 9	4
Turritella,	Species 1	5
	Species 3	6
Ampullaria,	Species 2	7
Nautilus,	Species 3	8
Ammonites calix	. . . .	9

Second Plate

Madrepora, Species 4	Fig. 1
Trigonia costata	2-3
Astarte ovata	4
Pecten equivalvis	5
Inoceramus	6
Terebratula spinosa.	7
Clypeus sinuatus	8

111
SAND AND SANDSTONE.
TESTACEA.
UNIVALVIA.
MULTILOCULAR UNIVALVES.
BELEMNITES.

Fig. 1, Sand and Sandstone Plate.
Tapering, apex of the alveolus central. Diameter two thirds of an inch.
Tucking Mill.

AMMONITES.
NO KEEL OR FURROW ON THE BACK.
SPECIES 1.

Ammonites, Species 4. *Marlstone*
Volutions about four, thick, the inner ones not much concealed, round on the back; radii very numerous, bifurcating at the middle; aperture round, lunate on the inner side.
Enstone.

A KEEL ON THE BACK
SPECIES 2.

Ammonites ellipticus? *Min. Conch.*
Yeovil.

SPECIES 3.

Ammonites, Species 8. *Marlstone.*

In this specimen, the radii are not so much bent in the middle as those in the marlstone.
a. Liliput. *b.* Tucking Mill.

SPECIES 4.

Fig. 2, Sand and Sandstone Plate.
Much depressed, volutions few, half exposed, quickly increasing, thin at the outer edge; radii small, numerous, twice rather obtusely curved, unequal in length uniting by pairs or more into short prominences

----

112

on the inner part: keel sharp; aperture two fifths of the longest diameter.
Yeovil.

BIVALVIA.
EQUIVALVED BIVALVES.
MODIOLA.

Fig. 3, Sand and Sandstone Plate.
Very much elongated with nearly parallel sides, acuminated at the extremities, gibbous diagonally from the beaks; posterior side, or hinge side, furrowed; lines of growth distinct, parallel to the margin. Length four or five times the breadth. The furrows on the back margin are oblique, short, and do not reach to the gibbous part.
Top of Frocester Hill.

MYA.

Mya, Species 1. *Fuller's Earth Rock.*
Enstone.

INEQUIVALVED BIVALVES.
AVICULA.

Avicula costata.
Enstone.

TEREBRATULA.

Terebratula ornithocephala. *Min. Conch.*
Enstone. A curious variety with flattened edges, similar to those from Tucking Mill and Sherborn in the under oolite.

113
MARLSTONE.
ZOOPHITA.
MADREPORA.

SPECIES 1.

Madrepora porpites. *Linn*
Tucking Mill.

PENTACRINUS.

SPECIES 1. ?

Fig.1 Marlstone Plate.
Vertebræ thin, acute, in the middle with five very prominent angles; vertebral column excavated at the meeting of the vertebræ between the prominent angles.
Churchill. Stone Farm, Yeovil. Kennet and Avon Canal.

SPECIES 2.

Vertebræ pentagonal, sides flat
Wotton under Edge.

TESTACEA.
UNIVALVIA.
HELIX.

Helix *Coral Rag and Pisolite.*
Wotton under Edge.

MULTILOCULAR UNIVALVES.
BELEMNITES.
SPECIES 1.

Large, squarish, with two obtuse furrows very near the apex.
Penard Hill.

R

114

An Alveolus of a large belemnite; very acutely conical, septa distant from each other one sixth of their diameter.
Foot of Frocester Hill.

Alveolus of a large belemnite; long, conical, septa numerous, distant from each other one seventh of their diameter.
Tucking Mill.
Long slender.
Fig. 2, Marlstone Plate.
a. Yeovil. *b.* Churchill. *c.* Tucking Mill. *d.* Enstone

NAUTILUS.

A depressed umbilicated Nautilus, resembling Nautilus lineatus, *Min. Conch.*is found in this stratum, with crystallized Carbonate of Lime in the chambers; the shell is striated longitudinally and appears to be very thin; the situation of the siphuncle has not been observed in the specimen.
Tucking Mill.

AMMONITES.
NO KEEL OR FURROW ON THE BACK.
SPECIES 1.

Depressed, volutions four or five, the back smooth, nearly flat, thicker than the other parts of the volution; radii distant, acute on the outer margin; aperture quadrangular, widest in the outer part.
Coal Canal.

SPECIES 2.

Depressed, volutions five or more, the inner ones more than a fourth concealed with many obtuse distant radii smoothed over the back; aperture elliptical, indented, length a fourth of the diameter. The radii are most prominent on the middle of the volution.
Coal Canal.

SPECIES 3.

Ammonites undulatus.
Fig. 3, Marlstone Plate.

115

Depressed, radii obtuse, mostly equal in length, twice curved, undulating the back; volutions four or more, depressed along the middle, the inner ones three fourths concealed: aperture very oblong, inner edges truncated.
The radii are obscure towards the center, twice curved, and on the back incline toward the aperture, and are so prominent as to give it the appearance of being folded or plaited. In some specimens the radii seem closer and more numerous on the outer volutions than on the inner.
Coal Canal.

SPECIES 4

Fig. 4, Marlstone Plate.
Volutions about four, thick, the inner ones not much concealed, round on the back; radii very numerous, bifurcating at the middle; aperture round, lunate on the inner side. Diameter three fourths of an inch to two inches and a half.
a. Coal Canal. *b.* Tucking Mill. *c.* Yeovil. *d.* Churchill.

SPECIES 5.

Ammonites communis. *Min. Conch.*
This shell varies much. These specimens are of the variety with an oblong aperture.
a. Near Bath. *b.* Tucking Mill. *c.* Coal Canal. *d.* Dundry.

SPECIES 6.

Large, volutions three, very quickly diminishing in depth and diameter, not at all concealed; radii, numerous irregular undulations, most distinct on the back, which is round; opening oval, the inner angles blunt, two fifths of the longest diameter. Diameter seven inches and a half.
Yeovil.

A KEEL ON THE BACK
SPECIES 7.

Volutions few quickly increasing, the inner ones more than half exposed, blunt: at the back, inner edges truncate and smooth; radii very numerous, most prominent on the outer part of the volution twice curved, the first bend in a slight spiral depression near the middle; keel small, acute; aperture narrow, more than two fifths as long as the diameter.
Longest diameter six inches.

R2

This is probably a different species from Ammonites elegans, *Min. Conch.* to which in many respects, it is very similar; the most essential distinctions are the bluntness or width of the back, and the greater exposure of the inner volutions.

a. Yeovil. *b.* Tucking Mill.

SPECIES 8.

Volutions few, the inner ones two fifths concealed, obtuse at the back, truncate at the inner angles; radii large, obscure on the inner half of the volution, conspicuous on the outer half, twice curved, the first bend in a spiral depression near the middle; aperture narrow, with subparallel sides, inner angles truncate. Diameter five inches.

This species differs from the preceding in the lesser number and greater size of its radii; in other respects perfectly similar.

a Stone Farm, Yeovil. *b* Penard Hill.

SPECIES 9.

Ammonites concavus. *Min. Conch.*

Coal Canal.

SPECIES 10.

Fig. 5, Marlstone Plate.

Depressed, volutions three or four, the inner ones almost half concealed; radii furcating from the inner part, bent in the middle, curved toward the keel in the outer part; back flattish, keel small acute: aperture narrow, inner angles truncate. Diameter between one and two inches.

a Coal Canal. *b.* Tucking Mill. *c.* Penard Hill. Dundry. Frocester Hill. Bathhampton, foot of inclined plane.

SPECIES 11.

Depressed, volutions four or five, convex, the inner ones a third concealed; radii many, obtuse, curving, unequal in length; septa rather distant, equal in number to the entire radii; aperture oval, a third as long as the diameter, without any truncation on the inner angles. Diameter about two inches.

Glastonbury.

A KEEL BETWEEN TWO FURROWS ON THE BACK.
SPECIES 12.

Volutions four, gibbous, almost wholly exposed; radii many, a little curved, undulating the inner margin; aperture squarish, with rounded angles.

Coal Canal.

SPECIES 13

Ammonites Walcotii. *Min. Conch.*

Fig. 6, Marlstone Plate.

Involute, depressed; volutions four, three fourths exposed. with a concentrate furrow; lunate undulations over half the sides; back with a keel between two furrows; aperture oblong, one third of the diameter long .

Each volution divided into two parts by an obtuse furrow; inner half nearly smooth.

Coal Canal. Glastonbury. Whitby

A FURROW ON THE BACK.
SPECIES 14.

Much depressed, radii entire, sharp, prominent and opposite on the outer margins; opening oblong, narrow, sides almost parallel, back concave along the middle.

Near Bath.

BIVALVIA.
INEQUIVALVED BIVALVES.
OSTREA.

Gryphea, Species 1. Lias Shd be Lias
Northeast of Newark.

PECTEN.

Fig. 7, Marlstone Plate.

Circular, depressed with many longitudinal obtuse ribs.
Kennet and Avon Canal. A mass. ? Lias Northeast of Newark. Do

---

TEREBRATULA.

Terebratula obsoleta. *Min.Conch.*

a. Churchill. *b.* Wotton under Edge.

The organized Fossils in the under part of the rock differ very materially from those in the upper, but these distinctions, with others relating to several of the preceding Strata, will be given in the subsequent part of the work.

OBSERVATIONS ON ECHINI.
CLASSICAL CHARACTERS.

Roundish, covered with a bony crust, more like a crustacean than a testaceous animal, with moveable spines, and two apertures, a mouth always on the base of the shell, and a vent variable in its position.

From the different situations of the vent the class is susceptible of three principal divisions:—*Anocysti, Pleurocysti, Catocysti.*

1. ANOCYSTI.

Mouth on the base of the shell; vent vertical.

Under this division are comprised two genera, Cidaris, and Clypeus.

CIDARIS.

GEN. CHAR.—Circular or ovate, with porous rays, diverging equally on all sides, from the vent to the mouth: vent vertical; central; mouth beneath, central.

CLYPEUS.

GEN. CHAR.—Circular, or suboval, irregular, with porous or striated rays.

2. PLEUROCYSTI.

Mouth on the base of the shell; vent on the side.

SPATANGUS.

GEN. CHAR.—Cordate or heart-shaped, with porous rays, and a groove or channel from the vertex to one end; mouth beneath, near the broad end, vent at the narrow end above the margin of the base.

GEN. CHAR.—Oblong, with ten biporous rays in five pairs; vent at one end, above the margin of the base; mouth beneath, almost central.

Echinites lapis cancri is of this Genus.

3. CATOCYSTI.

Both apertures on the base of the shell.

CONULUS.

GEN. CHAR.—Nearly circular, with porous lines from the vertex to the mouth: mouth beneath, central; vent on the circumference of the base.

GALEA.

GEN. CHAR.—Ovate, with porous rays from the vertex to the mouth, near the broadest end of the base; vent at the narrow end of the base.

The mouth of the Echinus is always in the base of the shell.

Central in Cidaris.

Nearly central in Clypeus.

Nearest to one end in Spatangus.

Excentric in Echinites lapis cancri.

Central in Conulus.

About one sixth of the length from the rounded end in Galea.

Nearly all the species of Echini agree in having ten rays of pores proceeding in five pairs from the vertex of the shell toward the mouth in the base, although they do not in all continue to the mouth (as in Scutum and other Genera).

The rays differ much in the number and arrangement of the pores; in the greater proportion of species, however, the rays are actually double, or each composed of two lines of pores.

The rays in Clypeus sinuatus are of a peculiar construction; they are transversely striated, with a line of pores on the side.

In Scutum, and some other recent genera, the rays make a floriform figure on the surface.

Many species of fossil mammellated Echini have articulating edges surrounding the small spherical tops of the mammellæ, which are generally punctated.

The Stratigraphical Table exhibits many instances of repetition of the same species in more than one stratum, and a little attention evinces the accuracy of an observation previously made, that *"similar strata contain similar fossils;"* Clypeus,. No.2., (clunicularis Llwyd), is a common instance. This species is repeated in five different strata, all of them calcareous, for

the fossils in the Clay over the upper Oolite lie within a small depth of the rock, and are generally filled with stony matter.

Yet although the same species is repeated in these different strata, a considerable difference in appearance may be traced between specimens from the Pisolite and others from the Combrash and Oolites. These last are thinner at the edge, with a more undulated base and flatter sides, particularly that side containing the groove.

The variation in the form of fossils, according to the nature of the stratum, is so remarkable, that in almost all the species which occur in different strata sufficient distinction may be perceived in the general appearance, to ascertain from what stratum they were collected.

Thus, where artificial specific differences fail, the natural features of relationship are sufficient for their identification.

Powerful glasses are required to discover the beautiful organization of petrified Echini, the delicate minutia of which is the more remarkable as the shells are now entirely converted into opaque crystals of Carbonate of Lime. The rhomboidal fracture of this carbonate of lime has long been considered characteristic of these shells and of their spines, and is common to no other organized fossils, except the Encrini.

Spines of Echini are generally more rare than the shells, but are so abundant in the Coral Rag as to be considered one of its best identifications.

The little fossil Clypeus being not only the common inhabitant of three rocks which have a general resemblance, but peculiar to the oolitic part of two of them, shows most distinctly the necessity and great utility of attending to their localities and to their peculiar sites in each stratum.

The stratigraphical table of fossil Echini comprises all the species enumerated in this work, and contains enough for the general purpose of identifying the British Strata.

By the table it appears that Echini are not common to more than eight Strata, Chalk, Green Sand, Coral Rag and Pisolite, Cornbrash, Clay over the Upper Oolite, Upper Oolite, Fuller's Earth Rock (rare), and Under Oolite.

Thence also it appears they are most abundant in the Chalk and in the Green Sand beneath it; the Genus Galea, containing eight species, is entirely peculiar to the Chalk.

The order Pleurocysti is found only in the Chalk and Green Sand, most of the species are found in the Chalk: three out of the five species of Conulus are found in the Chalk.

Clypeus sinuatus is characteristic of the Under Oolite, and occurs at many places in its course; a similar species is found rarely in the Coral Rag and Pisolite, but it is more convex, and larger.

STRATIGRAPHICAL SYSTEM OF ORGANIZED FOSSILS

PART II
CONTENTS.

———— ◆ ————

This section has been transcribed by the Editor from MS WS/F/1/3 in the William Smith Archive at the Oxford University Museum of Natural History. The MS consists of 48 foolscap folio pages of handwritten notes describing fossils from the:

BLUE MARL,

LIAS,

REDLAND LIMESTONE

MOUNTAIN LIMESTONE.

BLUE MARL.
[BM2]
ZOOPHITA.
Pentacrinus.

Rather large and hollowed between the angles which are rounded, vertebræ equal, thin.
Cheltenham – 1, small column.

[BM3]
TESTACEA.
UNIVALVIA.
MULTILOCULAR UNIVALVES.

A. Belemnites.
SPECIES 1.
Long large obtusely flattened ['on the' struck through] and four angled swelling at base terminating abruptly in the apex,[…] point of the Alveolus not central.
a.Yeovil – 2 b.Mudford -1.

SPECIES 2.
Very slender, long, depressed, four angled, pointed end flattened.
Mudford – 4

[BM4]
B. Ammonites.
No Keel or Sulcus on the Front.
SPECIES 1.
Ammonites planicosta, *Min. Conch.*
Marston Magna – 10

SPECIES 2.
Volutions from ['the diameter' struck through] three fourths of an inch diameter, not concealed fast increasing Radii sharpish, eighteen to twenty in a volution, on the front flattened and sharply curved toward the mouth, entire mouth oval widest near the front.
John St Bath – 1

SPECIES 3.
Volutions five in rather more than half inch diameter, not at all concealed, front broad. Radii numerous entire on the back, front nearly nearly obsolete and curved <u>from</u> the mouth; opening four angled, angles rounded, rather more than one fifth of the diameter.
a. Aston Somerville – 3 b. Cheltenham – 1

SPECIES 4.
Volutions four in three quarters of an inch diameter, regular widest at front, sides radiate. Radii many, rising into short tubercles on the margin of front. Front ['radii' struck through] striated opening, four angled, widest in front.
a. Cheltenham – 1 b. Aston Somerville – 1

[BM5]
A Keel on the Front.
SPECIES 5.
Very depressed, volutions four, the inner ones nearly half concealed, keel small. Radii curved dividing, and ending obsolete on the front, slight, obtuse. Opening oblong, deeply indented.
Aston Somerville – 1

A Keel between two Furrows.
Depressed volutions four or five, inner ones a third concealed. Keel obtuse, radii twenty to twenty four in volution, flattened, obtuse on the front, strong on the sides. Opening oblong evident on the front, narrow inwards; more than three-eighths of the diameter which is one to three inches.
Marston Magna -2

[BM6]
BIVALVIA.
EQUIVALVED BIVALVES.
C. Cardium.
SPECIES 1.
Cardium ( ) of the Fullers Earth Rock [Plate?]
Mudford -1

D. Tellina
SPECIES 1.
Oval transverse, very depressed, angled on one side, diagonally linear and with a fold. Front straightish. Beaks small. Lines of growth ? close, distinct, numerous a few longitudinal striæ. Length two thirds of the breadth, thickness a sixth of the breadth. Breadth one to two inches.
a. Mudford -5 b. South of Bedminster Down -2

INEQUIVALVED BIVALVES.

E. Plagiostoma.
SPECIES 1
Obtusely three angled, one side produced pointed. Eared [?] Many longitudinal sharp thin costæ. Length a quarter more than breadth; one and a sixth of an inch; rather gibbous.
South of Bedminster Down -1

[BM7]
F. Ostrea.
SPECIES 1.
Common Grypheus see Lias [Plate ?]
a. Gloucester and Berkley Canal -2 b. Cheltenham (open[?]) – 1 c. Batheaston Pit – 3

SPECIES 2.
See Lias No 2 south of Bedminster Down
Batheaston Pit – 3
NB [not use it ?]

[L1]
LIAS.
Amm. Walcotii diluvial near Shellingford [?]
[L2]
ZOOPHITA.

Tubipora ?

SPECIES 1.
Hemispherical, base flat showing the tubes ? radiating from the stem, top covered with polygonal points of coral concave and with transverse partitions seen at the sides. Points five to ten angled.
Purton Passage 1

SPECIES 2.
Tubes cylindrical with connecting transverse plates joining towards the base ['tubes hollow?' struck through]
Purton Passage

Madrepora.
Simple or one starred.
SPECIES 1.
Short conical, base flat, many lamelliform unequal, rays circular.
Weston-1

Many Starred.
Nearly hemi-spherical. Base flat with concentric rugæ and minute radiating striæ. Top convex with many round points which have serated edges. Diameter one inch. Porpital compound. Division of Park. Vol. 2, Page 68
Bath-1

[L3]
Pentacrinus.
SPECIES 1.
(Vertebræ). Thickness a sixth of the diameter; angles blunt, deeply hollowed between. Diameter a third of an inch.
a. Purton Passage (fine) mass b. Gloucester and Berkley [Canal] (mass) c. Keynsham two columns

SPECIES 2.
(Vertebræ) Thickness an eighth of the diameter which is a third of an inch, angles keen hollowed hollowed between.
Topcliffe mass
Gloucester and Berkley Canal mass with Sp. 1.

SPECIES 3.
Fine specimen of Briarean. Arms, joints, heads etc.
Charmouth-2

[L4]
TESTACEA.
UNIVALVIA.
A.Trochus.
SPECIES 1.
Trochus serrites[?] *Min. Conch.*
Conoidal, turriculated, volutions five or six, angular, flat at the upper part; three bands of spiral threads; the upper and lower bands set with nodular or tubercular eminences middle band of three threads smooth, part of the lower band hid by the lower turns; four threads in the upper band. No umbilicus, opening depressed guard angular, shell thick. Syn. Trochites medius clavellatus etc. *Llwyd* No 400.
a. Purton Passage (one with the shale)-2 b. Bath (casts outer and inner) -1 c. Charmouth (cast encrusted with pyrites)-1

SPECIES 2.
Conical, volutions five or six sides, even base flat reticulo-striated, striæ fine, perhaps umbilicate. Opening obliquely four angled, the bluntest angle upwards. Broader than long.
Bath -1

B. Solarium ?
SPECIES 1.
Depressed spire little extended of three or four roundish turns, aperture wide, depressed. Umbilicus large, a—cast imperfect.
a. Weston-1 b. Bath-1

[L5]
C. Natica ?
SPECIES 1.
Rhomboidal, acute; volutions four or five, upper part gibbous with a spiral depression beneath it. Umbilicate, striated (the lines of growth distinct). Opening oblong, semicircular, a little narrowed upwards, three fifths of the length it resembles N. glaucina. Length about half an inch.
Blue Lodge-2

N⁶ 6

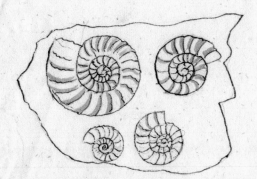

1

2

3

Fig. 1 Ammonites planicosta
Fig. 2 Ammonites [Sp. 6]
Fig. 3 Tellina Sp.1

PLATE 23 (AND FACING PAGE)

LOWER JURASSIC, BLUE MARL (unpublished) PLATE

1. Block with ammonites: *Promicroceras planicosta*
2. Ammonite: *Asteroceras smithi*
3. Bivalve: *Cardinia listeri*

0 cm 1 2 3 4 5

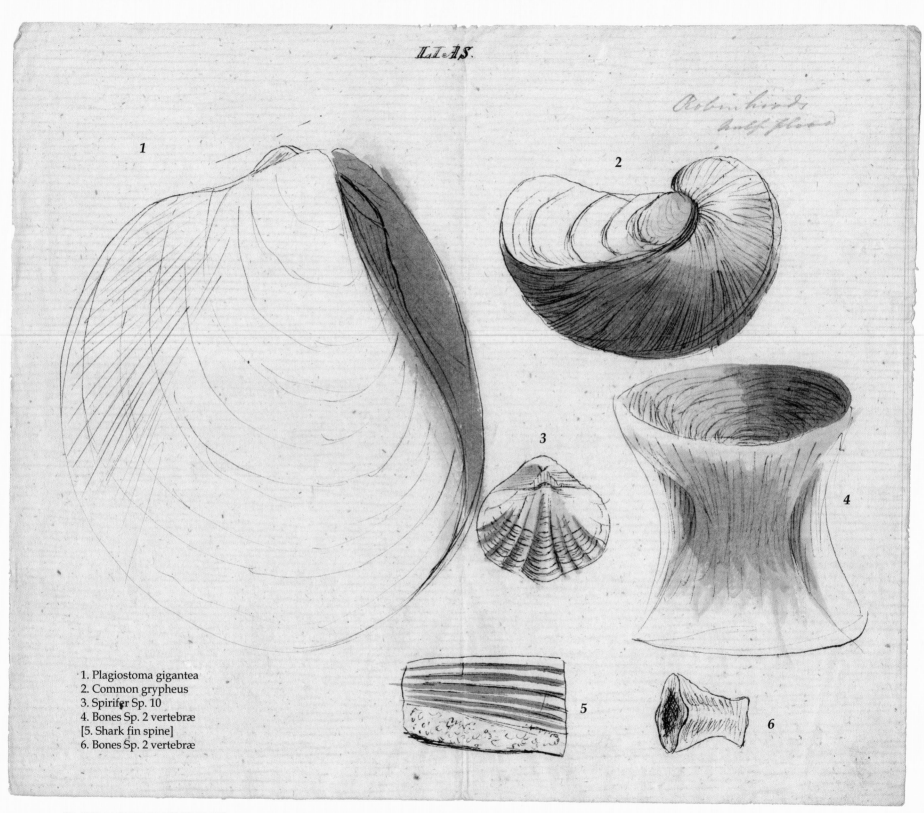

LIAS

1. Plagiostoma gigantea
2. Common grypheus
3. Spirifer Sp. 10
4. Bones Sp. 2 vertebræ
[5. Shark fin spine]
6. Bones Sp. 2 vertebræ

PLATE 24 (AND FACING PAGE)

120 | WILLIAM SMITH'S FOSSILS REUNITED

LOWER JURASSIC, LIAS (unpublished) PLATE 1

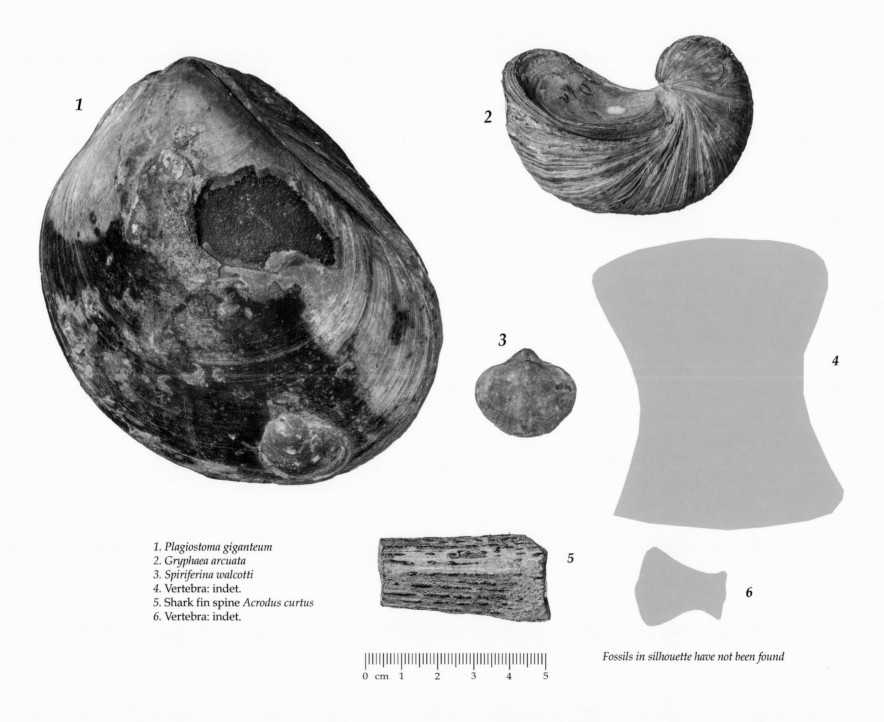

1. *Plagiostoma giganteum*
2. *Gryphaea arcuata*
3. *Spiriferina walcotti*
4. Vertebra: indet.
5. Shark fin spine *Acrodus curtus*
6. Vertebra: indet.

|||||||||||||||||||||||||||||||||||||||||||||||||
0 cm 1   2   3   4   5

Fossils in silhouette have not been found

MULTILOCULAR UNIVALVES.
D. Belemnites.

(Part) Large rather, form angular, sulcus deep. Alveolus conical, central—septa transverse concavo-convex numerous. A tenth of the diameter distant from each other.

Charmouth-1

[L6]
E. Ammonites.
No Keel or /Sulcus Furrow on the Front.
Radii entire.
*Radii straight.
SPECIES 1.

Much depressed, volutions five or six, the inner ones a third concealed. Front thinned and rounded. Radii straight very obtuse; and almost obsolete on the front opening long, oval, indented; a fourth of the diameter which is two to three inches.

Stony Littleton-1

SPECIES 2

Volutions four or five fast increasing, not at all concealed, thickest near the front; radii strong, obtuse, widened on the front, straight, fourteen to twenty in a volution. Opening oblong, narrow on the inner side, a third of the long diameter which is one and three fourths of an inch. It may be a variety of the next.

Charmouth-1

SPECIES 3.

Ammonites planicosta *Min. Conch.*

Charmouth -two or three

SPECIES 4.

Ammonites (   ). No. 2 of the Blue Marl

[L7]
** Radii curved.
SPECIES 5.

Large depressed keen edged, radii crossing diagonally (showing only near the front), numerous obtuse. Volutions five, the inner one a third concealed; thickest at the inner margin. Opening hastate [?], its length double the breadth. Diameter would be four inches or more (about half a turn)

Topcliffe

SPECIES 6.

Ammonites (   ) No 3 of the Marlstone [Plate]

Stony Littleton -2

Radii entire ***tubercled.
SPECIES 7.

Volutions five or six angular not concealed. Radii strong, large rising into strong tubercles on the margins of the front, obtuse on the front itself. About fifteen in a turn, inner margin waved. Opening squarish, about half and inch. Long diameter two inches.

Charmouth -1

SPECIES 8.

Volutions five to seven, depressed; angular not concealed. Radii many, tubercular on both margins, the outer row strongest. Radii obtuse on the front. Opening angular, square. Mouth one fourth the diameter which is one to two inches.

Charmouth -2

[L8]
Radii dividing.
SPECIES 9.

Ammonites communis. *Min Conch.*

The variety with oval mouth —

Bath -1

SPECIES 10.

Small volutions three or four, a little concealed, rather angular. Radii (merely striæ) dividing into three. Opening oblong two-fifths of the diameter. Diameter about an inch.

Brent -1

SPECIES 11.

Volutions four half concealed, fast increasing, deep as wide. Radii numerous strong, sharp, divaricating divisions strong. Opening broader than long, lunate. Diameter longest one inch and five eighths ['of an inch' struck through]

Charmouth-1

SPECIES 12.

Volutions four, deepest at the front. Front rounded radii numerous four or five unite into a tubercle on the margins, divided again on the front. Tubercles strong, eight to twenty in a turn. Mouth squarish evident at the front, a third the diameter which is an inch and one eighth.

Charmouth-1

[L9]
A Keel on the Front.
Radii entire.
SPECIES 13.

Thin as a wafer (perhaps compressed), volutions five, the inner ones a third concealed, a few radii show at the inner margin, smooth. Shell (copper coloured) with irridescent colours.

Watchet-4

SPECIES 14.

Ammonites (serratus?)

Blue Lodge-1 fine cast

SPECIES 15.

Very depressed, volutions four or five, front keen thin keel projecting; radii sharp straight with a slight curve at the margin, thirty in a turn, opening very oblong, sides parallel. Diameter two inches and a quarter.

a. Watchet-1 *b.* Gloucester and Berkley Canal-1 *c.* Charmouth -1

SPECIES 16.

Volutions four, fast increasing, not concealed, angular. Radii strong straight tubercular on the margin at the front. Keel small, striae diagonal on the back, some of the spaces between the ribs. Opening squarish. Shell white. Cast irridescent.

a. Stony Littleton-2 *b.* Charmouth (pyritous)-2

SPECIES 17.

Small, volutions five in three quarters of an inch, diameter angular, not concealed, radii numerous, straight, sharp, ending tubercular on the margins of the front. Keel very slight with many transverse striæ, front broad. Opening broader than long, pentagonal, sides rounded (may be a curious variety of the last).

Stony Littleton

SPECIES 18.

Volutions four in an inch diameter, angular widest at front, not concealed. Radii twenty in a volution, sharp, front wide; keel thin, sharp. Opening nearly circular.

Charmouth

A Keel between two Sulci on the Front.
SPECIES 19.

Volutions about six not concealed, squarish, flattened; radii showing very strongly on the outer margin. Front broad, keel and furrows strong. Opening an oblong square, about one inch and a half. Long diameter about six inches.

Syn. Walcot Fig. 40

Blue Lodge-1

SPECIES 20.

Volutions five or six, angular not concealed, depressed. Radii very numerous; about forty in a turn (near the end a little curved). Keel rather strong, furrows, slight, opening nearly circular a little oblong. Long diameter two inches and half. Mouth one fifth of the diameter.

a. Stony Littleton-1 *b.* Keynsham (part)-1

[L11]
A Sulcus on the Front.
SPECIES 21.

Very depressed sulcus narrow, volution little concealed. Radii many curved sharp. Front narrow, opening oblong.

Topcliffe-1

[L12]
EQUIVALVED BIVALVES.
F. Modiola.
SPECIES 1.

Modiola (   ) of Cornbrash [Plate]

Somerton-1

SPECIES 2

Flattened hinge linear, other side sharp. Beaks small, at one end. Breadth thrice the length which is three-quarters of an inch (cast).

Stony Littleton-1

G. Unio ?
SPECIES 1

Transverse depressed. Beaks at a third of the breadth from one end, the other pointed; transversely sulcated, hinge extended. Beaks small , close. Twice as broad as long.

Bath-1

SPECIES 2

Broader than long. Beaks thick gibbous, a third from one end which is blunt and gibbous, the other sharper. Deep as long. Front margin hollowed inwards. Length half the breadth.

Weston-1

SPECIES 3.

(Cast). Subelliptical, oblique, short side diagonally truncated near which is the beak. Three muscular impressions.

Bath-1

NB. All these have some appearance of a constriction or fold.

[L13]
H. Trigonia.
SPECIES 1.

Trigonia clavellata. *Park Vol. 3, Sowerby Min. Conch*

Bath 1

I. Mactra *Linn.*
SPECIES 1.

Mactra (   ) as at Crewkerne and Under Oolite [Plate?]

Bath 2

K. Cardium ?
SPECIES 1.

Circular subequilateral rather depressed, transversely and closely sulcated.

Syn. Walcot Fig.17-

Berkely-1

L. Tellina.
SPECIES 1.

(Cast) of a large broad depressed, one twice as broad as long. Beaks near one end. Depth is half the length. Two impressions with tetrahedral crystals of pyrites.

Walcot Fig. 14.

Newton-1

SPECIES 2.

(Cast) as in Blue Marl from Bedminster Down

Bedminster Down-4

[L14]
M. Mya ?
SPECIES 1.

Transverse, one side sharply and perpendicularly truncated. Beaks close to the truncated side, the other projecting, transversely sulcated. The breadth is to the length as 3 to 2.

Writhlington -3

INEQUIVALVED BIVALVES.
N. Plagiostoma, *Sowerby.*
SPECIES 1.

Plagiostoma gigantea, *Min. Conch.*

a. Topcliffe-1 *b.* Bath-3 *c.* Coal Canal-1 *d.* Stony Littleton (small) -1 ?

SPECIES 2.

Plagiostoma (striata)

a. Bath-2 *b.* Coal Canal-1

SPECIES 3.

Plagiostoma (—), oblique rather more than semicircular, the truncated side being the base, much depressed, eared, many longitudinal smooth projections with numerous intermediate decussated striæ. Length two to five inches. Depth one fourth of the length.

Bath-3

SPECIES 4.

Eared subovate, oblique, not truncated longitudinally threaded. Length an eighth to half an inch.

Breadstone – Mass.

[L15]
O. Ostrea.
Smooth or without projections, ribs, &c.
SPECIES 1.

Common grypheus. Lower valve very gibbous and much curved. Beak pointed a very little twisted, much projecting. Little lobate. Long oval. Upper valve concave, ovate. Length two to two and a half inches. Breadth about four-seventh of the length. NB. The Kelloways lobate oyster is more lobate, wider in the front, beak twisted, yet no so much produced.

Walcot 34., Parkinson Vol. 3 Pl. 15 Fig 3.

a. Gloucester and Berkley Canal-2 *b.* Purton Passage-1 *c.* Bath-3 *d.* Coal Canal-5 *e.* Weston-1 *f.* Stony Littleton-1

A variety with a small beak and the upper valve a little convex at its the apex.

SPECIES 2.

Oblong, lower valve convex, greatly twisted, oblique attached at the beak, upper valve oblong convex near its apex. The rest concave front margin reflected. One impression close to inner side of the arch or twist. Length half to one inch.

a. Bedminster Down-4 *b.* Bath-2

SPECIES 3.

Oblong or broad, irregular, rough, deep, oblique, imperfect.

Topcliffe in a mass-4

[L16]
SPECIES 4.

Oblong, narrow, very depressed or flat. Oblique lower valve convex, upper valve concave. Beak small pointed.

a. Tracey Park-1 *b.* Normanton Hill-1 *c.* Stokeleigh House, in stone-3

SPECIES 5.

Oblong broad in front. Lower ? valve like the hoof of a horse rising perpendicularly in the front and flat (attached ?) to the beak, the other a little convex with three or four irregular undulations. Shell thick. Length two or three inches.

Stony Littleton

With projections, ribs, &c

SPECIES 6.

Irregularly arched or twisted, oblique, flattsh; one valve concave at the apex and convex at the margin, the other convex at apex and concave at the margin. Ribed strongly, in a longitudinal and oblique direction. Ribs irregular twenty or more. Length two inches to two and a half -by mistake marked O7 ['in the account' struck through]

Stony Littleton

SPECIES 7.

Large as and nearly resembling the common Ostrea edulis. Flattish valve oblique, many irregular tubular projections marked O 6

Bath

SPECIES 8.

(rugosa?), a small specimen?, two inches long. It is more regular and more flattened —marked O9

Bath-1

[L17]
P. Pecten.
No tubercles, &c.
SPECIES 1.

Large very depressed. Ears long very straight and extended on one side, numerous fine longitudinal striæ. Length half and inch to three inches (in a Pyritous Ball). It may be Avicula.

Charmouth -2

SPECIES 2.

Flattened subcircular, equilateral, ears not large, many fine longitudinal threads and numerous minute transverse lines forming a kind of network. Length one inch and an eighth.

Beachley-1

SPECIES 3.

With prominences on the tubercles

Oblique, eared; one side produced, keenly pointed. Ribbed longitudinally, ribs sharp triangular set with small transverse eminences, many transverse striæ.

Bath-1

[L18]
Q. Terebratula.
SPECIES 1.

Terebratula ornithocephala, *Min. Conch.*
Very depressed, five angular, surface canullated
a. Crescent Fields-2 *b.* Stony Littleton-1

SPECIES 2.

Terebratula intermedia, *Min. Conch.*
Stony Littleton

SPECIES 3.

Terebratula obsoleta ?, small, *Min. Conch.*
Crescent Fields-8

SPECIES 4.

Terebratula tetraedia, *Min. Conch.*
Crescent Fields-1

SPECIES 5.

Terebratula media, *Min Conch.*
Bath (Crescent Fields)-1

SPECIES 6.

Terebratula acuta, *Min. Conch.*
Rhomboidal (looking on the lower valve), the beak fold and sides being the angles, gibbous, sides pointed with two or three strong plaits, fold very strong composed of one very strong, sharp plait. Length, breadth and depth equal, a quarter to half an inch.
a. Bath- *b.* Keynsham-1 [Species 6 description crossed out]

SPECIES 7.

Terebratula erumeria ? [?] *Min. Conch.*
a. Bath-1 *b.* Stony Littleton-2

[L19]
SPECIES 8.

Oblong, pointed, oblique. Plicæ few irregular dividing laterally. Beak with a round hole ? and a depression on each side (an irregular odd shell), most probably an ostrea.
Bath-7

The following Spirifer (Terebratula) have the hinge on a straight line and a fold on each valve from the apex to the front. The fold convex in the upper, concave in the lower valve.

SPECIES 9. [marked through]
Spirifer.

Rhomboidal, regular. Beak rather incurved, projecting. Folds very strong; upper valve triangular, the hinge being the base which is extended to the breadth of the shell, five or six deep sulci and projections on each side of the fold. Margin gibbous, deeply widened by the fold and the plicæ. Length and breadth of the larger valve equal, one inch, the greatest depth seven-eighths. Surface with minute eminences.
a. Bath-1 *b.* Stony Littleton-3

SPECIES 10.

Transversely subovate. Beaks greatly incurved, small. Folds not strong

about the curve of a 1/3 of a circle. Sulci and projections ten on each side of the fold. Hinge extended margin not pointed at the sides. Length half of one inch to an inch. Breadth three quarters to one and a half. Depth about half the breadth. Surface with minute eminences.
a. Keynsham -2 *b.* Bath 1-3

[L20]
BONES.
1.

Part of a fish, perhaps half, showing the rhomboidal coverings to the gills which are covered with small puncta. Scaly, the parts of the scales which appear are rectangular longest across the fish. Coloured dark by pyrites. Length four inches one quarter. Breadth three inches three quarters.
Charmouth

2.

Vertebræ concave at both ends, the thickness of the center of the hollow in one of the vertebra is a sixth of an inch, in another a third.
a. Charmouth, a fine section of two vertebræ shifted from their position, containing in the same mass bones, teeth etc and ammonites.
b. Keynsham, a separate vertebra showing the processes etc.

3.

Vertebra on the tail or fin of the turtle ?
Charmouth-1

4.

Part of jaws , with teeth in one, composed of coats one over another. In the bony parts of the jaws are layers of stone in cavities.
Charmouth

5.

Part of jaw with longitudinal twisted ridges on one edge and part of the sides, on the other side towards one end are disposed many eminences and a deep groove in which the teeth were perhaps placed. Length two inches
Walcot Fig. 65.
Charmouth 1

[L21]
6.

Masses of rounded bones, teeth etc. ? ['There are some coprolites of Lias at [west] Passage' script rotated 90 °]
Batheaston Pit,

7.

Shark's tooth with sharp edges and two minor teeth at the root, others in the mass.
Batheaston Pit, masses.

8.

Long, round, longitudinally sulcated. Length an inch, diameter about a third of an inch
Conichthyodontes striatus, *Parkinson.*
Keynsham 1

9.

Tooth of a cuttle bone (Sepia Loligo) ?
Weston ?

10.

Palatum limax [?], oblong, narrow, flattish, a longitudinal ['central' marked through] line, many fine striae divide from it, the margin nearest the line, arched inwards, the striæ meet in tubercles on it. Length an inch and a half. Breadth about three quarters of an inch.
Walcot Fig. , Parkinson Plate
a. variety

11.

Oblong pointed at the ends bulging in the middle. Line nearly on the middle, striæ branching from it. Length half an inch to one inch and half. Breadth in the middle half the length.
a. Keynsham-1 *b.* Bath-1

[RL1]
REDLAND LIMESTONE.
[RL2]
ZOOPHITA.
Tubipora.

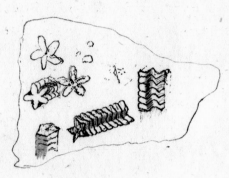
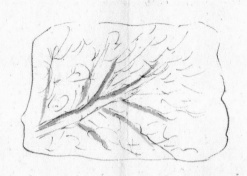

1. Pentacrinus Sp. 1
2. Pentacrinus Sp. 3
3. Trochus serrites [?]
4. Ammonites Sp. 16
5. Ammonites Sp. 9
6. Unio ? Sp. 2

PLATE 25 (AND FACING PAGE)

1. Crinoid, disarticulated: *Isocrinus psilonoti*
2. Crinoid, articulated: *Isocrinus psilonoti*
3. Gastropod: *Pleurotomaria* cf. *cognata*
4. Ammonite: *Euagassiceras sauzeanum*
5. Ammonite: *Zugodactylites braunianus*
6. Bivalve: *Pleuromya* aff. *uniformis*

0 cm 1 2 3 4 5

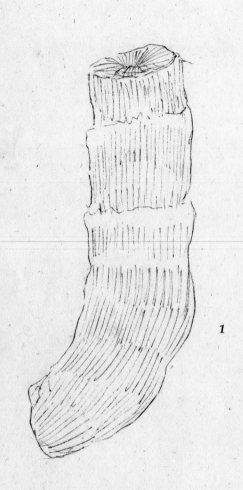
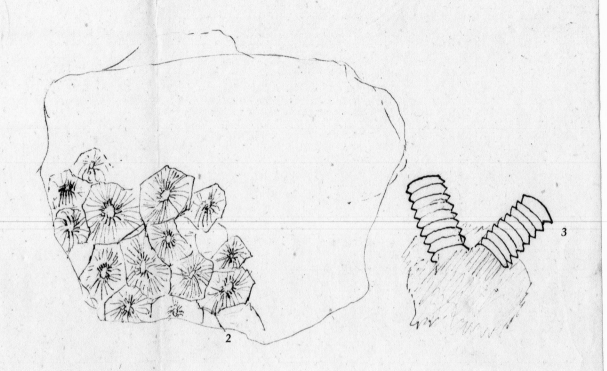

1

2

3

1. Madrepora turbinata
2. Madrepora Sp. 6
3. Encrinus Sp. 2

PLATE 26 (AND FACING PAGE)

CARBONIFEROUS, *(unpublished)* SMITH'S REDLAND LIMESTONE PLATE
now Carboniferous Limestone

1. Coral: *Amplexus coralloides* *
2. Coral: *Actinocyathus floriformis* *
3. Crinoid stems: indet.

0 cm 1 2 3 4 5

* similar fossil substituted from Smith's collection

SPECIES 1.
Tubipora strues[?] *Linn, Park*
    Mendip -1

SPECIES 2.
Tubipora catenulata *Linn, Park*
    Malvern -1 mass
    a. scale occurs [?...]

SPECIES 3.
This has been called, Tubularia indivisa
    Mendip -1

SPECIES 4.
Branching slender distinct set with holes and a projecting scale over each making a rough surface. This is perhaps a Millepora.
    Malvern -1

Madrepora.
Simple, composed of a single star
SPECIES 1.
Mycetita of a compressed conical figure.
    Hutton Hill-1

SPECIES 2.
Madrepora turbinata, elongated variety. Elongated, bent, rough closely striated, many circular projections, one over the other. Top concave, radii close numerous sometimes a smooth outer covering.
    Parkinson Vol. 2, Plate 4, Fig. 8, 13, 14
    a. Mendip -1 *b.* Hotwells -2 *c.* Worcestershire -1 *d.* small specimen, Malvern -1.

[RL3]
Compound composed of many stars.
Fasiculated.
SPECIES 3.
Nearly resembles Madrepora flexuosa, *Linn., Ellis &c.*, but differs in their stars in this they are convex.
    Arbury, Staffordshire -1

SPECIES 4.
Branching distinct striated longitudinally, branches around. Top edged radiated, radii unequal.
    a. Near Wells -1 *b.* Mendip -1 *c.* Sodbury -1
Aggregated.
SPECIES 5.
Branches round, rough, striated. Top radiate with two or three circular intermissions; the radii double in number on the outer margin. It resembles *Plate 5, Fig. 8 of Parkinson, Vol.2.*
    Hotwells -1

SPECIES 6.
Star concave irregularly, angular unequal, center large radiate, the space between that and the parietes finely varied with angular points. Parietes crenated, the crenations being opposite give it a chain-like appearance. Center light red with deep brownish red border, the parietes white.
    a. Hotwells-1 *b.* Farley-1, alluvial from Mendip.

[RL4]
SPECIES 7.
Stars regular, hexagonal, concave radiated, no central rising. Sides longitudinal striated, transversely lamellated. *Parkinson Vol.2 Plate 5, Fig.9.*

    a.Ubby Hill-1
    b. Slabhouse   } Mendip
    c. Tusons Farm -1

SPECIES 8.
Stars irregular, hexagonal and pentagonal, concave, with a sharp rising in the centre and a flat around it, radiated. Parietes keen, thin, strong, dividing from the pedicle in four principal branches, each subdivided striated.
    Hotwells -2

SPECIES 9.
Closely striated, stars concave with a thick blunt rising, closely radiated. Parietes indistinct, broad crossed by the radii. Stars large.
    Hotwells -1

SPECIES 10 ?
Branches round with many circular furrows and longitudinal striæ; curved divided stars, concave radiated branching at first in two divisions and separate (This is only a part of No.8.) [all descriptive text for Species 10 struck through]
    Hutton Hill

[RL5]
SPECIES 10/11.
Columnar, regular; striated and radiated, tops a little rounded. A variety of Madrepora basaltiformis Lithostrotion &c Llwyd.
    Stowey -1

Porpital Compound Madreporites
Parkinson Vol. 2, Page 66.
SPECIES 12
Very large base, flat with many concentric rugæ and numerous radiating striæ. Upper side composed of coats or layers covered with small angular stars. Diameter six to nine inches.
    Malvern -1

[RL6]
Encrinus.
Vertebra equal.
SPECIES 1.
Vertebræ equal, even, many; stem sometimes one inch diameter. In the cast the spaces between the vertebræ angular projecting and when bent sometimes are divided on the outer side of curve.
    Milsinley, Yorkshire -3
    Mells (cast) -2 *Plate 6, Fig. 8, Parkinson Vol. 2.* [Pl. 6 is entirely corals, the likely candidates are Plate 13 *Fig. 10* or Plate 15. *Fig. 8*]

SPECIES 2 ?
(Cast) Spaces between the vertebræ thin angular keen, vertebrae equal, even; one fifth as thick as their diameter. Top finely articulated.
    Mells (in the same specimens as No.1) -1

SPECIES 3.
(Long stems) vertebræ in both stems equal projecting. In one they are rounded and thick, six in an inch; in the other angular nine in an inch. Diameter half an inch. Columns four to six inches long. Probably different parts of the stem of one Encrinus.
    Dudley -2 long stems

SPECIES 4 ?
Vertebræ equal, even, round, thick; small hole large central articulations five. Diam[eter] quarter of an inch.
    High Hang Hill, Yorkshire 4

SPECIES 5.
Vertebræ equal, oval, even finely articulated , thickness one third of the diameter, small.
    High Hang Hill, Yorkshire -2

SPECIES 6.
Vertebrae unequal, sometimes projecting, the longer one about twice as thick as the other, rounded.
    a. Mathon *b.* Ticknal

[RL7]
TESTACEA.
UNIVALVIA.

A. Euomphalus.
SPECIES 1.
Euomphalus catillus, *Min. Conch.*
var.? the ridge nearest the outside.
    Clifton-1

MULTILOCULAR UNIVALVES.
B. Nautilus.
SPECIES 1.
(Cast) spine rounded concealed with a slight longitudinal depression; opening lunate half the diameter (reckoning to the angles); more than twice as broad as long.
    Clifton-1

C. Amplexus.
SPECIES 1.
Amplexus coralloides, *Min. Conch.*
Tube irregular bent, longitudinally striated; margins of the septa deeply reflexed and regularly plaited.
    Mendip

[RL8]
BIVALVIA.
EQUIVALVED BIVALVES.
D. Mactra ? *Linn.*
SPECIES 1.
Transverse, beaks gibbous contiguous; near one end, the other fine and pointed, closed. Longitudinal projections, transverse furrowing, margin thick. Length and depth about equal. Breadth three inches and a quarter, double the length.
    Aberthaw ? -1

E. Venericardia ?
SPECIES 1.
(Cast) Subcordate very oblique, gibbous. Beaks thinned, hooked; margin keen, two impressions. Length one inch and half. Breadth two inches.
    Wales (Sth. Coast)-1

[RL9]
INEQUIVALVED BIVALVES.
F. Productus.
Longest valve gibbous, its beak curved over the hinge, the other valve flat or concave.

SPECIES 1.
Productus scoticus, ? large very gibbous, breadth twice the length margin rounded.
    a. Hotwells-1 *b.* Near Mells-2 [possibly Wells] *c.* Redland (near Bristol) -1

SPECIES 2.
Productus scabriculus, *Mineral Conchology.*
    Conch. Anomia scabriculus *Martin* [Petrif. Derb.]
    Longest valve flattish, its beak curved over the hinges, the other gibbous, short.
    Near Mells *-4 [possibly Wells]

SPECIES 3.
Hinge extended straight, the gibbous valve flattish at the beak, bulging towards the front. The other valve flattish at the front and convex at the beaks, set with short small spines showing stronger toward the edge. Striae strong, many, a depression on the gibbous valve, many transverse wrinkles.
    Clifton-1

SPECIES 4
Three fourths circular, beak of the flatter valve small, pointed just rising over the hinge. Upper valve very gibbous in the middle, sides keen, front one-waved , wave inflected on the gibbous valve. Many decussated striae, a few transverse. Length half to an inch.
    Malvern -10 -4

SPECIES 5
Valves convex gibbous in the middle, sides keen, front one-waved on the short valve, sides reflected on the long valve. Striated striæ smooth unequal in front.

[RL10]
G. Terebratula.
SPECIES 1

Terebratula media.

With a straight extended hinge and a fold from apex to margin on each valve.

Malvern -2

SPECIES 2

Terebratula ( ). *No. 9 of the Lias* [Plate]

Clifton -1

[RL11]
CRUSTACEA.
Trilobites *Parkinson*.
SPECIES 1.

Oval or oblong, broadest at the head, trilobate; the lower end blunt, the whole surrounded by a defined border. Head or upper part nearly semicircular. Tripartite, the middle lobe rounded, gibbous with 2 two round protuberences on each side, the lower ones longest; the other on each side part appearing to be eyes. On the back are placed transverse triarcuate segments or ridges folding under each other, about twenty on each lobe; on the side lobes, between each segment is a small ridge. Length about two inches; breadth at the head an inch and a quarter. The animal had the power of rolling itself up, <u>perhaps an insect</u>.

Parkinson [Vol 3] *Plate 17, Fig. 11, 14, Page 263-264 &c.*

A small one has been found at Fadley[?] in the alluvial bed of the River Frome.

Dudley

SPECIES 2.

A produced point from the tail, middle lobe smallest. Ribs or segments distant, lobes ending obtusely.

Parkinson [Vol 3] *Plate 17, Fig. 17, &c.*

Malvern

MOUNTAIN LIMESTONE.
[ML2]
ZOOPHITA
Tubipora.
SPECIES 1.

Tubipora catenulata, *Linn.*

Lincoln Hill

Madrepora.
Simple composed of one star
SPECIES 1.

Mycetita of a compressed-conical figure.

a. Derbyshire-1 b. Critch-3 c. Mynedd Carreg -2

Compound composed of many stars
*Fasiculated.

SPECIES 2.

Madrepora ( ), *No. 4 of Redland Limestone* [Plate]

Buxton

***Porpital compound.

SPECIES 3.

Madrepora ( ), *No. 12 of Redland Limestone* [Plate]

This might have been placed last

**Aggregated.

SPECIES 4.

['Lithostrotium basaltiformis of *Llwd*' struck through]. Columnar, the columns four, angular, aggregated striated. ['Top radiates' struck through] Top radial, probably a variety of the next.

Steeraway Wrekin-1

SPECIES 5.

Lithostrotion basaltiformis of *Llwd* &c.

Steeraway Wrekin-1

[ML3]
Encrinus.
Vertebræ Equal, *oval.
SPECIES 1.

Oval, vertebræ equal, similar, projecting, angular, top concave, a raised surface of the radii from the center to each end.

a. Bonsal -4 b. Richmond -2 c. Mynedd Carreg 3

** circular

SPECIES 2.

Round, equal, even top slightly concave. Radii (articulations) close. Hole central

a. Bonsal -4 b. Mynedd Carreg-1

SPECIES 3.

Vertebrae, equal, projecting.

Hole central, pentagonal, large.

a. Bonsal-5 b. Mynedd Carreg-4 c. Merthyr Tydvil-1 d. Clithero 4

SPECIES 4.

Encrinus ( ) as *No. 1 of the Redland Limestone* [Plate] (Casts).

a. Derbyshire b. Nenthead

Specimens of the marble Clithero Whally &c.
Vertebræ unequal

SPECIES 5.

Alternately large and small, projecting.

a. Mynedd Carreg-4 b. Richmond-1 c. Bonsal 4 d. Whally (in the stone)-1

[ML4]
SPECIES 6.

A column in which the vertebræ are first, one large and two small (for two series), then one large and three smaller (for three series) lastly one large and four smaller vertebræ projecting, angular.

NB. When there are three small, the middle one is larger than the other two and when four smaller the two middle ones larger than other two.

Derbyshire (the column)-1 Bonsal (two series) -1

Pentacrinus.

Angles keen, hollow between vertebræ, thin projecting.

Derbyshire (with No. 6)-1

[ML5]
TESTACEA.
UNIVALVIA

A. Helix ?
SPECIES 1.

(Part). Volutions nearly round with two raised projections on the middle of the front. Upper side indented by the preceding turn, striated across the spine. Conoidal opening, roundish. Umbilicus large.

Bonsal -1

AB. Euomphalus *Sowerby* ?
SPECIES 1.

Euomphalus nodosus, *Min. Conch.*

Upper side having a nearly central ridge, underside a row of rather large nodular projections: aperture nearly round.

Spofforth.

MULTILOCULAR UNIVALVES.
B. Ammonites *Sowerby*.
SPECIES 1.

Ammonites sphericus, *Min. Conch.*

Derbyshire-1

[ML6]
BIVALVIA.
INEQUIVALVED BIVALVES.
C. Productus *Sowerby*.

**Longest valve gibbous, its beak curved over the hinge. ['The other flat concave' struck through]

SPECIES 1.

Conch Anomia productus, *Martin Petrif. Derb. Tab. 22, Fig. 1, 2, 3.*

a. Derbyshire -4

b. Wrekin-1

SPECIES 2.

Large valve very gibbous and cylindrically produced. Hinge straight short, a broad flat or slightly concave fold on the valve, striæ numerous close with small projections. On each side the fold, three or four projections formed by the meeting of the striæ, a few transverse wrinkles near the beak.

Derbyshire-1

SPECIES 3.

Conch Anomia striatus.

**** Longest valve flattish, its beak curved over the hinge.

SPECIES 4.

Valves both convex, the lower valve flattest. Transversely ovate, longest valve with a concave fold, the other with a slightly convex one. Hinge extended, rounded at the sides. Striae extremely close and numerous, striae sometimes raised into minute points, margin reflected toward the flatter valve. Not described P. striatus[?].

Derbyshire -1

EDITOR'S NOTE

In this book I have re-formatted William Smith's original text of A Stratigraphical System of Organized Fossils, the text has been re-flowed into a three column format and the font size considerably reduced. The format of the original pages is indicated by dotted lines separating Smith's pages and the original page numbers have been retained. Also, Smith had locations printed in a tabular list, one under the other, in this book they are shown in a linear form across the page. In my MS transcription of Part II, the same format has been followed. Part II was hand written on Foolscap folio pages without page numbers, the sequence of the original pages is shown by the square bracketed letters and following numbers. [BM n..] is Blue Marl, [L n..] Lias, [RL n..] Redland Limestone and [ML n..] Mountain Limestone.

WILLIAM SMITH'S MAPS AND HIS FOSSIL LOCATIONS

William Smith did not show the locations of his fossils on any of his published maps. However, in the memoir to his 1815 map he discussed ways of representing the locations of fossils. He wrote: "one of the greatest difficulties in understanding such an extensive branch of natural history arose from the want of some method of generalizing the information, which could only be supplied by a map that gives, in one view, the locality of thousands of specimens. By strong lines of colour, the principal ranges of strata are rendered conspicuous, and naturally formed into classes, which may be seen and understood at a distance from the map, without distressing the eye to search for small characters. This is the advantage of colours over any other mode of representation".

Smith was careful to document both the stratigraphic and geographic positions of his fossils. From his publications it has been possible to identify nearly 1,400 specimens from over 350 separate locations which were included in the sale to the British Museum in 1817. Some of Smith's location names were to a general area, e.g., Cotswold Hills or Kent and a few could not be found. The positions of the fossils are shown on Map 1, with the size of each marker point indicating the number of specimens at each location. From the map it is evident that the majority of specimens are from Mesozoic and Tertiary rocks with relatively few from older Paleozoic rocks in the west and north of the country. Indeed, nearly two thirds of the localities and the vast majority of actual specimens are from the English counties of Somerset, Gloucestershire, Wiltshire and Oxfordshire. To the east of the country the counties of Norfolk and Suffolk contain around ten percent of total localities.

The position of each location was determined through use of the online Gazetteer of British Place Names (Association of British Counties) and geologically refined through use of the British Geological Survey online viewer of the Geology of Britain, at a scale of 1:50,000. In choosing maps on which to locate Smith's fossils it was thought appropriate to use examples of Smith's own geological maps. Through implementation of a Geographic Information System (GIS), several Smith maps were re-projected to the British National Grid. These maps are over 200 years old and show a number of spatial inconsistencies but in general fit well with the real world coordinates used for the fossil locations. The base-map for Map 1 is a later issue William Smith 1815 Map (P), with key map outlines for Maps 2-8. Each of these maps includes parts of various William Smith's geological maps of England and Wales overlain with his fossil locations. The earliest Smith map shown is a facsimile copy of his 1799, 1½" to 1 mile, map around Bath (see Map 8), portions of Smith's 1815 map (early issue, unsigned "A"), 1" to 5 miles, has been used as a base for Maps 3, 5 and 6. Map 7 also uses part of the A map together with a section of Smith's 1819 County Geological Map of Wiltshire (approximately 1" to 1 mile). The latest map used is an 1828 issue of Smith's reduced scale (1" to 15 miles) New Geological Map of England and Wales (1820) and has been utilized in Maps 2 and 4. Geological legends for both the 1815 and 1820 maps are reproduced on Map 1 and relate to subsequent maps.

Map 2 shows the distribution of pre-1817 fossils from more northerly parts of England which Smith sold to the British Museum. The number of fossil locations is small compared to the rest of the country but it should be remembered that after 1819 Smith and John Phillips spent several years in the north collecting more fossils and revising the geology. Of interest is the area around the Vale of Pickering. Smith's initial interpretation of fossils from Whitby (339) was that they were from the Clunch Clay (Oxfordian) and that this clay encircled the North York Moors and parts of the Vale of Pickering. At a later date Smith realized that the clay at Whitby was Liassic and rectified his mistake, although not on his maps. Interestingly, although the 1820 map shows Red Marls at Topcliffe (334), on the 1820 Yorkshire county map Smith shows a small outcrop of Lias and correctly records Lias fossils at that location. The oldest fossils recorded by Smith are from the Carboniferous (Mountain) Limestone of Derbyshire and Cumbria. To the southwest of the map, fossils from various older

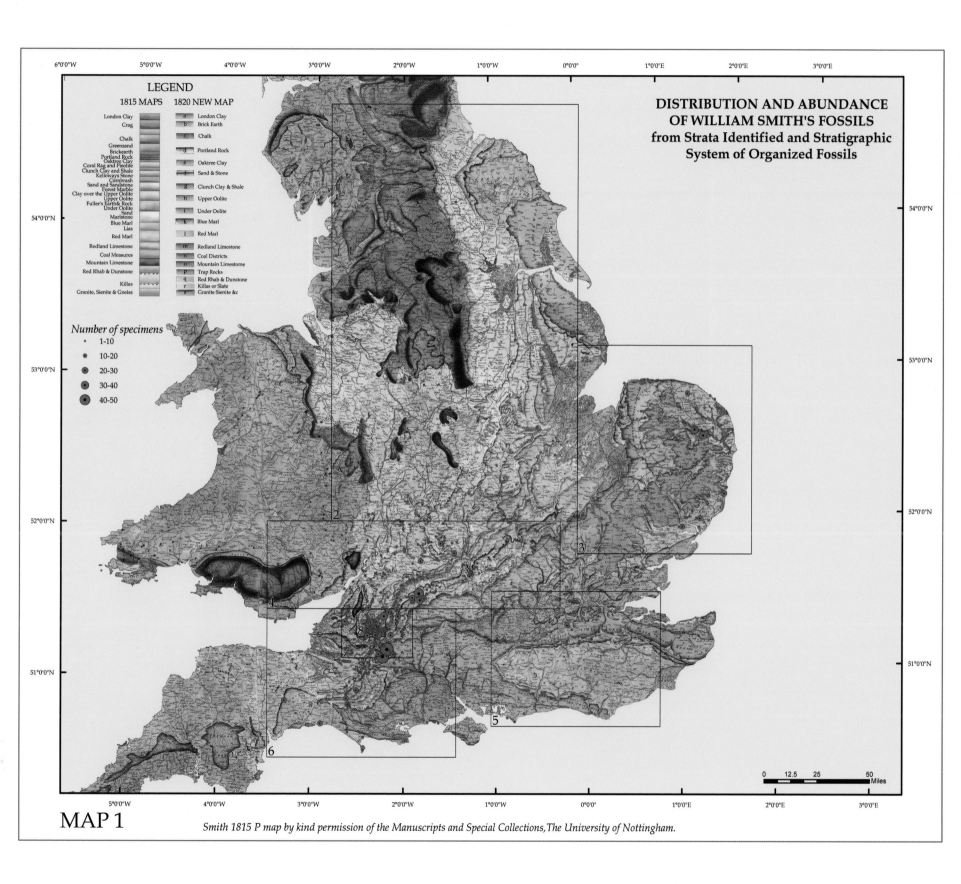

LEGEND

1815 MAPS

London Clay
Crag

Chalk
Greensand
Brickearth
Portland Rock
Oaktree Clay
Coral Rag and Pisolite
Clunch Clay and Shale
Kelloways Stone
Cornbrash
Sand and Sandstone
Forest Marble
Clay over the Upper Oolite
Upper Oolite
Fuller's Earth& Rock
Under Oolite
Sand
Marlstone
Blue Marl
Lias

Red Marl

Redland Limestone

Coal Measures

Mountain Limestone

Red Rhab & Dunstone

Killas

Granite, Sienite & Gneiss

1820 NEW MAP

a London Clay
b Brick Earth
c Chalk
d Portland Rock
e Oaktree Clay
f Sand & Stone
g Clunch Clay & Shale
h Upper Oolite
i Under Oolite
k Blue Marl
l Red Marl
m Redland Limestone
n Coal Districts
o Mountain Limestone
p Trap Rocks
q Red Rhab & Dunstone
r Killas or Slate
s Granite Sienite &c

Number of specimens

- 1-10
- 10-20
- 20-30
- 30-40
- 40-50

DISTRIBUTION AND ABUNDANCE OF WILLIAM SMITH'S FOSSILS
from Strata Identified and Stratigraphic System of Organized Fossils

0   12.5   25   50
Miles

MAP 1

Smith 1815 P map by kind permission of the Manuscripts and Special Collections, The University of Nottingham.

limestones are shown around the Wrekin (300), Dudley (299) and Malvern area (286). These are named by Smith as either Redland or Mountain Limestone, it is now known that these limestones are mostly Silurian, a system defined much later by Roderick Murchison in the 1830s. Smith's principal outcrop of his Redland Limestone is shown by the blue coloured outcrop running centrally north to south and marked with the letter "m". To the east of Spofforth (332) Smith recorded a specimen of Euomphalus (Gastropod) within his Redland Limestone. Smith knew the area well as he had been engaged in a coal trial there in 1803 (Phillips, J. 1844, p. 54).

Map 3 illustrates the pattern of Smith's collecting in Norfolk, Suffolk and north Essex. Smith knew the area well mostly from his work at the Holkham estate and various drainage and sea defence projects. Most of the locations are in his Crag (Plio-Pleistocene). He recorded a number of samples from a cliff section at Happisburgh (317) which he interpreted as belonging to the London Clay which he incorrectly thought to be younger than the Crag. The ammonites which he collected there were actually not *in situ* and were derived from glacial till. His 1815 map does not show London Clay at Happisburgh but has two small inliers of London Clay to the east of Norwich, one of which to the south of location number 309 is correct. Most of the other locations are within the Chalk, but with one location at Grimston (314) on his Brick Earth (now Gault).

Map 4 shows locations with a spectrum of age from the oldest in the Mountain (Carboniferous) Limestone at Merthyr Tydfil to the west and includes a complete Jurassic sequence traversing eastward across the escarpment. The youngest fossils located on the map are from the Chalk at Upton (203). Of interest, are the large numbers of Corallian (Oxfordian) fossils named by Smith as being from the Coral Rag and Pisolite. Smith collected a number of specimens (mostly Under Oolite) from his birthplace at Churchill (256) and also has specimens (Brick Earth) from Prisley [Priestly] Farm (268) close to the bog he successfully drained for the Duke of Bedford in 1802-1803.

Much of the area of Map 5 comprises the Weald of Sussex and Kent, an area about which Smith knew little. He prepared a cross-section across the Weald which demonstrated the general anticlinal structure of the Weald with the chalk dipping to the north and the south. However, he wrongly interpreted the age of the thick section in the core of the anticline as Oaktree Clay and older (Smith Strata Numbers 8-13). This was understandable because he had never encountered the thick Wealden (Lower Cretaceous) section between the Greensand-Gault and Portland-Purbeck stone. For obvious reasons, he could not have known that the Weald had been an actively subsiding basin during the Mesozoic which had subsequently been inverted and un-roofed. Further north, in the London area, Smith figured a number of localities containing fossils from the London Clay. These were often from deep wells (e.g., 173) and house foundations but the most spectacular man-made exposure was at Highgate Archway (204) where a tunnel through Highgate Hill collapsed in 1812. A contemporary painting by C.A. Pugin clearly shows the extent of the excavations with London Clay capped by sandy Claygate and Bagshot beds. Smith also listed London Clay fossils at Bognor (10) and Bracklesham Bay (9) but on the map showed the outcrop as Crag (on another version of the 1815 map (P) there is a small outcrop of London Clay shown on Selsey Bill).

Map 6 extends from South Wales, Devon and Somerset in the west, across Dorset to Wiltshire (the inset is the outline of Map 7). On the South Wales coast Smith showed Redland Limestone at Aberthaw ?(150) and also at Nether Stowey (56) and the Mendips (100, 103). Aberthaw is actually on Lias so Smith's samples were probably east of Porthkerry where outcrops of Carboniferous limestone occur. The fossils from Nether Stowey are of interest. It is known that as a young man in 1791 Smith walked over 100 miles from Burford to Nether Stowey in order to survey an estate (Phillips, J. 1844, p.7.) He became familiar with the area and noted the occurrence of Red Marl, also at some time later he collected a coral from a limestone, now known to be of Devonian age (Rodhuish Limestone). Limestone is not show on the 1815 A map but does occur

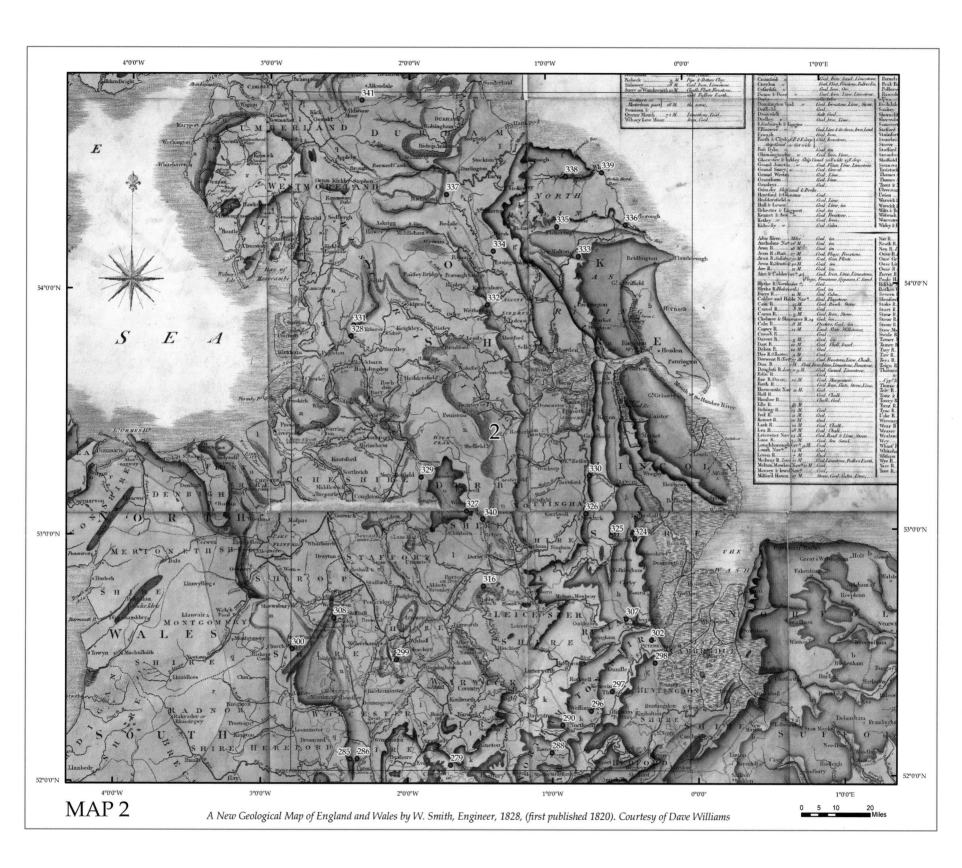

MAP 2

A New Geological Map of England and Wales by W. Smith, Engineer, 1828, (first published 1820). Courtesy of Dave Williams

0 5 10   20
Miles

on some other issues. Most of the other locations are from the Lias up section to the Portland Stone and Greensand, going northeast up the Vales of Blackmore and Wardour. From his Blue Marl at Marston Magna (27), Smith collected specimens of an ammonite now known as *Asteroceras smithi*, which was named for him by James Sowerby who wrote "This is named in honor of Mr. W. Smith, the Author of a Geological map of England, etc. whose discoveries of the regular succession of the strata, and the means of distinguishing them by their organised contents, has laid the foundation of all our Geological knowledge of England." (*Mineral Conchology* vol 4, page 148, plate 406). The location at Bruham Pit (53) is significant because in 1805 William Smith visited this trial for coal at Cook's Farm and was able to confirm through his knowledge of the fossils he found that, far from being in the Coal Measures, the miners were in fact in the Kellaways, much higher up in the succession (Torrens, H.S. 2002, p. 101-118) and that coal could not be found. The actual specimen which Smith used to identify the Kellaways at Bruton is shown in Plate 13 Fig. 5. This was one of the first applications of stratigraphy to commercial endeavor, albeit in a negative way. In the eastern coastal region at Barton, Hordle Cliff and Mudeford (4-8), Smith lists fossils from the London Clay and also shows it on his map. Although now considered to be part of the Barton and Bracklesham beds, Smith was still close to the mark in his interpretation. Smith shows some fossils from Dorset but it is probably true to say that he was an infrequent visitor to the county (Hugh Torrens, pers. comm.). Across the border in Devon samples are recorded from fossiliferous Greensand beds on the Blackdown Hills (15) which represent the most westerly occurrence of fossils from that formation.

The area encompassed by Maps 7-8 can fairly be said to be the cradle of stratigraphy, for it is here in the region of the Somerset Coal Canal that Smith developed his new science. On Map 7, oldest rocks are to the west becoming younger to the east. The base-map displayed is a composite image derived from Smith's 1815 map (to the west) and part of his 1819 County Map of Wiltshire (to the east). Smith listed a number of localities in the Mendip Hills area, to the west of the map, from which he obtained fossils which he identified as from Redland Limestone. Smith had defined the Redland Limestone ("Magnesium Limestone") in Yorkshire and Nottinghamshire and chose, mistakenly, to correlate this stratum across country to the Mendips. This was an important mistake as the Mendips are actually Carboniferous (Mountain) Limestone. However, he clearly defined the Carboniferous Coal Measures of the Somerset coal fields (mines shown with crosses) but, surprisingly, did not list any fossils from Coal Measure localities. In the Bath region Smith lists several hundred fossil specimens from close to fifty localities. The maps also demonstrate how Smith developed his ideas on various versions of his map. The locality (62) is at Longleat Park. Thomas Davis, the land-steward to the Marquis of Bath, was friends with Smith and it was from outcrops at Longleat that Smith was able to collect a very distinct fossil assemblage including species of *Trigonia*. This assemblage he later used to define his Coral Rag and Pisolite. The Coral Rag does not appear on early versions of his maps but in 1816, after examining a sequence from a deep well near Swindon (193, Map 4), Smith found a similar assemblage and afterwards mapped the Coral Rag as a distinct formation on later issues of his 1815 map.

Map 8 shows a facsimile of Smith's circular 1799 map of the area around Bath and is probably one of the earliest geological maps ever made. Some of Smith's fossil locations are overlain on the map, also shown are localities marked in green which are from Richard Warner's Fossilogical Map of the Country Five Miles around Bath which he published in his New Guide to Bath in 1811. Richard Warner (1763–1857) was a clergyman and antiquarian who wrote early travel guides. Also, under the pen name of Peter Paul Pallet, he wrote somewhat scurrilous satirical pieces on Bath life and its people. Warner was acquainted with Smith and in his History of Bath (1801) refers to him as "the very ingenious Mr Smith of Midford". In this work he published a fairly detailed sequence of the stratigraphic succession around Bath, obviously told to him by Smith. His 1811 map must have been plagiarized from Smith but Warner makes no acknowledgement of him in the text. At each location he showed the name of the locality together with the rock type, some of these locations are close to Smith's others are different but almost certainly all came from Smith.

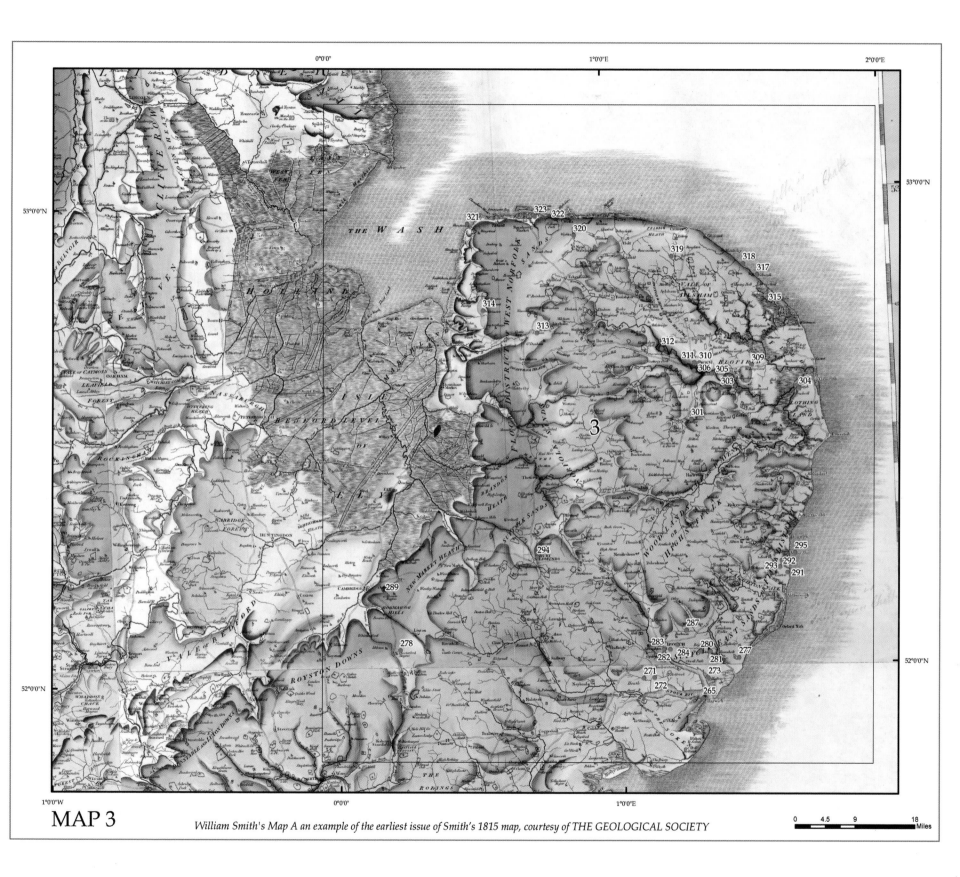

MAP 3

William Smith's Map A an example of the earliest issue of Smith's 1815 map, courtesy of THE GEOLOGICAL SOCIETY

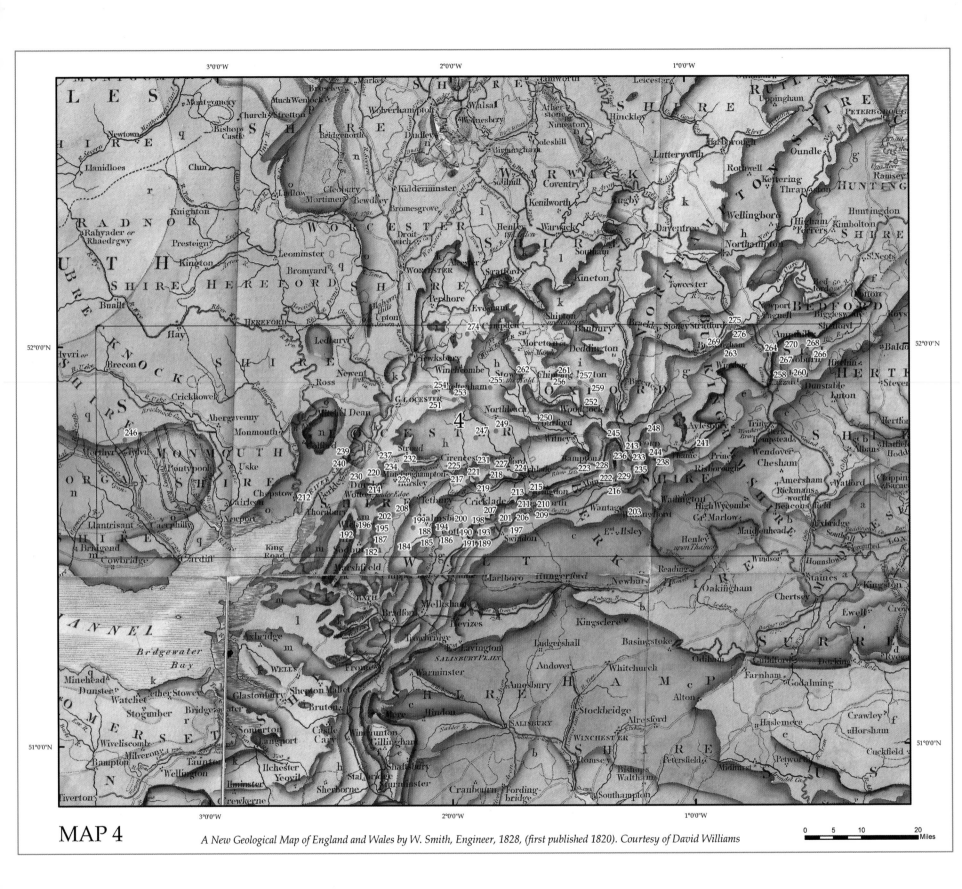

MAP 4

A New Geological Map of England and Wales by W. Smith, Engineer, 1828, (first published 1820). Courtesy of David Williams

MAP 5

William Smith's Map A and example of the earliest issue of Smith's 1815 map, courtesy of THE GEOLOGICAL SOCIETY

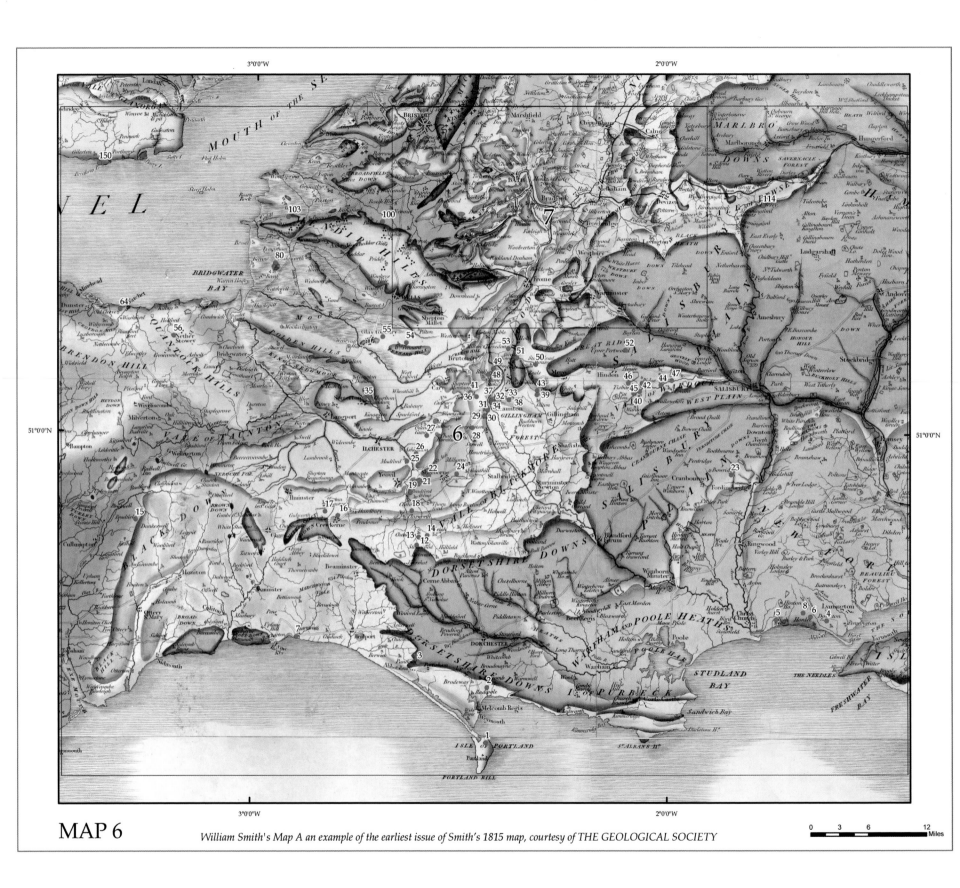

MAP 6

William Smith's Map A an example of the earliest issue of Smith's 1815 map, courtesy of THE GEOLOGICAL SOCIETY

MAP 7

William Smith's Map A, an example of the earliest issue of Smith's 1815 map, courtesy of THE GEOLOGICAL SOCIETY merged with a composite image from his 1819 Geologic Map of Wiltshire (UKOGL)

2°0'0"W

0   1.25   2.5   5
                    Miles

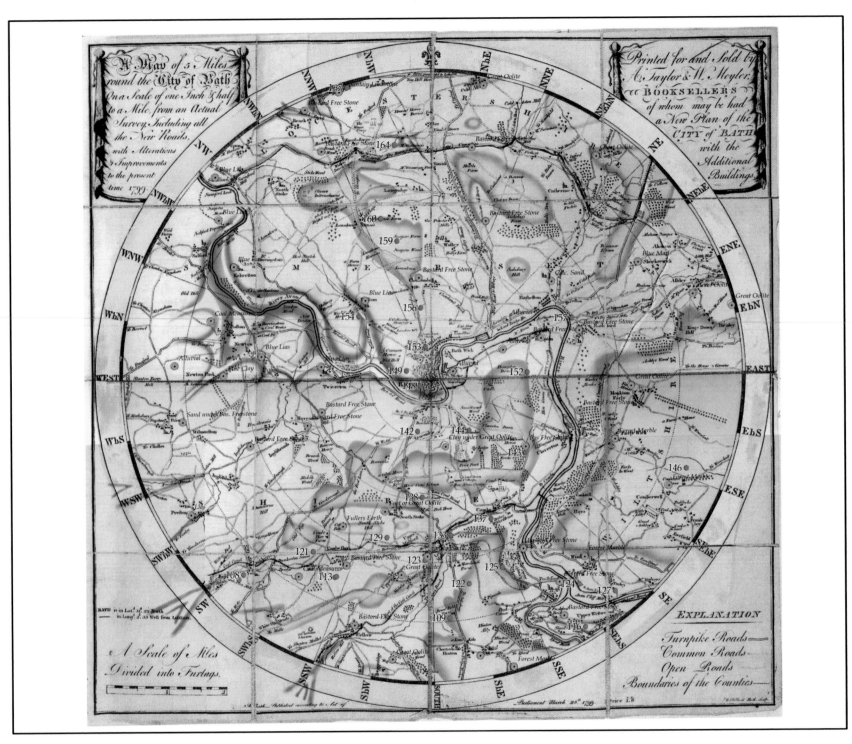

MAP 8

Facsimile copy of William Smith's Geological Map of Bath, 1799, courtesy of Peter Wigley.
Green locations, FOSSILOGICAL MAP of the Country Five Miles round BATH, R. Warner 1811.

SMITH'S FOSSIL LOCATIONS (by number)

No	Location	No	Location	No	Location	No	Location
1	Portland	87	Hardington	173	Well at Brixton Causeway	259	Gagenwell (nr)
2	Between Weymouth and Osmington	88	Tinhead	174	Northfleet	260	Puddle hill, near Dunstable
3	Abbotsbury (nr)	89	Laverton	175	Blue Lodge	261	Chipping Norton
4	Hordel Cliff [Hordle]	90	Mesterham, out of a deep well [Westerham]	176	Tytherton Lucas	262	Stow on the Wold
5	Muddiford [Mudeford]	91	Road, Coal Experiment [Rode]	177	Sheppey	263	Little Harwood
6	Barton Cliff	92	Road [Rode]	178	Redland (nr Bristol)	264	Little Brickhill
7	Charmouth	93	Writhlington	179	Hilmarton	265	Harwich
8	Barton	94	S. W. of Tellisford	180	Kelloways	266	Westoning
9	Bracklesham Bay	95	Tellisford (SW)	181	Near May Place	267	Woburn
10	Bognor	96	Stoney Littleton	182	Hinton	268	Prisley Farm [Priestley]
11	Newhaven Castle Hill	97	Steeple Ashton	183	Woolwich	269	Thornbury Bucks [Thornborough]
12	Evershot	98	Wick Farm	184	Castle Combe	270	Steppingley Park
13	Melbury	99	Trowle	185	Draycot	271	Bentley
14	Bubdown [Bubb Down]	100	Ubby Hill, Mendips [Ubley]	186	Christian Malford	272	Tattingstone Park
15	Blackdown	101	Farley Castle	187	Cross Hands	273	Trimingsby
16	Crewkerne	102	Farley	188	Well at Seagry	274	Aston Somerville
17	Chillington	103	Hutton Hill	189	Wotton Basset (nr) [Royal]	275	Stony Stratford
18	Closworth	104	Pottern[e]	190	Wilts and Berks Canal	276	Woolverton
19	Stoford	105	Westwood	191	Wotton Basset (nr) [Royal]	277	Alderton
20	Clayton Hill	106	Ladydown Farm	192	Sodbury	278	Chesterford
21	Yeovil	107	Coal Canal	193	Well near Swindon, Wilts and Berks -Canal	279	Ilmington
22	Between Sherborn and Yeovil [Sherborne]	108	Dunkerton	194	Dauntsey House	280	Brightwell
23	Damerham	109	Hogwood Corner	195	Between Cross Hands and Petty France	281	Newborn [Newborne]
24	Sherborn	110	Kennet and Avon Canal	196	Little Sodbury	282	Holywell
25	Stone Farm Yeovil	111	Elmcross	197	Swindon	283	Stoke Hill
26	Mudford	112	Below Combe Down Caisson	198	Banner's Ash	284	Ipswich
27	Marston Magna	113	Rowley Bottom	199	Norton	285	Mathon
28	Charlton Horethorn	114	Pewsey	200	Brinkworth Common	286	Malvern
29	North Cheriton	115	Kennet and Avon Canal, near Trowbridge	201	Even Swindon	287	Playford
30	Sattyford [Lattiford]	116	Avoncliff	202	Petty France	288	Towcester ?
31	Wincanton (SW)	117	Bradford Lock	203	Upton	289	Cherry Hinton
32	S.W. of Wincanton	118	Canal at Bradford	204	Highgate Archway	290	Northampton (NW)
33	Bayford (south)	119	Poulton Quarry, Bradford	205	Highgate	291	Thorpe Common
34	Wincanton	120	Grip Wood	206	Stratton	292	In the parish of Leiston
35	Somerton	121	Combhay	207	North Wilts Canal	293	Leiston, Old Abbey
36	Wincanton (West)	122	Pipehouse	208	Didmarton	294	Bury St. Edmonds
37	Wincanton (north side)	123	Mitford [Midford]	209	Wilts and Berks Canal near Shrivenham	295	Minsmere Iron Sluice
38	South of Bayford	124	Winsley	210	Near Shrivenham	296	Wellingborough
39	Silton Farm	125	Limpley Stoke	211	Stanton near Highworth	297	Woodford
40	Tisbury	126	Bradford	212	Beachley	298	Near Stilton
41	Turnpike near Bratton	127	Berfield	213	Highworth	299	Dudley
42	Chicksgrove	128	Devizes	214	Wotton under Edge	300	Wrekin
43	Dun's Well, Silton Farm [Dunn's]	129	Stoke [South ?]	215	Coleshill	301	Foxhole
44	Teffont	130	Smitham Bottom	216	Marcham	302	Peterborough (nr)
45	Lady Down	131	Near Devizes	217	Thames and Severn Canal [nr South Cerney]	303	Bramerton
46	Fonthill	132	Devizes (nr)	218	Down Ampney	304	Burgh Castle
47	Dinton Park	133	Tucking Mill	219	Latton (north)	305	Writlingham
48	Redlynch (nr)	134	Canal at Seend	220	Dursley	306	Norwich
49	Redlynch	135	Kennet and Avon Canal at Seend	221	Latton	307	North of Stamford
50	Stourhead	136	Holt	222	Shippon	308	Steeraway Wrekin
51	Alfred's Tower	137	Monkton Combe	223	Hinton Waldrish	309	Between Norwich and Yarmouth
52	Great Ridge	138	Combe Down	224	Dudgrove Farm	310	Moushold
53	Bruham Pit	139	Rundaway Hill [Rounway]	225	Siddington	311	North of Norwich
54	Penard Hill	140	Croydon	226	Nailsworth	312	Taverham
55	Glastonbury	141	Carshalton	227	Maisey Hampton [Meysey]	313	Lexham
56	Stowey [Nether]	142	Devonshire Buildings, Bath	228	Dry Sandford	314	Grimston (nr)
57	Chute Farm [Shute Farm]	143	Vinyard Down [Vineyard]	229	Sunningwell	315	Hickling
58	Horningsham	144	Smallcombe Bottom [Vale]	230	Breadstone	316	Ticknal[l]
59	Crockerton	145	Sutton	231	Poulton	317	Happisburgh
60	Knook	146	Wraxhall	232	Minching Hampton Common	318	Keswick
61	Heytesbury	147	Bath	233	Sandford Churchyard	319	Aldborough
62	Longleat Park	148	John St Bath	234	Frocester Hill (top)	320	Wighton
63	Mazen Hill	149	Crescent Fields	235	Kennington	321	Hunstanton Cliff
64	Watchet	150	Aberthaw	236	Bagley Wood Pit	322	Holkham Park
65	Norton Bavant	151	Westbrook	237	Frocester Hill (foot)	323	Burnham Overy
66	Chittern [Chitterne]	152	Bathhampton	238	Garsington Hill	324	Sleaford
67	Near Warminster	153	Bath (nr)	239	Gloucester and Berkley Canal	325	Normanton Hill
68	Marston, near Frome	154	Weston	240	Purton Passage	326	Newark (NE)
69	Warminster	155	Dundry	241	Thame	327	Bonsal [Bonsall]
70	Between Nunny and Frome [Nunney]	156	Near Bath	242	Heddington Common	328	Whaley
71	Leigh upon Mendip	157	Batheaston Pit	243	Heddington Common	329	Buxton
72	Wells (nr)	158	Keynsham	244	Shotover Hill	330	Newton [on Trent]
73	Slabhouse, Mendips	159	Lansdown	245	Ensham Bridge	331	Clithero
74	Black-Dog Hill, near Standerwick	160	Near Lansdown	246	Merthyr Tydvil	332	Spofforth
75	Mells	161	Bedminster Down (S)	247	Foss Cross	333	Malton
76	Dilton	162	Bedminster Down	248	Stanton	334	Topcliffe
77	Guildford	163	Derry Hill	249	Broadfield Farm	335	Kirby Moorside
78	Berkley	164	Liliput	250	Fulbrook	336	Scarborough
79	Oldford near Frome	165	Pickwick	251	Crickley Hill	337	Richmond
80	Brent	166	Calne	252	Stunsfield [Stonesfield]	338	Danby Beacon (nr)
81	North of Reigate	167	Tracey Park [Tracy]	253	Dowdswell Hill	339	Whitby
82	Orchardleigh	168	Wilts and Berks Canal, near Chippenham	254	Cheltenham		
83	Reigate (north)	169	Hotwells	255	Naunton (nr)		
84	Lullington	170	Reading	256	Churchill		
85	Godstone (nr)	171	Clifton	257	Enstone		
86	Near Godstone	172	Sheldon	258	Leighton Beaudesert		

APPENDIX: PLATE FOSSIL LISTING

PLATE NO	SMITH STRATA NAME	MODERN STRATA	PLATE REF	SMITH FOSSIL NAME	REVISED NAME	SMITH CODE	NHM REG	LOCATION	NOT FOUND	SUBSTITUTE	NOTE
Frontispiece	Frontispiece	Pliocene-Pleistocene Crag	Frontispiece	Large Extinct Animal Tooth Norfolk	*Anancus arvernensis*		M1983	Writlingham			1
1	**London Clay**	**Eocene (mostly), London Clay**									2
–	–	–	1-1	Vivipara fluviorum	*Viviparus suessoniensis*		G1677	Well at Brixton Causeway			
–	–	–	1-2	Tellina, &c.	*Abra splendens*		L1426	Sheppey ♠			
–	–	–	1-3	Arca Linn. Pectunculus Lam.	*Glycymeris brevirostris*	Q 3	G1430	Bognor ♠			3
–	–	–	1-4	Chama	*Chama squamosa*			Hordwell Cliff	*		
–	–	–	1-5	Voluta spinosa	*Volutospina luctator*			Barton	*		
–	–	–	1-6	Voluta	*Volutospina denudata*	A 1	G1563	Bognor			
–	–	–	1-7	Cerithium	*Brotia melanioides*	D 1 a	G1567	Woolwich			
–	–	–	1-8	Large Shark's tooth	*Otodus obliquus*		P4829	Sheppey			
–	–	–	1-9	Small Shark's tooth	Shark's tooth indet.			Highgate	*		
–	–	–	1-10	Pectunculus decussatus	*Striarca wrigleyi*	Q 1	L1435	Highgate			
–	–	–	1-11	Ammonites communis	*Dactylioceras commune*			Happisberg	*		4
–	–	–	1-12	Calyptrea Lam.	*Sigapatella aperta*			Barton Cliff	*		5
–	–	–	1-13	Crab	*Zanthopsis* sp.		(I 749)	Sheppey		*	
2	**Crag (Craig)**	**Pliocene-Pleistocene, Crag**									6
–	–	–	2-1	Murex contrarius	*Neptunea angulata*	B 4 a	G1546	Alderton			
–	–	–	2-2	M. striatus	*Nucella incrassata* with encrusting barnacles	B 2 e	G1536	Bramerton			
–	–	–	2-3	Turbo littoreus	*Littorina littorea*	F 1 c	G1558	Thorpe Common			
–	–	–	2-4	Turbo Linn. Turritella Lam.	*Potamides tricinctus*			Thorpe Common	*		
–	–	–	2-5	Patella Fissura Linn. Emarginula Lam.	*Emarginula fissura*			Bramerton, Harwich, Holywell	*		7
–	–	–	2-6	Balanus tessselatus	*Balanus* sp.		I 747	Bramerton			
–	–	–	2-7	Arca Linn. Pectunculus Lam.	*Glycymeris variabilis*	Q 2 b	L1409	Tattingstone Park			
–	–	–	2-8	Cardium Linn.	*Cerastoderma hostei*	R 1 a	L1410	Tattingstone Park		*	
–	–	–	2-9	Mya lata	*Mya arenaria* (hinge only)		(L1413)	Bramerton			8
–	–	–	2-10	Short vertebra of a fish	teleost indet.		P4832	Thorpe Common			
–	–	–	2-11	Elongated or Hourglass vertebra	*Platax woodwardi*		P4839	Thorpe Common			
–	–	–	2-12	Vertebra worn	teleost indet.		P4839	Thorpe Common			
–	–	–	2-13	Vertebra showing six costa forming a sort of star	half a teleost vertebra indet.		P4833	Thorpe Common			
–	–	–	2-14	Vertebra showing six costa forming a sort of star	half a teleost vertebra indet.		P4833	Thorpe Common			
–	–	–	2-15	Palate bone of a fish	?*Aetobatus* sp.		P4834	Tattingstone Park			
–	–	–	2-16	Large Shark's tooth (worn)	*Isurus*' sp.		P4835	Stoke Hill			
–	–	–	2-17	Large Shark's tooth perfect, worn smooth	?Lamnid		P4836	Reading			
–	–	–	2-18	Large Shark's tooth perfect state, worn smooth	Shark's tooth, ?Laminid			Reading	*		
–	–	–	2-19	Large Shark's tooth perfect state, worn smooth	Shark's tooth, 'Odontaspid' type		P4837	Reading			
–	–	–	2-20	Quadrupeds bone	Toe phalange, possibly gazelle		M1990	Tattingstone Park			9
–	–	–	2-21	Angular stalactite				Burgh Castle	*		
3	**Upper Chalk**	**Upper Cretaceous, Upper Chalk**									
–	–	–	3-1	Alcyonium Flint, others in Chalk	*Sporadoscinia alcyonoides*		S9863	Wighton			
–	–	–	3-2	Alcyonium Flint, others in Chalk	*Toulminia catenifer*		S9866	Chittern ♠			
–	–	–	3-3	Serpula	?*Filogranula* sp.			Norwich	*		
–	–	–	3-4	Valves of Lepas, Linn.	*Regioscalpellum maximum*		I 750	Norwich			
–	–	–	3-5	Hollow Valve of Ostrea	*Pycnodonte vesicularis*		L1446	Norwich			
–	–	–	3-6	Flatter Valve of Ostrea	*Pycnodonte vesicularis*			Norwich	*		
–	–	–	3-7	Flatter Valve of Ostrea attached to Belemnite	Oyster with *Belemnitella mucronata* attached	G 1	L1446	Norwich			10
–	–	–	3-8	Pecten	*Mimachlamys mantelliana*		L1441	Norwich			
–	–	–	3-9	Terebratula subundata, (long variety)	*Concinnithyris subundata*		B1392	Norwich			
–	–	–	3-10	Echinus	*Echinocorys scutata*	(D 1 a)	(E552)	North of Norwich		*	11
–	–	–	3-11	Palate of a fish	*Ptychodus mammillaris*		P4813	Warminster			
–	–	–	3-12	Part of Echinus	basal plate of a cideroid with boss for spine			North of Norwich	*		12
–	–	–	3-13	Echinus Spine	spine of a cideroid			North of Norwich	*		
–	–	–	3-14	Shark's Tooth with 2 ridges	*Enchodus* sp. (fish)		P4816	North of Norwich			
–	–	–	3-15	Shark's Tooth serrated	'Corax'-tooth			North of Norwich	*		
–	–	–	3-16	Vertebrae	Vertebra indet. (possibly shark)			North of Norwich	*		
4	**Lower Chalk**	**Upper Cretaceous, Lower Chalk**									
–	–	–	4-1	Inoceramus Cuvieri	*Volviceramus involutus*		L1444	Heytesbury			
–	–	–	4-2	Inoceramus	*Mytiloides labiatus*		MB1147	Wilts (Warminster)			
–	–	–	4-3	Cast of a Trochus	*Bathrotomaria* sp.		G1571	Mazen Hill			
–	–	–	4-4	Ammonites	*Schloenbachia subtuberculata*	(H 2 a)	(C619)	(Rundaway Hill)		*	13
–	–	–	4-5	Cirrus depressus	*Bathrotomaria* sp.		G1573	Warminster			
–	–	–	4-6	Terebratula	*Gibbithyris semiglobosa*	I 2 a	B1387	Heytesbury			14
–	–	–	4-7	Terebratula	*Orbirhynchia cuvieri*		(B1396)	Heytesbury		*	
–	–	–	4-8	Terebratula subundata	*Gibbithyris semiglobosa*	I 2 a	B1387	Heytesbury			15
–	–	–	4-9	Sharks teeth	Sharks tooth indet.		(P4819)	(no location)		*	16
5	**Green Sand**	**Lower-Upper Cretaceous, Upper Greensand**									
–	–	–	5-1	Alcyonite (funnel form)	*Pachypoterion compactum*		P3030	Warminster			
–	–	–	5-2	Alcyonite (doliform)	*Siphonia tulipa*		P3018	Pewsey			
–	–	–	5-3	Venus angulata	*Epicyprina angulata*	P 2	L1455	Blackdown			
–	–	–	5-4	Murex Linn.	*Cretaceomurex calcar*		G1584	Blackdown			17
–	–	–	5-5	Turritella Lam.	*Torquesia granulata*	C 1	G1581	Blackdown			
–	–	–	5-6	Pectunculus Lam.	*Glycymeris sublaevis*	K 1	L1448	Blackdown			
–	–	–	5-7	Cardium	'*Mactra*' angulata (on block)		G1583	Blackdown			18
–	–	–	5-8	Rostellaria Lam.	*Drepanocheilus calcaratus* (on block)		G1583	Blackdown			
–	–	–	5-9	Trigonia alaeformis	*Pterotrigonia* cf. *aliformis* (on block)		G1583	Blackdown			
–	–	–	5-10	Cucullaea. Lam.	?*Idonearca* sp. (on block)		G1583	Blackdown			
6	**Green Sand**	**Lower-Upper Cretaceous Upper Greensand**									
–	–	–	6-1	Vermicularia (chambered)	*Rotularia concava*	E 1	A121	Near Warminster			19
–	–	–	6-2	Solarium Lam.	*Nummogaultina fittoni*	B 1	G1580	Rundaway Hill			20
–	–	–	6-3	Pecten (echinated)	*Merklinia scabra*		L1470	Chute Farm			
–	–	–	6-4	Terebratula pectinata	*Dereta pectita*		B1407	Chute Farm			
–	–	–	6-5	Terebratula lyra	*Terebrirostra lyra*			Chute Farm	*		
–	–	–	6-6	Terebratula	*Cyclothyris latissima*		B1406	Chute Farm			
–	–	–	6-7	Chama haliotoidea	*Amphidonte obliquatum*	R 1 f	L1462	Alfred's Tower			
–	–	–	6-8	Pecten quadricostata	*Neithea gibbosa*		L1468	Near Warminster			

PLATE NO	SMITH STRATA NAME	MODERN STRATA	PLATE REF	SMITH FOSSIL NAME	REVISED NAME	SMITH CODE	NHM REG	LOCATION	NOT FOUND	SUBSTITUTE	NOTE
–	–	–	6-9	Pecten	"Chlamys" aff. subacuta		L1473	Chute Farm			
–	–	–	6-10	Ostrea (Gryphea Lam.)	Amphidonte obliquatum	S 2 a	L1464	Stourhead			21
–	–	–	6-11	Echinus with a singular anal appendage	Salenia petalifera	C 1	E476	Chute Farm			
–	–	–	6-12	Echinites Leske	Discoides subuculus		E487	Warminster			
–	–	–	6-13	E. lapis cancri	Catopygus columbarius	C 1 No 3	E485	Chute Farm			
–	–	–	6-14	Spatangus Leske	Holaster laevis	B 3	E483	Chute Farm			
–	–	–	6-15	Cyclolites Lam.	Microbacia sp.			Chute	*		
–	–	–	6-16	Madreporite	indet.			Chute Farm	*		
–	–	–	6-17	Alcyonite	Barroisia sp.			Chute Farm	*		
7	Brick Earth	Lower Cretaceous, Gault Clay									
–	–	–	7-1	Ammonites	Hoplites dentatus		(C627)	(Steppingley Park)		*	22
–	–	–	7-2	Hamites	Idiohamites sp.		C628	Nr. Grimston			
–	–	–	7-3	Echinus Linn. Spatangus Leske	Pliotoxaster sp.		E489	Near Devizes			
–	–	–	7-4	Belemnites	Neohibilites minimus		(C626)	(Nr. Grimston)		*	23
–	–	–	7-5	Belemnites	Neohibilites minimus		C625	Prisley Farm			24
8	Portland Stone	Upper Jurassic, Portland Stone									
–	–	–	8-1	Cast of Natica Lam.	Neritoma sinuosa		G1587	Swindon ♦			
–	–	–	8-2	Turritella inside cast	Aptyxiella portlandica		G1585	Portland			
–	–	–	8-3	Cast of Venus Linn.	Eomiodon sp.	E 2	L1486	Swindon ♦			
–	–	–	8-4	Trigonia	Myophorella incurva	(2)	(L1484)	(Swindon)		*	25
–	–	–	8-5	Venus, inside cast	Protocardia dissimilis		L1487	Swindon			
–	–	–	8-6	Pecten	Camptonectes lamellosus		L1492	Swindon			
–	–	–	8-7	Fossil Wood	Section of larger piece of conifer		(V745)	(Woburn)		*	26
9	Oak Tree Clay	Upper Jurassic, Kimmeridge Clay									
–	–	–	9-1	Melania Heddingtonensis	Pseudomelania heddingtonensis			North Wilts Canal	*		27
–	–	–	9-2	Turbo	Gastropod indet.			North Wilts Canal	*		
–	–	–	9-3	Trochus	Bathrotomaria reticulata		24817	North Wilts Canal			
–	–	–	9-4	Ampullaria	Ampullina sp.			North Wilts Canal	*		
–	–	–	9-5	Chama	Nannogyra nana	2 b	L53452-3	North Wilts Canal			28
–	–	–	9-6	Ostrea delta	Deltoideum delta	D 1 b	L1495	North Wilts Canal			
–	–	–	9-7	Ammonites	Pictonia baylei		37847	Wooton Basset			29
–	–	–	9-8	Venus	Neocrassina ovata		L256	No locality			
–	–	–	9-9	Terebratula	Torquirhynchia inconstans		(B1409)	(Bagley Wood Pit)		*	30
10	Coral Rag and Pisolite	Upper Jurassic, Corallian Oolite									
–	–	–	10-1	Madrepora	Isastrea explanata		R1076	Stanton near Highworth			
–	–	–	10-2	Madrepora	Confusastrea depressa		R1079	Steeple Ashton			31
–	–	–	10-3	Madrepora	Thecosmilia annularis		56336	Steeple Ashton			
11	Coral Rag and Pisolite	Upper Jurassic, Corallian Group									32
–	–	–	11-1	Turbo	Ooliticia muricata	B 2 b	G1594	Derry Hill			
–	–	–	11-2	Ampullaria	Ampullospira sp.	D 1 a	G1599	Longleat Park ♠			
–	–	–	11-3	Melania striata	Bourguetia saemanni	(B 3)	(G1646)	(Caisson ♦, Wilts & Berks Canal)		*	33
–	–	–	11-4	Ostrea crista galli	Actinostreon gregarium	(K 1 a)	(L1533)	(Wilts) ♠		*	34
–	–	–	11-5	Cidaris	Paracidaris smithii	(?A 3)	(E492)	(Hilmarton)		*	35
–	–	–	11-6	Clypeus	Nucleolites clunicularis		E495	Meggot's Mill, Coleshill			36
12	Clunch Clay and Shale	Middle-Upper Jurassic, Oxford Clay									
–	–	–	12-1	Large Belemnites	Cylindroteuthis puzosiana	C 1 a	C640a	Dudgrove Farm			
–	–	–	12-2	Gryphrea dilatata lower valve	Gryphaea dilatata	(F 1 b)	(L1518)	(Derry Hill)		*	37
–	–	–	12-3	Gryphrea dilatata upper valve	Gryphaea dilatata		(L1518)	(Derry Hill)		*	
–	–	–	12-4	Ammonites armatus ?	Kosmoceras spinosum		C636	Thames and Severn Canal			38
–	–	–	12-5	Serpula	Genicularia vertebralis			Wilts and Berks Canal, near Chippenham	*		39
–	–	–	12-6	Serpula	Genicularia vertebralis			Wilts and Berks Canal, near Chippenham	*		40
13	Kelloways Stone	Middle Jurassic, Kellaways Rock									
–	–	–	13-1	Rostellaria	Dicroloma sp.			Kelloways, Wilts & Berks Canal, nr Chippenham	*		
–	–	–	13-2	Ammonites sublaevis	Cadoceras sublaevis		C748	Kelloways			
–	–	–	13-3	Ammonites Calloviensis	Sigaloceras calloviense		C642b	Kelloways			41
–	–	–	13-4	Ammonities	Proplanulites koenigi		C643	Kelloways			
–	–	–	13-5	Gryphea incurva	Gryphaea dilobotoes	I1 c	L1778	Ladydown			42
–	–	–	13-6	Terebratula ornithocephala	Ornithella ornithocephala		B1417	Wilts and Berks Canal, near Chippenham			
14	Cornbrash	Middle Jurassic, Cornbrash									
–	–	–	14-1	Natica?	Ampullospira sp.	E 1 a	G1605	Road			
–	–	–	14-2	Ammonites discus	Clydoniceras discus		C649	S.W. of Wincanton			
–	–	–	14-3	Modiola	Modiolus imbricatus	F 1 b	L1536	Wick Farm			
–	–	–	14-4	Trigonia costata	Trigonia crucis		L1551	North side of Wincanton			
–	–	–	14-5	Venus Linn.	Protocardia buckmani	L 1 a	L1556	Trowle ♦			
–	–	–	14-6	Cardium	Pholadomya deltoidea	K 1	L1552	Road			
–	–	–	14-7	Unio ?	Pleuromya uniformis	M 3 b	L1543	Road			
–	–	–	14-8	Avicula echinata	Meleagrinella echinata		L1579	Draycot			
–	–	–	14-9	Terebratula digona (var. gibbosa, rotunda)	Digonella siddingtonensis		B1423	Latton			
15	Forest Marble	Middle Jurassic, Forest Marble									
–	–	–	15-1	Patella rugosa	Symmetrocapulus tessoni			Minching Hampton Common	*		
–	–	–	15-2	Ancilla	Cylindrites archiaci		G1608	Farley Castle			
–	–	–	15-3	Rostellaria ?	Rostellaria in block		L1596	No location, probably Poulton			
–	–	–	15-4	Ostrea	Catinula sp.		L1589	Wincanton			
–	–	–	15-5	Pecten	Plagiostoma subcardiiformis	I 1 a	L1591	Siddington			
–	–	–	15-6	Pecten	Camptonectes auritus	I 4	L1594	Farley Castle			
–	–	–	15-7	Oval Bufonite	?Eomesodon sp. (splenial bone)		(P4826)	(Stunsfield)		*	
–	–	–	15-8	Round Bufonite	?Lepidotes sp.			Stunsfield, Pickwick, Didmarton	*		
–	–	–	15-9	Fish Palate	?Asteracanthus magnus		P4820	Pickwick			
–	–	–	15-10	Cap-formed Palate	Asteracanthus tenuis		P4823	Pickwick			

PLATE NO	SMITH STRATA NAME	MODERN STRATA	PLATE REF	SMITH FOSSIL NAME	REVISED NAME	SMITH CODE	NHM REG	LOCATION	NOT FOUND	SUBSTITUTE	NOTE
–			15-11	Shark's Teeth	teeth: probably 1 shark, 1 teleost			Stunsfield, Pickwick, Farley Castle	*		
16	Clay over the Upper Oolite	Middle Jurassic, Bradford Clay									
–	–	–	16-1	Pear Encrinus	Apiocrinus elegans		E559	Bradford			43
–	–	–	16-2	Pear Encrinus Clavicle	Apiocrinus elegans		(unreg)	Farley Castle		*	44
–	–	–	16-3	Pear Encrinus root and stems	Apiocrinus elegans		E559	Bradford			45
–	–	–	16-4	Tubipora	Serpulid worm, Filograna sp.			Broadfield Farm, Farley Castle	*		
–	–	–	16-5	Millepora	Terebellaria ramosissima		D34537	Hinton			
–	–	–	16-6	Chama crassa	Praeoxygyra crassa			Stoford	*		
–	–	–	16-7	Plagiostoma	Plagiostoma cardiiformis	I 3	(L1605)	(Combhay) ♠		*	46
–	–	–	16-8	Avicula costata	Oxytoma costata		(a) 43258	Bradford			
–	–	–	16-8	Avicula costata	Oxytoma costata	N 1 b	(b) L1611	Hinton			
–	–	–	16-9	Terebratula digona the long variety	Digonella digona	O 1 a	B1424	Farley Castle			
–	–	–	16-10	Terebratula reticulata	Dictyothyris coarctata	O 3 a	B1430	Farley Castle			47
17	Upper Oolite	Middle Jurassic, Great Oolite							*		
–	–	–	17-1	Tubipora	Lochmaeosmilia radiata			Broadfield Farm, Combe Down, Westwood	*		
–	–	–	17-2	Tubipora	Lochmaeosmilia radiata			Combe Down	*		
–	–	–	17-3	Madrepora turbinata	Montlivaltia sp.			Farley Castle, Broadfield Farm	*		
–	–	–	17-4	Madrepora porpites	Chomatoseris porpites			Broadfield Farm	*		48
–	–	–	17-5	Madrepora flexuosa	Cladophyllia babeana		unreg.	Castle Combe			
18	Fullers Earth Rock	Middle Jurassic, Fuller's Earth									
–	–	–	18-1	Nautilus	Nautiloid indet.			Lansdown	*		
–	–	–	18-2	Ammonites modiolaris	Tulites modiolaris			Dundry, Rowley Bottom			
–	–	–	18-3	Modiola anatina	Modiolus anatinus		66930	Avoncliff			
–	–	–	18-4	Cardita	Ceratomya aff. striata		L53451	Hardington ♠			
–	–	–	18-5	Cardium	Pholadomya aff. lirata	K 1	L1685	Charlton Horethorn			
–	–	–	18-6	Tellina	Cercomya aff. pinguis	G 3 a	L1689	Avoncliff			49
–	–	–	18-7	Ostrea acuminata	Praeexogyra acuminata			Orchardleigh, Avoncliff, Caisson, Stamforth (N)	*		50
–	–	–	18-8	Ostrea Marshii	Actinostreon marshii	P 1 b	LL40856	Cotswold Hills			
–	–	–	18-9	Terebratula media	Rhynchonelloidella media		(B1488)	(Near Bath)		*	51
19	Under Oolite (unpub) 1st	Mid Jurassic, Inferior Oolite									52
–	–	–	19-1	Melania Sp 2	Pseudomelania sp.	B 2 b	G1644	Tucking Mill			
–	–	–	19-2	Trochus Sp 1	Pyrgotrochus conoideus	C 1	G1647	Near Bath			
–	–	–	19-3	Trochus Sp 6	Pyrgotrochus sp.	C 6 a	G1653	Coal Canal			
–	–	–	19-4	Trochus Sp 9	Pleurotomaria granulata		G1655	Sherborne			
–	–	–	19-5	Turitella Sp1	Nerinea sp.	E 1 a	G1661	Smallcombe Bottom			
–	–	–	19-6	Turitella Sp 3	?Nerinea sp.	E 3 a	G1663	Churchill			
–	–	–	19-7	Ampullaria Sp 2	Ampullina sp.	F 2 b	G1665	Bath			
–	–	–	19-8	Nautilus Sp 3	Cenoceras excavatus	H 3 a	C666	Sherborn ♠			
–	–	–	19-9	Ammonites calix	Teloceras calix	K 2	C671	Sherborn			
20	Under Oolite (unpub) 2nd plate	Middle Jurassic, Inferior Oolite									53
–	–	–	20-1	Madrepora Sp 4	Coral indet.			Dundry, Tucking Mill, Crickley Hill	*		
–	–	–	20-2	Trigonia costata	Trigonia costata	N 1 a	L1694	Cotswold Hills			
–	–	–	20-3	Trigonia costata	Trigonia costata	N 1 f	L1699	Tucking Mill			
–	–	–	20-4	Astarte ovata	Astarte elegans	Q 1 b	L1719	Coal Canal			54
–	–	–	20-5	Pecten equivalvis	Variamussium cf. pumilum	(W 2)	(L1730)	(Churchill)		*	55
–	–	–	20-6	Inoceramus	Fragment of large Trichites ploti		L1733	Bath			
–	–	–	20-7	Terebratula spinosa	Acanthothyris spinosa	X 3 c	(B1501)	(Churchill)		*	56
–	–	–	20-8	Clypeus sinuatus	Clypeus ploti	B 1 f	E538	Naunton (nr)			
21	Sand & Sandstone (unpub sketch)	Lower Jurassic, Upper Lias Bridport Sand									57
–	–	–	21-1	Belemnites	Belemnopsis sp.	1 b	C669	Tucking Mill			
–	–	–	21-2	Ammonites Sp. 4	Pleydellia burtonensis	B 4	C684	Yeovil			
–	–	–	21-3	Modiola	Inoperna sowerbyana	C 1	L1734	Frocester Hill ♠			
22	Marlstone (unpub sketch)	Lower Jurassic, Middle-Upper Lias									58
–	–	–	22-1	Pentacrinus	Crinoid: indet.			Churchill, Stone Farm Yeovil, Kennet & Avon	*		
–	–	–	22-2	Belemnites Sp 1	Belemnite: indet.			Yeovil, Churchill, Tucking Mill, Enstone	*		
–	–	–	22-3	Ammonites undulatus	Tragophylloceras undulatum	C 3	C33499	Coal Canal			
–	–	–	22-4	Ammonites Sp 4	Zugodactylites sp.	C 4 a	C710	Coal Canal			
–	–	–	22-5	Ammonites Sp 10	Witchellia sp.	C 10 c	C700	Penard Hill			
–	–	–	22-6	Ammonites Walcotii [Walcotti]	Grammoceras striatulum	C 13 b	C703	Glastonbury ♠			
–	–	–	22-7	Pecten	Pseudopecten equivalis		L1774	Kennet and Avon Canal			
23	Blue Marl (unpub sketch)	Lower Jurassic, Lias									59
–	–	–	23-1	Ammonites planicosta	Promicroceras planicosta		C736	Marston Magna ♠			60
–	–	–	23-2	Ammonites Sp (6)	Asteroceras smithi		C737	Marston Magna			61
–	–	–	23-3	Tellina	Cardinia listeri	D 1 a	L1765	Mudford			
24	Lias (unpub sketch)	Lower Jurassic, Lias									62
–	–	–	24-1	Plagiostoma gigantea	Plagiostoma giganteum	N 1 b	L1780	Bath			
–	–	–	24-2	Common grypheus	Gryphaea arcuata	O 1 a	L1737	Gloucester and Berkley Canal			63
–	–	–	24-3	Spirifer	Spiriferina walcotti	Q 10 a	B1504	Keynsham			
–	–	–	24-4	Fish Vertebra	Vertebra: indet			Charmouth, Keynsham	*		64
–	–	–	24-5	Bones	Shark fin spine Acrodus curtus		P4841	near Lyme			
–	–	–	24-6	Fish Vertebra	Vertebra: indet			Charmouth, Keynsham	*		
25	Lias 2nd (unpub sketch)	Lower Jurassic, Lias									65
–	–	–	25-1	Pentacrinus Sp 1	Isocrinus psilonoti		E561	Gloucester and Berkley Canal			
–	–	–	25-2	Pentacrinus Sp 3	Isocrinus psilonoti		E542	Charmouth			
–	–	–	25-3	Trochus Sp 1	Pleurotomaria cf. cognata	A 1 a	G1670	Purton Passage			
–	–	–	25-4	Ammonites Sp 16	Euagassiceras sauzeanum	E 16 a	C83396	Stony Littleton			
–	–	–	25-5	Ammonites Sp 9	Zugodactylites braunianus	E 9	C723	Bath			
–	–	–	25-6	Unio ? Sp 2	Pleuromya aff. uniformis		L1769	Weston			
26	Redland Limestone (unpub sketch)	Carboniferous Limestone									66
–	–	–	26-1	Madrepora Sp 1	Amplexus coralloides	(C 1)	(R1069)	Leigh-upon-Mendip ♠		*	
–	–	–	26-2	Madrepora Sp 6	Actinocyathus floriformis		(R1067)	Hotwells		*	
–	–	–	26-3	Encrinus Sp 3	Crinoid stems: indet		E548	Mells			

Note No.	PLATE	PLATE NOTES
1	Frontispiece	The Mastodon tooth from Norfolk, its locality was first recorded by Smith's pupil R.C. Taylor in the April 1827, Philosophical Magazine (series 2, vol. 1, pages 283-284) as "from Whitlingham, near Norwich". This was then confirmed by Smith himself in March 1836. (pers. comm., Hugh Torrens).
2	Plate 1	Includes specimens from the Woolwich (older) and Barton, Bracklesham and Hordle Cliff (younger).
3	1-3	Q 3 is written on the specimen. It is likely that this is a mistake on Smith's part and it should be Q 2.
4	1-11	Smith later corrected to Lias Fossil Diluvial [transported in the glacial till]. No London Clay at Happisburgh.
5	1-12	There is no entry for Fig. 12 in SS and neither Calyptraea nor its relatives are listed - ? Ever reached BM.
6	Plate 2	Smith places the Crag beneath the London Clay but later realised it was younger. The spelling 'Craig' on the plate is probably an error. It is Crag in the texts.
7	2-5	Only Bramerton is listed in SS. ? figured specimen was from a missing locality and never came to BM.
8	2-9	Apart from the cast, only hinges are listed in SS. It is possible no whole specimens reached the BM.
9	2-20	If the identification of gazelle is correct it would be the earliest occurrence in the UK.
10	3-7	Fig. 7 is not mentioned in SS, probably because the oyster is the same sp. and location as Figs 5 & 6.
11	3-10	The figured specimen E551, (near Norwich, Norfolk) is on exhibition (2017) in the King's Library, BM.
12	3-12	The specimen is not listed in SS. It is possible that it never came to the BM.
13	4-4	H 2 a = Greensand code but *Scholoenbachia* is a Lower Chalk specimen. Substitute not identical but same species.
14	4-6	SS not listed as figured, but description fits I 2 a.
15	4-8	SS not listed as figured, but description fits I 2 a.
16	4-9	SS not listed as figured for Lower Chalk teeth. Substitute has no location.
17	5-4	Murex is not listed at all in SS. The location of Blackdown on the label matches SIOF.
18	5-7	None of the specimens on block are specified as figured in SS, except Fig. 10.
19	6-1	Fig. 1 not listed in SS, but specimen matches Vermicularia Sp. 1.
20	6-2	The photographed specimen is a close match and from the only location mentioned in SS.
21	6-10	Stourton (SIOF) and Stourhead (SS) are the same location.
22	7-1	A specimen in fragments may have been the figured one. Pyrite decay is a common problem of Gault fossils.
23	7-4	Smith's figured specimen is slightly larger than the photographed one. The location fits SS.
24	7-5	There is no entry for Fig. 5 in SIOF but Figs 4 & 5 are referred to the same species in SS. The locations match.
25	8-4	Substitiute is a trigonid from Swindon. Locations in SIOF match Sp. 1 in SS but description matches Sp. 2 as on specimen.
26	8-7	The photographed image is just a small portion of a larger piece.
27	9-1	*Melania Heddingtonensis* is named in SS (p.41) but no mention that it is figured.
28	9-5	We believe the photographed specimens with the code 2 b to be the figured one yet the locations listed in SS for Sp. 1 includes the Well near Swindon as in SIOF.
29	9-7	This is the correct specimen but Wootton Bassett is not mentioned in either SIOF or SS for this species.
30	9-9	The substitute is the same species from the same location. He adds '[on]ly one [rem]aining [wi]th septaria' so maybe the specimen figured in SIOF was lost at an early stage.'
31	10-2	Smith lists this species in SS (p.47) but does not mention that it is figured.
32	Plate 11	Smith indicates in SS which species are figured but does not number the figures.
33	11-3	The drawing of Fig. 3 Gastropod: Bourguetia saemanni G1646 is a somewhat enigmatic. Smith's plate specimen is remarkably like the one found in the collection with the 'Under Oolite' specimens. 'B3 Caisson' is written on the specimen which fits with the numbering system and place for the Under Oolite in SS and the Caisson was constructed within the Inferior Oolite. As the range of this species extends from the Bajocian to the Upper Oxfordian we feel justified in photographing it for the Coral Rag & Pisolite plate. There is no similar specimen in that collection.
34	11-4	K 1 a matches SS but none of the specimens match Smith's exactly.
35	11-5	Substitute is larger than Smith's but it is the same species from the same location.
36	11-6	Smith notes (SS p. 20): This latter specimen, as shown in my "Stratigraphical Table of Echini" is one of the characteristic distinctions of the Pisolite part of the rock.
37	12-2	None of the specimens from Derry Hill match exactly.
38	12-4	Fig 4 on plate is captioned Ammonities armatus ?, the text description is Ammonites.
39	12-5	No Fig. is detailed against Serpula in SS (p.55). It is detailed as Serpula, Sp. 2 Oaktree Clay yet there is no Sp. 1.
40	12-6	Location is different in SS (Steeple Ashton).
41	13-3	Smith's figured specimen is on tour in Singapore (2017). Substitute is the same species from the same location (C642a).
42	13-5	Figure 5 Gryphea incurva was found by Smith at the Bruham Coal Trial and helped him prove that the miners were far to high in the succession to ever encounter coal.
43	16-1	Fig1 Captioned Pear Encrinite in text and as Pear Encrinus on the plate.
44	16-2	Fig 2 Captioned Vertebrae ditto in text and as The Clavicle on the plate.
45	16-3	Fig 3 Captioned Stems ditto in the text and as The Roots and Stems on the plate.
46	16-7	Substitute is not from the same location but is same species, albeit somewhat smaller. Location tallies with Plagiostoma Sp.2 Variety in SS (p.80).
47	16-10	O 3 a is written on the specimen which seems to match the figured specimen well, Smith code probably O 5 a.
48	17-4	This specimen does not appear to be listed in SS so may not have come to BM.
49	18-6	There is only one species of Tellina (labelled Fig. 6) so we believe the code should read G 1 a.
50	18-7	As Fig. 7 is not listed in SS the specimen may not have come to BM. However, at a later date Smith notes beside Fig. 9 that 'Fig. 7 numerous'.
51	18-9	This specimen is also known as *Rhynchonelloidella smithi* .
52	Plate 19	Proposed Plate species listed in SS p. 110.
53	Plate 20	Proposed Plate species listed in SS p. 110.
54	20-4	Smith writes 'Oak-tree Clay' after his identification of Astarte ovata and indeed it is figured on that plate (Fig. 8 - it is the type specimen). This is the same genus but we believe it to be Astarte elegans.
55	20-5	No specimens for Sp. 1 have been found and so Sp. 2 has been substituted.
56	20-7	Substitute is same species as the one Smith lists under Sp. 4 but slightly less well preserved. The X 3 c code is marked on the specimen chosen but it is not the Obsoletirhynchia obsoleta listed under Sp.3 in SS.
57	Plate 21	Figures Detailed in SS p. 111-112. Smith's Sand and Sandstone mostly refers to a group of Upper Liassic Sandstone now grouped as the Bridport Sand.
58	Plate 22	Figures Detailed in SS p. 113-118. Smith's Marlstone refers a number of Middle-Upper Lias silty and calcareous sediments in part marly members of the Bridport Sand, at Glastonbury and Pennard Hill they constitute the Dyrham Formation. At Churchill the equivalent is the Whitby Mudstone Formation.
59	Plate 23	SS Part 2. Specimens selected to match sketch WSF12-01 courtesy of OUMNH. Smith shows his Blue Marl as a formation above the Blue Lias and indeed there are Blue marls recognised in the Middle Lias. However, the specimens his lists from his Blue Marl at Marston Magna and Mudford are from older Liassic rocks (Blue Lias).
60	23-1	This is the famous Marston Magna Stone.
61	23-2	Sp. 6 is not specified in SS, only ' a keel between two furrows' following Sp. 5. The fossil was named for Smith by James Sowerby.
62	Plate 24	SS Part 2. Specimens selected to match sketch WSF12-02 courtesy of OUMNH.
63	24-2	SS labels Ostrea 'C' but it should logically be 'O'.
64	24-5	No fin spines are listed, nor any locations 'near Lyme' (pp 19-20).
65	Plate 25	SS Part 2. Specimens selected to match sketch WSF12-03 courtesy of OUMNH.
66	Plate 26	SS Part 2. Specimens selected to match sketch WSF12-04 courtesy of OUMNH. Smith's failure to publish this plate saved him from emphasising one of his most serious mistakes because all the specimens shown on Smith's sketch are from the Carboniferous limestone (his Mountain /Derbyshire Limestone) in the Bristol-Mendip area and not from his Redland Limestone ("Magnesium Limestone"), (Cox. L.R 1942 p. 55). Initially, Smith showed this mistaken correlation of the Mendip Limestones with his Redland Limestone in Yorkshire on his 1815 map. However by the time his Gloucestershire map was published in 1819 he shows the limestones around Bristol to be older Mountain Limestone suggesting that he had, at least in part rectified his mistake.

All NHM Registration numbers have the prefix NHMUK with invertebrates adding PI and vertebrates PV

SIOF refers to *Strata Identified by Organized Fossil* s. In the original, the plates are un-numbered in this new publication they have been numbered for ease of reference.

SS refers to *A Stratigraphical System of Organized Fossils with reference to the specimens of the original geological collection in the British Museum.*

BM = British Museum, transferred to the BM (Natural History) in 1880s. Now the Natural History Museum.

OUMNH = Oxford University Museum of Natural History, where the William Smith Archive is kept.

♣ Location marked on the specimen

AFTERWORD

William Smith is known today as 'The Father of English Geology'. A towering figure in the history of our science, his story is all the more fascinating given the challenges he faced in the social and academic world of the war-torn early nineteenth century.

When the third edition of the Geological Society's own Map of England and Wales was issued in July 1865, it was under the revised title 'A Physical and Geological Map of England & Wales by G B Greenough, FRS (on the basis of the original map of Wm Smith 1815)'. Smith's contribution to the science of geology had already been recognised and acknowledged by a Society which had long overlooked his work, but his contribution to Greenough's map in particular was, with this new edition, finally addressed.

The story of these two maps – Smith's virtually solo effort and Greenough's collaborative one – had begun decades before. Within a few months of the founding of the Geological Society by thirteen gentlemen at the Freemason's Tavern, Longacre, in November 1807, its President George Bellas Greenough and several other founding members condescended to accept an invitation to visit Smith's house in Buckingham Street to view his fossils and maps. Smith, by then, had already made a name for himself as an engineer and surveyor, first for the Somerset Coal Company and later as either, or both, for hire. Despite his growing reputation, the gulf in social class between Smith and his visitors meant that he was never invited (nor could he have afforded) to join the new Geological Society.

Already at work on his great map, the visit was for Smith an opportunity to obtain assistance from the Society and its wealth of resources and knowledge. The Fellows, however, left unimpressed. Failing to grasp the importance of Smith's ideas on stratigraphy, they embarked shortly after on their own map, eventually published in 1820, just five years after Smith's.

Smith's relationship with the Society is, in some ways, a familiar tale; a working scientist pitted against the privileged and wealthy members of a learned society whose membership was closed to him. Unlike so many similar stories, there was at least a happy ending, of sorts – before his death in 1839 Smith was recognised for his achievements by a new generation of geologists, who dubbed him 'The Father of English Geology' and awarded him the Geological Society's first Wollaston Medal in 1831 – still our highest award.

As one of the most recent in the long line of Geological Society Presidents since Greenough's three tenures, I am ever conscious of the story of William Smith's relationship with the Geological Society and its first President; not least as a reminder of the importance of ensuring our science is as inclusive and welcoming as possible. Today, strength in diversity is one of the Society's core messages, embedded in our most recent ten year strategy. It is hard not to wonder what more might have been achieved in those early days of stratigraphy, had the Society worked with Smith and engaged with his research as it should have done.

Today, Smith's memory is revered; alongside our Wollaston Medal, the Society also awards a William Smith medal annually to those who have made significant contributions to applied or economic aspects of geoscience. Whilst he is remembered most for his extraordinary map, this new volume bringing together his ground breaking publications on stratigraphy, his now treasured fossil and rock collections, and James Sowerby's wonderful engravings of them, can only serve as a further reminder to today's geologists of how much is owed to him.

Malcolm Brown
President of The Geological Society of London 2016-2018

SELECTED REFERENCES

Cox, L. R. 1930. On British fossils named by William Smith. *Annals and Magazine of Natural History Series* 10 Vol. 6: 287–304.

Cox, L. R. 1942. New light on William Smith and his work. *Proceedings of the Yorkshire Geological Society* 25: 1–99.

Eyles, J. M. 1967. William Smith: The sale of his geological collection to the British Museum. *Annals of Science* 23: 177–212.

Eyles, J. M. 1969. William Smith (1769-1839): A bibliography of his published writings, maps and geological sections, printed and lithographed. *Journal of the Society for the Bibliography of Natural History 5*: 87-109.

Henderson, P. 2015. James Sowerby: The Enlightenment's Natural Historian. Royal Botanic Gardens.

Morrell, J. 2005. John Phillips and the Business of Victorian Science (Science technology and culture. 1700-1945). Aldershot, Ashgate Publishing Ltd.

Phillips, J. 1844. Memoirs of William Smith LLD. London: John Murray.

Phillips, J. 1860. Presidential Address, QJGS Vol. 16 xxvii-lv.

Riches, P. 2016-2017. William Smith's problems with the correlation of the post-chalk section in East Anglia, as revealed in his geological sections. *Bulletin of the Geological Society of Norfolk* 66:45-53.

Sowerby, J. 1812-1818. The mineral conchology of Great Britain; or, Coloured figures and descriptions of those remains of testaceous animals or shells, which have been preserved at various times and depths in the earth (vi-vii). B. Meredith.

Torrens, H. S. 2001. Timeless order: William Smith (1769–1839) and the search for raw materials. In: *The Age of the Earth: from 4004 BC to AD 2002*, edited by C. L. E. Lewis and S. J. Knell, 61–93, Special Publication 190. London: Geological Society of London.

Torrens, H. S. 2002. The Practice of British Geology. Aldershot: Ashgate—Variorum.

Torrens, H. S. 2003. An Introduction to the life and times of William Smith (1769-1839). In: *Memoirs of William Smith LL.D by his Nephew and Pupil John Phillips 1844, Reprinted with Additional Material.* Bath: Royal Literary and Scientific Institution.

Torrens, H. S. 2016. William Smith (1769-1839): His struggles as a consultant, in both geology and engineering, to simultaneously earn a living and finance his scientific projects, to 1820. *Earth Sciences History* Vol. 35, No. 1, 2016 pp. 1–46.

(Editor's note: more information on William Smith can be found at the UKOGL Website www.Strata-Smith.com. A detailed version of the current Appendix, including comparative information, prepared by Diana Clements is also available on this website.)

SELECTED INDEX OF FOSSIL LOCATIONS, AND WILLIAM SMITH FOSSIL NAMES

SMITH FOSSIL NAMES